Beginnings of Interior Environment

FIFTH EDITION

Fabrics and sample books for cover photo courtesy of China Seas, Inc. and Scalamandré, Inc.

Macmillan Publishing Company
866 Third Avenue, New York, New York 10022

Collier Macmillan Canada, Inc.

Library of Congress Cataloging in Publication Data

Allen, Phyllis Sloan.
    Beginnings of interior environment

    Bibliography: p.
    Includes index.
    1. Interior decoration—Handbooks, manuals, etc.
I. Title
NK2115.A59   1985   728   84-27397
ISBN 0-02-301800-3

Printing: 7   8   9   10   11   Year: 9 0

ISBN 0-02-301800-3

Dedicated to all beginning interior designers, professional and nonprofessional, on whom the quality of America's future interior environment depends.

Contents

ONE

Our Domestic Architectural Heritage

TWO

The Modern House and Future Trends

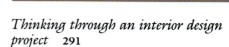

TWELVE

Interior Design as a Career

Foreword

Most people spend the greater part of their time inside—in offices, classrooms, stores, and factories, but most of all, in their homes. In an era grown increasingly complex and stressful, the home has become the last bastion of protection, privacy, and emotional shelter. One's truest life is lived in the home.

Theorizing about the importance of intelligent responses to functional and aesthetic requirements in the home is unnecessary. Most people realize this importance already. What is needed is simply to learn how to achieve these responses. It is widely accepted that the organization and visual character of homes are critical and major influences on all people. The question is, however: Where do we go from here?

Creating an interior atmosphere appropriate to individual life-styles and within available economic means does not, unfortunately, come naturally to most people. This ability must be learned. Further, if a home's interior is to be effective, this learning must include the knowledge that design is not done for design's sake but rather to make a home workable—not only aesthetically and physically but also emotionally—for those living there.

The learning process in interior design, however, is not that difficult or mysterious. Phyllis Sloan Allen demonstrates this well in *Beginnings of Interior Environment*. Her step-by-step process takes the novice interior designer from the fundamentals to the final stages of interior design. Students of all ages will be helped enormously by this text. Students will learn how to bring new life and personality to their own home interiors, and some will be launched by the learning experience this text offers into distinguished careers as professional interior designers.

For these reasons, I recommend this remarkably clear and well-organized text. If the student heeds the advice, engages the exercises, and practices all that Phyllis Allen teaches, an exciting and deeply satisfying dimension can be introduced into his or her life and into the livability of the interiors he or she creates.

MILO BAUGHMAN

Preface

The fifth edition of *Beginnings of Interior Environment* provides the basis for a comprehensive introductory course in interior design. The aim in this new, revised edition is to acquaint students with basic design principles and integrate these principles with today's living spaces and activities. Although the book has served teachers and students for more than ten years with its practical approach to design and furnishing, the new edition recognizes many changes in the way Americans live and in the general philosophy of interior design.

Today, convenience and efficiency are essential to the modern life-style, and space is often limited as more people choose to live in apartments, condominiums, or mobile homes. The need for energy conservation affects every aspect of the home or business environment. In addition, the products of our newest technologies must be accommodated in the process of interior planning.

With these changes in mind, the fifth edition of *Beginnings of Interior Environment* helps design students to enrich interior spaces both practically and aesthetically. The growing field of professional interior design will be well served by this book of "beginnings," which establishes a framework for future career studies. Information on how to be creative within the bounds of good taste and good design principles is presented in a somewhat structured fashion in the belief that a solid foundation in these principles and guidelines is necessary before a designer can depart from them with success.

The new edition has been thoroughly rewritten and updated, with new or expanded sections on lighting, windows, ceilings, doors, computer-aided design, and careers in interior design. Hundreds of new photos and line drawings help clarify concepts, and an enlarged, illustrated glossary will aid students in understanding new terminology. At the ends of Chapters 3, 4, 5, 6, 9, and 11, specific projects have been assigned to test the student's competency in those particular areas. The worksheets for these assignments will be found in the Student Packet prepared to accompany the text.

The Instructor's Guide, coordinated to the new edition, includes a daily schedule for the entire course based upon 43 class periods of 50 minutes each. It contains suggestions and supplementary materials for class demonstrations and projects, outline forms for correcting projects, a number of quizzes, a midterm examination, and a journal or file assignment.

Chapter 1, Our Domestic Architectural Heritage, presents an overview of the history of the American home. This chapter will give students an appreciation for the timelessness of good architectural design, and a foundation of knowledge that will be invaluable in future architectural or design studies.

Chapter 2, The Modern House and Future Trends, discusses today's house and surveys the options for homes currently available: from the traditional custom-built house to the recreational home on wheels to houses designed to conserve energy.

Chapter 3, Floor Plans, focuses on determining the best possible arrangement of a given space. The designer's goal is to provide comfort and efficiency for the homeowner or family based on an analysis of their needs.

Chapter 4, Design Theory and Application, is concerned with the development of good taste through a knowledge of the principles of design and their application in interior space.

Chapter 5, Color, explores the power of color as the single most important element in home design. Meaningful projects help students to create *livable* color schemes.

Chapter 6, Fabrics, concentrates on the many uses of fabric in creating interiors. Through study and practical projects, students learn that with skillful handling, fabric can establish beauty, comfort, mood, style, and a unity in decoration impossible to achieve through any other element of furnishing.

Chapter 7, Floors, Walls, and Ceilings, is a survey of the most up-to-date treatments for floors, walls, and ceilings, with charts showing characteristics and uses of each treatment; a discussion of the boom in the carpet industry, with an emphasis on fiber characteristics and their uses for beauty and durability; and a study of wallpaper with its many decorative uses in today's interiors.

Chapter 8, Windows and Doors, considers various types of windows and methods of treatment. Emphasis is given to the importance of windows in today's dwindling living spaces, and suggests ways of treating them to conserve energy.

Chapter 9, Furniture, discusses the considerations involved in furniture selection. It also points out the most important things to look for when buying wood and upholstered furniture, and includes sketches of various furniture pieces with their identification. Furniture styles are treated here only briefly. A study of this vast and complex topic is beyond the scope of a general introductory course. Both historic and contemporary furnishings deserve separate and complete courses on a more advanced level.

Chapter 10, Furniture and Wall Arrangement, treats the arrangement of furniture to achieve the most efficient use of interior space and the design of successful wall compositions.

Chapter 11, Unifying the Interior Environments, brings together the principles and elements of design and applies them to the problems of designing various rooms of a home to create a workable and unified whole.

Chapter 12, Interior Design as a Career, explores the field of interior design and considers the qualifications and responsibilities, preparation, opportunities, and future challenges of the professional interior designer.

Acknowledgments

I am indebted to many people for their invaluable help in making this revision of *Beginnings of Interior Environment* possible: the great number of students at Brigham Young University who, for over ten years, have used and expressed enthusiasm for the previous editions, and have given helpful suggestions; the many instructors across the country who have used this text and have taken the time to suggest minor changes and additions; and my colleagues in the Department of Interior Design at BYU, who have reinforced my efforts by offering useful suggestions. For expert professional advice I am grateful to Professor Wilford Tolman, Department of Computer Technology, and Professor Evelyn Lee, Department of Clothing and Textiles, both at Brigham Young University. I thank the many individuals and firms who have so generously furnished excellent black-and-white and colored photographs.

I would like to acknowledge Beverly Gooch of Bauder Fashion College for her contribution to Chapter 12 and her review of the text. Other reviewers who lent their experience and expertise to this revision include the following instructors: Kerry Albanese, University of Akron; Reed Benhamou, Purdue University; William Erdahl, University of Maryland—College Park; Betsy Gabb, Oklahoma State University; Bill Greer, University of Georgia—Athens; Stu Fullarton, University of Wisconsin—Stout; Dee Ginthner, University of Minnesota; Agnes Hartnell, Phoenix College; Jeannie Ireland, Illinois State University; Margaret Nagy, Texas Tech University; Susan Reedy, Michigan State University; John Olvera, North Texas State University; Curt Sherman, San Diego State University; and Lynda Shindala, Mississippi State University.

To Nancy Crochiere, my editor at Burgess Publishing Company who provided steady support, cooperation, and wise judgment in supervising the progress of this book, I am deeply indebted. And to all others at Burgess who collaborated on the publication of this edition I offer my gratitude.

Special appreciation is due my husband, Mark K. Allen, for lending his expertise in photographing numerous illustrations, for his encouragement and help in many ways, and for his patience, without which this text never would have appeared in print. I am also grateful to my four children, who urged me to teach and write in the first place, and who have always supported me wholeheartedly.

Introduction

Ever since prehistoric times, when primitive drawings decorated the walls of caves, humans have been concerned with the embellishment of their dwellings. Throughout history, people have considered their home as their castle, and the pride they have taken in its beautification is well known.

Interior design in its contemporary sense, however, began in 1897, when Edith Wharton and Ogden Cadman wrote a book entitled *The Decoration of Houses*, which they claimed to be the first book on decoration to be published in 50 years. In the early twentieth century, Elsie deWolfe's book *The House of Good Taste*, published in 1913, gave respectability and great impetus to the profession of decorating. For several decades, however, interior decoration was highly restrictive, for the services of the interior decorator could be had only by the rich. Today nearly every reputable furniture and department store has one or more interior *designers* (no longer called "decorators") on its staff, whose services are available free of charge to clients who make their purchases through the store.

For years the "decorator" too often applied modern materials and technology in creating interiors only as he or she thought they should be, with little regard for the client's preferences and needs. This practice, too, has changed. The new emphasis today in interior design is on *people*.

Today's challenge for the interior designer is to use present materials and technology to create environments that are responsive to the needs of people—environments that are efficient but flexible, and concerned not only with function and efficiency but also with psychological and spiritual needs. No longer will the trained designer encourage people to adjust their lives to the *designer's* notion of what an environment should be. Rather, the designs of environments must grow out of the needs of the people who inhabit them.

Because of today's complex social and economic problems, the high cost of leisurely pursuits, the need for energy conservation, and the changing life-style, the home (although becoming increasingly smaller) is rapidly evolving into the center of people's lives. Benefits deriving from this change can be many and positive if the home is given top priority and if household values are reordered for home-centered living. The home environment can be substantially improved to meet total needs, thereby adding to pleasure while increasing the quality of household life.

People today are demonstrating an unprecedented interest in interior design. Never before has there been such an abundance of materials from which the interior designer may choose—nor in such a wide price range. Articles for function and beauty from the past and present and from all countries of the world are readily attainable. Today's market abounds in dirt-defying materials and soil-preventive devices that were unheard of a few years ago. Through these, the common problems of maintaining a well-groomed home for an active household have been cut to a minimum.

A life worth living should have beauty, and beauty is everywhere. We need only to learn to *see* it. Elizabeth Gordon, former editor of *House Beautiful*, said of beauty, "If you can't afford it when you are poor, you won't likely have it when you are rich." Acquiring the ability to see beauty means developing an acute awareness of the world—an awareness of color, texture, light, and form as they relate to each other and to other objects. It means learning to see beauty in simple and commonplace things, such as the subtle coloring in the bark of a tree and in the softness of new moss, the exquisite form of a simple glass vase, or the wealth of color in the glaze of a cookie jar. It means enjoying the feel of soft wool and the mellow patina of well-cared-for wood, or sensing how the filtered light through sheer curtains can relax the nerves. The therapeutic value of seeing beauty in everyday life is worth any amount of effort.

In recent years much has been said about a return to elegance. What is true elegance? Is it reserved for only the wealthy? The answer is no. True elegance is not for purchase; it is not a show of affluence nor a superficial display. Elegance is a certain refinement that comes from understanding the lasting beauty of simplicity in one's environment. Because the physical environment has such a subtle but powerful influence on one's personal life, care should be taken in designing and arranging daily surroundings in the best possible manner. Great comfort and reassurance are derived from seeing familiar things, such as the same rooms, furniture, paintings, books, and personal belongings. Through day-to-day observation of these elements, values and attitudes are established that are often difficult to change.

Shaping the environment with good taste is important, and good taste has little to do with cost. Through the knowledge and application of accepted principles of art and design, good taste may successfully be cultivated. People live today surrounded by so much luxury that too often they lose sight of the importance of the little things that can frequently make the difference beween a house and a home. Finding a room that cannot be improved in some way is uncommon, and the smallest change that corrects an irritating problem or adds a touch of beauty may make a major contribution to the ease and pleasure of daily living. With the mounting pressures of modern life, it is increasingly important that environments provide feelings of serenity and well-being. True peace may come from within, but a well-planned environment can nurture and preserve that peace.

Humans function at their best in an atmosphere free from irritation and frustration. Conscious and constant refining in daily life can contribute immeasurably to feelings of repose and well-being. As people change, their needs change, and finding solutions to these changing needs is a constant challenge for the professional interior designer. Designs should reflect clients' varied interests in books, music, hobbies, and religion. A sense of appropriateness for individual life-styles should be maintained. Someone once said that people's homes are reflections of the way they live and think. Could it also be said that as a home is, so will the people dwelling within it live and think?

*Beginnings
of Interior
Environment*

CHAPTER ONE

Our Domestic Architectural Heritage

How a nation lived in its homes is now recognized as having far greater importance than facts as to how many of the same people perished and how.
—ANONYMOUS

- weather
- supplies
- national home life

The history of the American home is the history of our nation. Where did that history begin? Although some claim that the first white person settled in what is now New Mexico in 1536, and records confirm that St. Augustine, Florida, was founded in 1565, the general agreement is that the mainstream of American culture stems from those English colonists who founded Jamestown in 1607 and landed in Plymouth in 1620.

The dwellings of the earliest colonists were merely crude shelters against the elements. Soon, however, settlers in divergent areas ranging from New England to Louisiana, living under particular circumstances and using *indigenous* materials, constructed houses that filled their individual needs and expressed their distinctive characteristics. Through this process a variety of architectural styles evolved gradually and naturally. Because

Figure 1.1 The oldest-known stone house still standing in what was once colonial America. Built in 1639 for Reverend Henry Whitfield in Guilford, Connecticut, Old Stone House remains today a glimpse of seventeenth-century America. (Photograph by Elliott Erwitt, courtesy of Magnum.)

speed was necessary in providing all early shelter, it was an important factor in determining a principal characteristic common to early *colonial* architecture: simplicity.

An understanding of the traditional styles of American architecture is necessary to the interior designer and should be of interest to the home owner. This knowledge can deepen an appreciation of our architectural heritage and can provide a foundation for better understanding the present. Rarely are the colonial styles copied precisely today, but many individual elements such as roofs, doors, windows, and other architectural details may be used to give a feeling of a particular style. Exteriors of a particular period may be adapted to fit today's floor plans and still retain the desired *traditional* appearance. One advantage of a well-designed period house is that as current styles come and go, it will never be dated.

Of equal necessity and importance to the interior designer and the home owner is an appreciation for modern architecture. Just as the well-designed *period style* will endure, so will the well-designed modern style.

The Spanish influence

Where did the history of American houses begin? The first explorers to land on American soil are believed to have been the Spaniards, who landed in Florida and Louisiana 100 years before the Pilgrims arrived in Plymouth. Some 40 or 50 years later, however, the first settlers introduced the Spanish style of architecture into the South. Of these homes, practically none remain. Damp climate, frequent hurricanes, and persistent fires have destroyed them. One house in St. Augustine, Florida, however, still stands on its original foundation. It was built in the late 1500s and was restored in 1888. This house is claimed by some as the oldest in the United States and is called Oldest House.

THE SPANISH HOUSE

Spanish architecture has always had a romantic appeal for Americans, and when well designed, this type of home has a definite charm. Many examples may be found in southern California, especially in the Santa Barbara area, where many Spanish-style buildings have been restored and opened to the public. (An example is Casa Covarrubias.) The Spanish house is particularly suitable for warm, dry climates, restricting its practical use to the South and West.

The following are the general characteristics of the Spanish house:

- Stucco-covered walls, white or tinted
- Low-pitched tile roof with broad overhang
- *Arcaded* porches surrounding an inner court (frequently)
- Floors paved with brick or tile
- Beautiful wrought-iron decoration
- Colorful tile trim around doors and on stair *risers*

Spanish

In the sixteenth century, Cortez introduced the Spanish influence into Mexico, where it took on a colonial atmosphere unique to the area. The early Spanish colonial style was simple because of unskilled Indian labor and crude materials. Its charm, however, has become a favorite in warm areas of the United States, and from time to time—during the 1920s, for instance—it has had an active revival. During the 1960s, with the popularity of the Mediterranean influence in decorating, Spanish colonial architecture again found favor in many parts of the country.

Figure 1.2. Oldest House (1565), St. Augustine, Florida. The house rests on its original foundation and is claimed by some as the oldest house in the United States. (Courtesy of the St. Augustine Historical Society.)

Figure 1.3. Santa Barbara's Street in Spain, built around an adobe hacienda dating from 1827. The tile-roofed adobes bring to life the Spanish influence of Old California. (Courtesy of the Santa Barbara Chamber of Commerce.)

THE SOUTHWEST ADOBE HOUSE

In 1605 Southern colonists traveled to the area that is now New Mexico, where they found Indians living in **pueblos**. Taos Pueblo, first visited by Captain Alvarado in 1540, is considered the oldest, and perhaps the largest, continuously occupied apartment dwelling in the United States. Today it houses about 1500 Pueblo Indians, whose way of life has changed little in 800 years.

In 1610 Santa Fe became the capital for Spain, later for Mexico, and finally for New Mexico. In that same year, Palace of the Governors, which is the oldest public building in the United States, was built on the site of an old Indian pueblo. An ancient **adobe** structure known as Old House, near the San Miguel Mission in Santa Fe, is claimed by some as the oldest house in the United States. Whether this structure is older than Oldest House in St. Augustine is not definitely established. The adobe houses built today, mainly in Arizona and New Mexico, follow the same basic style as the early adobes.

Pueblo or adobe

The following are the general characteristics of the Southwest adobe house:

□ Thick adobe walls that provide good insulation against heat

□ Rectangular construction with one or more stories

□ Rough-hewn pole **beams** projecting through walls

□ Deep-set windows

□ Pole ladders on exterior in place of interior stairs

Figure 1.4 (*top*). Taos Pueblo (ca. fifteenth century), Taos, New Mexico. (Courtesy of the New Mexico Department of Development.)

Figure 1.5 (*bottom*). Palace of the Governors (1610), Santa Fe, New Mexico. The oldest public building in the United States. (Courtesy of the New Mexico Department of Development.)

Figure 1.6. Old House, Santa Fe, New Mexico. Considered by some as the oldest house in the United States. (Courtesy of the New Mexico Department of Development.)

THE MONTEREY HOUSE

The Monterey house is a blending of the Spanish, French, and New England architecture that had its birth in California when that state was a colony of Spain and Monterey was the most important seaport on the West Coast. Since lumber was plentiful but workers were scarce, builders employed Indians, skilled in the use of adobe, for constructing the thick walls. The Spanish influence was seen in the red tile roofs, and the overhanging *balconies* with their wrought-iron railings reflected the French houses of New Orleans. The basic style had already been established when the settlers arrived from New England with their English ideas, but they contributed doors, windows, and moldings, some of which they brought with them. The result of this happy blend was the Monterey house, which after a hundred years, continues to be a popular style of architecture in some areas of America today, particularly California.

The following are the general characteristics of the Monterey house:

□ Adobe, stucco, or whitewashed brick walls—sometimes tinted

□ Flat-pitched tile roofs

□ Wide overhangs to shade windows

□ Second-story balcony

□ Woodwork showing New England influence

The Monterey style is suitable for most areas of the country. Many fine examples may be seen in the peninsula towns south of San Francisco, notably Monterey and Palo Alto.

Four adobe structures of particular interest are Old House, Santa Fe, New Mexico; S. Parson's House, Santa Fe, New Mexico; Palace of the Governors, Santa Fe, New Mexico; and the University of New Mexico, Albuquerque, New Mexico.

THE CALIFORNIA RANCH HOUSE

The California ranch house is a mixture of the Spanish style and the western farmhouse. The structure is low and rambling, and developed from an informal life-style and ample building space. This type of house is currently popular in the West and meets many families' needs. The term *ranch style* has been used so freely that many people think it means merely a long, low house. A true California ranch house, however, has several identifying characteristics:

□ Structure hugging a relatively flat ground

□ Low roofline

□ Wide, low overhangs, supported by posts

□ Indigenous materials used for construction, such as adobe, wood, stucco, or brick

□ Wing-sheltered *patio,* easily accessible from most rooms

California ranch house

Monterey

16th century. mid-evil

Our English heritage

Although the history of American architecture began with the Spanish colonists, who in the sixteenth century settled in the area now known as Louisiana and Florida, the mainstream of American culture began at Jamestown and Plymouth in the seventeenth century. The culture that British colonists brought to the new land when they settled along the Atlantic seaboard had a far greater influence on America than all other cultures combined.

TUDOR AND ELIZABETHAN PROTOTYPES

THE THATCHED COTTAGE

Perhaps most familiar to the early English settlers was the simple thatched cottage with walls of wattle and daub (interlaced boughs covered with clay and mud), which was the *prototype* of their earliest dwellings. Of the many thatched English cottages, the charming Ann Hathaway's Cottage is the most famous.

THE TUDOR HALF-TIMBER MANOR HOUSE

Having been long used in Europe, the *half-timber* house reached its most elaborate form in England in the latter part of the sixteenth century. Half-timber construction consists of large wooden columns and beams for structural components, with sections in between filled with plaster or masonry. When used in America, half-timber construction is usually simulated by placing boards on the surface, which gives the appearance of the original construction. This style, founded on the *Gothic,* is commonly referred to as *Tudor.*

Figure 1.7. Ann Hathaway's Cottage, Welford-on-Avon, Warwickshire, England. A sixteenth-century thatched and timbered construction. (Photograph by Mark K. Allen.)

TUDOR

Figure 1.8. Agecroft Hall (sixteenth century), a handsome half-timber Tudor manor house, formerly stood in Lancashire, England. In 1925 it was transported to Windsor Farms near Richmond, Virginia, where it was reconstructed. (Photograph by Miriam Stimpson.)

The half-timber Tudor house is characterized by the following:

- Two to three stories
- Half-timber construction
- Second-story overhang (frequently)
- Sharp *gables*
- Many columned chimneys
- Small-paned windows

Tudor half-timber

One picturesque half-timber manor house built in England in the sixteenth century and removed to America in 1925 is Agecroft Hall.

THE ELIZABETHAN MANOR HOUSE

During the reign of Elizabeth I, the Gothic design in architecture was merged with the new Dutch influence and resulted in the great, ornate-gabled house known as the Elizabethan.

The Elizabethan manor house is characterized by the following:

- Rambling design—often E-shaped
- Two to three stories hugging the ground
- Stone and brick construction
- Sharp gables, reflecting Dutch influence
- Gables crowned with *balustrades* (frequently)
- Many bay windows with small, leaded panes
- Doorways recessed in round or *Tudor-arch* framing
- Numerous columned chimneys; exterior chimneys common

Virginia House

A fine example of Elizabethan architecture is Virginia House, a majestic structure that was once the county seat in Warwick, England, during the time of Elizabeth I. Virginia House was moved to America in 1925 and now stands reassembled at Windsor Farms near Richmond, Virginia. The Elizabethan house built in America today follows the same general style as its prototype and is adaptable to many areas of the country.

THE STONE COTTAGE

A sixteenth-century English cottage, typical of houses in the *Cotswold* area, can be seen in Dearborn, Michigan. The cottage was moved to Dearborn, from its original setting. Houses of this type and others of English origin have had an important influence on American domestic architecture from its beginning, and from time to time have had a resurgence.

THE MEDIEVAL LOOK IN AMERICA: SEVENTEENTH AND EARLY EIGHTEENTH CENTURIES

JAMESTOWN AND SURROUNDING AREA

The shelters constructed by the British settlers who landed at Jamestown in 1607 were at first little more than caves dug in the earth or crude thatched huts. Some

Figure 1.9. Old Cotswold Cottage, sixteenth-century English medieval. Reassembled in Dearborn, Michigan. (Courtesy of the Henry Ford Museum, Dearborn, Michigan.)

Cotswold (English cottage)

Thatched cottage

huts for survival were copied from native Americans. As soon as initial hardships were overcome, however, settlers began building more substantial houses based on those they had known in England. Having come primarily from the upper classes, these colonists preferred brick, the material to which they were accustomed. This construction was made possible by local clay and lime for the mortar, which was plentiful in seashells.

Although almost nothing remains of the earliest dwellings around Jamestown, two extant brick structures build in the seventeenth century reflect their English prototypes. Adam Thoroughgood House, *circa* 1636, Norfolk, Virginia, with its brick construction, sharp gables, massive exterior chimneys, small diamond-paned windows, simple doorway, and vertical aspect, is in the *medieval* tradition of the late sixteenth century English houses and is probably the oldest brick house in America. The more complex development of the midcentury plantation houses is seen in Bacon's Castle, Surrey County, Virginia, circa 1655. Bacon's Castle is a two-story rectangular block with a high-pitched roof and unique decorative end-gables. Its most distinctive feature, however, is a projecting tower in the center of both the front and back, which rises above the *eaves*. Bacon's Castle is considered the most *authentic* Tudor-Gothic in Virginia and is the only surviving house of the period in America.

Figure 1.10. Adam Thoroughgood House (ca. 1636), Norfolk, Virginia. The oldest brick house in America, with a style reminiscent of its English ancestry. (Courtesy of Haycox Photoramic, Inc., Norfolk, Virginia.)

Bacon's Castle

NEW ENGLAND

The Pilgrims who first landed at Massachusetts Bay were for the most part from a lower economic class and were seeking political and religious freedom. Although ill equipped to meet the hardships that awaited them, they were courageous, vigorous, and religious zealots who responded to the challenge of establishing a home in a harsh and unknown land. The Pilgrims' first shelters were little more than dugouts or crude huts of boughs covered with clay (wattle and daub); yet by the middle of the seventeenth century, their homes had a surprising degree of comfort.

Because the land was heavily wooded and had to be cleared for dwellings, wood was the logical choice for construction material. In addition, adequate tools

Figure 1.11. Witch House (ca. 1642), restored, Salem, Massachusetts. An architectural treasure with distinctive medieval features. (Courtesy of the Chamber of Commerce, Salem, Massachusetts.)

were in short supply, and speed in construction was a necessity—two factors that accounted for distinctive characteristics of the seventeenth-century New England house: wood construction and simplicity. Early houses, which were built from memory, were derived from English folk architecture of the late medieval and Elizabethan period. Through the forthright use of local materials and necessary *adaptations,* the result was a unique provincialism that expressed the vigor of the early colonists. Fortunately, the sharp gables, steep roofs, large chimneys, and small-paned windows, to which the colonists had been accustomed, were practical for the severe New England climate.

The strong Tudor and Elizabethan influence in early New England architecture can be seen in many houses still standing that were built in the seventeenth century. A New England parsonage in Springfield, Massachusetts, built in 1639 of half-timber construction and with a projecting tower, reveals its English ancestry.

A unique example of a stone house in the medieval tradition is Old Stone House in Guilford, Connecticut (see Figure 1.1). Built in 1639, its 2-ft-thick walls are made of local stone and mortar, mixed with yellow clay and pulverized oyster shells. The simple vertical facade, with its tiny windows and large exterior chimneys, reveals its medieval ancestry. Its uniqueness lies in the stone construction, which was rare in the area due to lack of materials. Old Stone House remains the oldest stone house in New England today.

A notable architectural treasure of the seventeenth century is Witch House in Salem, Massachusetts, built circa 1642 and now restored. Owned by Jonathan Corwin, a judge in the witchcraft court, Witch House is believed to have been a site for some of the witch trials of the century. Other important seventeenth-century New England houses in the medieval tradition are House of Seven Gables, 1668, Salem, Massachusetts; Whipple House, 1638, Ipswich, Massachusetts; Strawberry Hill, or Proctor House, circa 1670, Ipswich, Massachusetts; Fairbanks House, 1636, Dedham, Massachusetts; John Ward House, 1684, Salem, Massachusetts; and Ironmaster's House, 1636, Saugus, Massachusetts.

TYPES OF SEVENTEENTH-CENTURY NEW ENGLAND HOUSES

Because of the circumstances peculiar to the environment, the homes of the New England settlers took on characteristics that became uniquely American.

DEVELOPMENT OF THE NEW ENGLAND
HOUSE

1650
Half-house

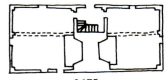

1675
Two-room or double house

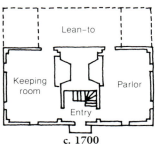

c. 1700
Lean-to or saltbox

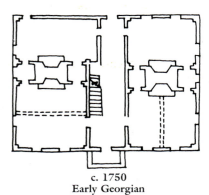

c. 1750
Early Georgian

THE HALF-HOUSE

The first houses were but a single room (half-house) with the chimney on the side wall. The door opened into a tiny entrance that abutted the chimney; from there, steep stairs rose to an attic.

THE TWO-ROOM OR DOUBLE HOUSE

Soon a second room was added on the other side, and the fireplace became the central core of the house. John Howland House, built in 1666 in Plymouth, Massachusetts, the only extant house in which Pilgrims once lived, shows the original medieval-like half-house and the 1750 addition. John Alden House, built in 1653 (now restored), is an example of a two-room house in the medieval tradition.

THE SALTBOX

To provide additional space, a lean-to that usually became the kitchen was added to the two-room house. Late in the century, the lean-to was often part of the original plan. This type of house, called a "saltbox" because the shape resembled the boxes in which settlers stored their salt, became the most characteristic silhouette of the early colonial houses. Three noteworthy examples ex-

tant today are John Quincy Adams House, 1675, Quincy, Massachusetts; Jethro Coffin House, 1686, Nantucket Island; and Ogden House, 1690, Fairfield, Connecticut.

Saltbox

THE GARRISON

In many houses, the second story extended beyond the first floor, a carry-over from medieval England. The overhang had end brackets with hand-carved *pendants*. This house is commonly called a "garrison." The garrison-style Parson Capen House in Topsfield, Massachusetts, built in 1683, is a superb example of medieval framing in America. Three other garrison houses of particular interest are Paul Revere House, 1650, Boston's oldest house; John Ward House,

Figure 1.12. Howland House (1666), Plymouth, Massachusetts. The only house still standing in Plymouth in which Pilgrims once lived. (Courtesy of the Pilgrim John Howland Society, Plymouth, Massachusetts.)

Figure 1.13. Parson Capen House (1683), Topsfield, Massachusetts. A garrison type and a superb example of medieval framing in America. (Photograph by Sydney B. Brimhall.)

Garrison

1684, Salem, Massachusetts; and Scotch-Boardman House, 1651, Saugus, Massachusetts.

THE GAMBREL

Another modification had a double-pitched roof made of two sections of rafters. This roof style was inexpensive to build and permitted more headroom in the attic. The *gambrel roof* is often incorrectly called "Dutch colonial." Seventeenth-century examples of the gambrel-roofed house are Fairbanks

Gambrel

House, 1636, Dedham, near Boston; Harlow-Holmes House, 1649, Plymouth, Massachusetts; and Glebe House, 1690, Woodbury, Connecticut.

THE CAPE COD (TRANSITIONAL)

During the final decade of the seventeenth century, one of America's best-loved houses made its appearance. This style was an outgrowth of the half-house and the two-room or double house. What has come to be known as the "Cape Cod" was a humble cottage that retained much medieval character. Covered with clapboards or shingles, the structure had a central chimney, a simple plank doorway, and small-paned win-

Cape Cod

dows—often two on one side of the entrance and one on the other. The Cape Cod derived its name from the great number of these houses that were built on Cape Cod.

Early in the eighteenth century, the Cape Cod house took on some of the features of early *Georgian* architecture, such as *dormers, dentil-trim cornices,* impressive end-chimneys and symmetrically arranged *double-hung windows*. A paneled central doorway had a transom (small window above a door or window) of small glass panes topped by a flat cornice. Later in the century, a *pedimented* doorway was sometimes added. The Cape Cod has been copied and adapted more often than any house in America, and is appropriate for almost any area in the country. Although the style often took on a more formal aspect in the eighteenth century, the quaint seventeenth-century form with the low roofline has persisted virtually unchanged to the present. Two seventeenth-century Cape Cod houses of particular interest are Jabez Wilder House, circa 1690, Hingham, Massachusetts, and Jonathon Kendrick House, late seventeenth-

Figure 1.14 (*above, left*). Jonathon Kendrick House (late seventeenth century), South Orleans, Massachusetts. An early Cape Cod style. (Photograph by Arthur Haskell, courtesy of the Library of Congress.)

Figure 1.15 (*above, right*). Brush-Everard House (1717), an early eighteenth-century transitional style. Tall windows, dormers, and dentil trim show Georgian influence. (Courtesy of the Colonial Williamsburg Foundation.)

century, South Orleans, Massachusetts. Two transitional structures built early in the eighteenth century that show the Georgian influence that followed are Brush-Everard House and Raleigh Tavern, both in Colonial Williamsburg, Virginia.

Despite their distinguishing characteristics, the four seventeenth-century New England houses share a number of features:

- Rectangular plan
- Wood construction
- Central chimney
- Small casement windows
- General asymmetry
- Simple medieval character

Numerous examples of original seventeenth-century houses can still be found throughout New England; many furnished in the manner of the period are open to the public. Massachusetts has more of this type of house than any other state, and Ipswich, Massachusetts, probably has more than any other community.

THE GEORGIAN PERIOD IN AMERICA (Circa 1720–1790)

While settlers were getting established in their adopted homeland, a new style of

architecture was developing in England, which subsequently had a deep and lasting influence in America. In the 1600s, Inigo Jones had introduced the *Renaissance* style from Italy into England, where Sir Christopher Wren became its foremost exponent. In his capable hands, it developed into a gracious architectural style, adaptable to both manor house and modest dwelling. Because this style flourished during the reigns of George I, George II, and George III, it became known as "Georgian." Although Sir Christopher Wren never came to America, his influence was the dominant force in American architecture during the early Georgian period (circa 1720–1750). The latter part of the Georgian period was dominated by the *Palladianism* of another eminent English architect, James Gibbs.

By the second decade of the eighteenth century, the colonies had grown, and the people prospered due largely to the expansion of shipping and commerce. English craftspeople and builders, laden with tools and architectural drawings, arrived in the colonies. There they worked with local craftspeople, and the rugged simplicity of the earlier houses soon gave way to the new and grander Georgian styles. At the time of the

American Revolution, the new style had become familiar in American facades from Jamestown to Portsmouth.

THE EARLY GEORGIAN OR WREN-GEORGIAN STYLE (Circa 1720–1750)

The early Georgian house in America retained the basic elements, fine proportions, and symmetry of its English prototype, but took on local differences.

The following are the general characteristics of the Wren-Georgian house:

☐ Rectangular plan

☐ General feeling of dignity and formality

☐ 2½ or 3 stories with dormers

☐ *Hip roof,* often with *captain's walk*

☐ Tall end-chimneys

☐ Symmetrically placed sash windows with small panes

☐ Central doorway flanked by *pilasters* and crowned by one of the four pediment forms

☐ Prevalence of dentil-trim cornices

☐ Corner *quoins* (frequently)

☐ Bands of stone between stories

☐ Sometimes crowned by a *parapet* and a *cupola*

Wren-Georgian

The English craftspeople who arrived in the colonies in the eighteenth century brought with them handbooks for builders, filled with uniform structural information and carefully drawn decorative detail. The widespread dissemination of these manuals accounts in large

PEDIMENT FORMS

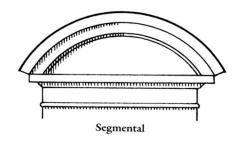

Segmental

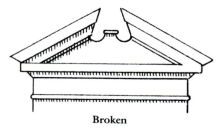

Broken

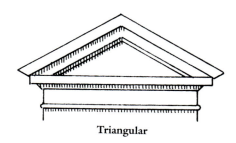

Triangular

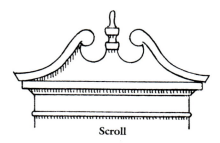

Scroll

measure for the similarity seen in the architecture of the period. This style of architecture, commonly known as "Georgian," was first seen in the colonies in Virginia, and the earliest structure was the Wren Building at William and Mary College in Williamsburg. (According to some, it was designed by Wren himself or by someone in his office, but this has not been documented.) The Wren-Georgian style, however, reached its greatest refinement in the gracious mansions that plantation owners built along the lower James River. One splendid and thoroughly English example of these early eighteenth-century houses—extant and in a remarkable state of preservation—is Westover (1730–1740). The wings were a later addition. Two other notable examples of the period and built in the area are Berkeley, 1726, on the James River, and Stratford Hall, circa 1730, on the Potomac River.

As the new style spread, great brick and wood mansions were built in the new Georgian manner but with regional differences. Rooflines varied from the hipped style to sharp gables and gambrel. Since wood was plentiful, it continued as the common building material; and although Georgian houses in the North lacked some of the formal elegance of southern mansions, they reflected

Figure 1.16. Westover (1730–1740), near Richmond on the lower James River. Typical of Georgian plantation houses, it was reputed to have the most beautiful doorway in the colonies. (Courtesy of the Convention and Visitor's Bureau, Richmond, Virginia.)

the formal grandeur of the Wren-Georgian style. Some examples of Wren-Georgian architecture in the North are MacPheadris-Warner House, 1718 to 1723, Portsmouth, New Hampshire; Ropes Memorial, 1719, Salem, Massachusetts; Hunter House, 1746, Newport, Rhode Island; and Wentworth-Gardner House, 1760, Portsmouth, New Hampshire.

THE LATE GEORGIAN OR GIBBS PALLADIAN STYLE (Circa 1750–1790)

The Roman Palladian style (developed by Andrea Palladio, an Italian Renaissance architect), which became popular with the English aristocracy in the early eighteenth century, was introduced into America near midcentury, primarily through books. Among the many builders' manuals that made their way to the colonies, perhaps most important was James Gibbs's (1682–1754) *A Book of Architecture,* first published in England in 1728 and believed to have reached the new land in 1751. Intended as a pattern book, its simple and conservative style had an immediate appeal to the colonists, and exerted a powerful influence on American architecture. Although buildings retained the basic Wren-Georgian style, Gibbs's new Palladianism offered a more monumental quality and a greater degree of formality than did earlier buildings.

The following are the general characteristics of the Palladian house in America:

□ Features of basic structure essentially Wren-Georgian

□ Classical details such as pilasters and pediments

□ Central section of facade emphasized by pedimented *pavilion* extending above the roofline

□ Pavilion sometimes flat, sometimes projecting *portico* form

□ Side dependencies or wings connected to the main block, sometimes by open *colonnades*

□ *Palladian window* prevalent.

Palladian influence seen in side dependencies

Gibbs-style pedimented pavilion

In the South the Palladian influence was seen in the symmetrical villa-like plan with its central block and side dependencies extending on either side. One of the first of this type was Carter's Grove, built 1750 to 1753. Its central block was in the Wren style, but its symmetrical wings reflected the new Palladianism. Some outstanding Palladian houses in the South are Tyron Palace, 1760, New Bern, North Carolina; Hammond-Harwood House, 1773 to 1774, Annapolis, Maryland; and Miles Brewton House, 1765 to 1769, Charleston, South Carolina.

In the Middle Atlantic states, side dependencies (when used) were usually detached from the central block. Mount Pleasant, built in 1761 in Fairmount Park, Philadelphia, was the most imposing house of the area. Another great mansion with a formal Gibbs facade in Fairmont Park is Woodford (1742–1756).

Figure 1.17. Hunter House (1746), Newport, Rhode Island. Typical of the Wren-Georgian style in the North, it ranks among the ten best examples of colonial residential architecture in America. (Photograph by John T. Hopf, courtesy of the Newport County Chamber of Commerce.)

Figure 1.18. Carter's Grove (1750–1753). One of the first houses to show the Palladian influence in the side dependencies. (Courtesy of Colonial Williamsburg Foundation.)

Figure 1.19. Mount Pleasant (1761), Fairmount Park, Philadelphia, Pennsylvania. The imposing mansion with its formal Gibbs-style facade was considered one of the grandest in the colonies. (Courtesy of the Convention and Tourist Bureau, Philadelphia, Pennsylvania.)

Figure 1.20. Longfellow Home (1750), Cambridge, Massachusetts. Its classical detail with the triangular-topped pavilion reveals Gibbs's Palladianism. (Courtesy of the U.S. Department of the Interior, National Park Service.)

In the North after 1750, wood continued as the principal material used for construction, and side dependencies were rarely added. Only the facades revealed Gibbs's Palladianism with their triangular-topped pavilions, the *classical* detail of which was more authentically done than anywhere in the colonies. Examples of particular merit are Longfellow (vassal) Home, 1750, Cambridge, Massachusetts; Lady Pepperell Mansion, circa 1760, Kittery Point, Maine; Shelton's Tavern, 1760, Litchfield, Connecticut; and Jeremiah Lee House, 1768, Marblehead, Massachusetts.

Neoclassicism in America (circa 1790–1845)

Neoclassicism in America, which covered the last decade of the eighteenth century and the first four decades of the nineteenth century, is made up of two periods: *federal* and *Greek revival.* Between Georgian Palladianism, federal, and Greek revival, however, no clear lines of demarcation exist. Rather, one style gradually blends into the other. Much neoclassicism was communicated to the colonies through books; yet in the fervor of achieving national identity, young men were encouraged to go abroad and study classical architecture. This effort resulted in a group of trained and highly motivated American-born architects. In the early nineteenth century, British and French architects began arriving on the scene—among whom English-born Benjamin Latrobe (1764–1820) was the first—and European ideas were further infused into American architecture.

THE FEDERAL PERIOD
(Circa 1790–1825)

The decades following the revolutionary war were eventful for America. The tendency was to break with anything reflecting English dominance, and interest in French *modes* grew. Consequently, when the excavation of *Pompeii* captured the interest of French designers during the reign of Louis XVI, as well as the interest of the Adam brothers in England, the new classical style rapidly superseded the Georgian. Although America was reluctant to adopt this style from England, the style exerted great influence during the period following the adoption of the Declaration of Independence. The architectural style of the early federal period, influenced primarily by the designs of the Adam brothers, was concentrated in the North, but the later phase, which was dominated by Thomas Jefferson, occurred in the South.

Two main factors brought about this change in America: (1) the need for an official architecture and (2) Thomas Jefferson's enthusiasm for the new classicism, together with his distaste for English-Georgian architecture. Jefferson was a scholar and a skillful architect, and his designs for the new capitol of Virginia at Richmond, inspired by the Maison Carrée in France, established the columned portico as the essential motif of American official architecture. His home, Monticello, strongly influenced the design of domestic buildings. Jefferson's support of architects such as Latrobe, who was trained in the new classicism, enabled the classical revival to attain a greater vogue in America than it did in England. Young architects traveled to Greece and Rome, where they took exact measurements of Greek temples and adapted them to American buildings. Throughout the colonies, buildings had columns that were capped with one of the three famous Greek orders (i.e., *Doric, Ionic,* or *Corinthian*). Columns also appeared inside, separating rooms and supporting mantels. Triangular pediments were placed over doorways, windows, and fireplaces; *reeding, bead-and-reel, egg-and-dart,* the urn, and all manner of classical decorations were employed both inside and out. Around 1820, Jefferson classicism had developed

CLASSIC GREEK ORDERS

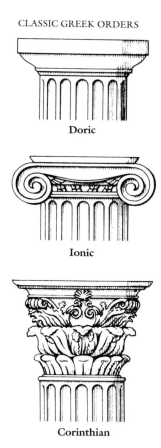

Doric

Ionic

Corinthian

Figure 1.21. Monticello (1769–1809), home of Thomas Jefferson, Charlottesville, Virginia. (Courtesy of the Thomas Jefferson Memorial Foundation.)

Figure 1.22. Pingree House (1804), Salem, Massachusetts. A dignified federal period mansion designed by Samuel McIntire. (Courtesy of the Chamber of Commerce, Salem, Massachusetts.)

into a full-blown Greek revival. The Wren-Georgian style was not immediately discarded, however. The basic style of the Georgian house continued to be used, and only the details, particularly the addition of the pillared portico, indicated the postrevolutionary date.

In the residential work of the federal period, four names stand out as representing the best architectural design: Samuel McIntire of Salem, Charles Bulfinch of Boston, John McComb of New York, and Benjamin Latrobe in the South. Among these architects, the first is probably the best known. McIntire planned three-story, square, dignified mansions with exquisite detail and simplicity. McIntire's influence was largely responsible for transforming the small seaport town of Salem, Massachusetts, into the city that became known as the "New World Venice." The elegant three-story porticoed homes that he designed

Federal

for well-to-do citizens have been considered as representative of one of the purest styles of architecture ever developed. Salem remains today the most typical example of an American city of the federal period.

The following are the general characteristics of the federal period house:

□ Main structure usually in early Georgian style and often three stories high

□ A columned portico in front

□ Doorway sidelights (frequently); entrance topped by *elliptical fanlight*

□ Windows crowned by pediments (frequently)

□ Balustrade above cornice, concealing roof (frequently)

Excellent examples of houses of the federal period extant today are Pierce-Nichols House, 1782, Salem, Massachusetts; Pingree House, 1804, Salem, Massachusetts; Harrison Gray Otis House, 1796, Boston, Massachusetts; Monticello, completed 1769 to 1809, Charlottesville, Virginia; Homewood, circa 1800, Baltimore, Maryland; Nathaniel Russell House, 1809, Charleston, North Carolina; and The White House, present structure completed 1829.

THE GREEK REVIVAL PERIOD (Circa 1825–1845)

Although the neoclassic style reached the South later than it did the North, the style of the Greek revival period—the final phase of neoclassicism—perhaps became more predominant in the South than anywhere else. The size and elegance of the plantation mansion, the ample space for expansion, and the luxurious manner of living lent themselves well to the new style. The architects in the South did not merely build *replicas* of Grecian temples, but adapted the *classic* style to meet the needs of the hot climate. Two-story columns framed the cool *verandas,* which often encircled the entire house.

Greek revival—isolated temple form

On a more modest scale, the Greek revival house was a simple pitched-roof structure much like earlier houses, but the short end faced the street. Authentic Greek details were applied to the front corners. The house had Doric pilasters, above which was a flat *entablature* and a pediment with full entablature around the cornice. The door was usually asymmetrically placed, and the whole structure was painted white.

Greek revival—end turned to street

The Greek revival house is characterized by the following features:

▫ Precise adherence to Greek proportions, orders, and ornaments

▫ Isolated temple form

▫ Profuse use of two-story columns on more pretentious houses

▫ White exterior

▫ House often built with gable end to street, with or without proper colonnaded portico attachment

▫ In absence of a portico, placement of pilasters, frieze, and classically framed doorway

Figure 1.23. Abraham Hasbrouck House (1692–1712). One of the original stone houses still standing along Huguenot Street in New Paltz, New York. (Courtesy of the Huguenot Historical Society, New Paltz, New York.)

▫ Straight, square, sturdy windows

▫ Two-story columns across front or on all sides

Some examples of Greek revival houses are Andalusia, 1836, Bucks County, Pennsylvania; Wilcox-Cutts House, 1843, Orwell, Vermont; Alvin T. Smith House, 1850s, Forest Grove, Oregon; and Stanton Hall, 1852 to 1857, Natchez, Mississippi.

Other foreign influences

THE FRENCH HOUSE

The heartland of America—the area between the Allegheny and the Rocky mountains, from Canada to the Gulf of Mexico—was controlled by France for a hundred years; yet during this time, little of the area was colonized.

THE NORMAN COTTAGE

French colonists who came to America in the seventeenth century settled mainly along the St. Lawrence River and in the South along the Mississippi River. The houses they built in the North often had hipped roofs and rounded corner towers with whitewashed exteriors, reminiscent of the *châteaus* and manor houses the colonists had known in France. In 1678 French *Huguenots* founded a settlement at New Paltz, New York. Five of the original stone houses built there are standing today along what is called "Huguenot Street." One of these houses is the Abraham Hasbrouck House (1692–1712).

Early Norman cottage in the North

THE FRENCH PLANTATION HOUSE

In the South, the basic structure of the northern cottage was retained, and was adapted to the climate by adding an encircling porch covered by a broad roof (bonnet roof). The roof provided shelter from frequent rains and gave a pavilion-like appearance. Another practical adaptation was raising the house to allow an air passage underneath, which helped to keep the house dry and cool. Due to the

Pavilion house with bonnet roof

Pavilion house with stone foundation

Posts and an encircling gallery replace stone foundation

The zenith of the French plantation house during the Greek revival period

high water table, basements were impossible. A further variation was the raised cottage, in which the ground floor was built of brick or stone, topped by a white plastered wooden pavilion. *French doors* opened on all sides onto the porch, which served as a hallway.

With the passage of time, new architectural influences were evidenced in the evolution of the French house. The masonry wall of the lower floor was replaced by posts that supported an encircling balcony. When neoclassicism swept the country, posts gave way to classical columns on both upper and lower stories, and windows were surmounted by pediments.

During the prosperous decades that preceded the Civil War, the Greek revival period reached its zenith in the great plantation mansions of the South. Two-story Greek columns swept from ground to roofline. Delicate wooden balustrades enclosed upper *galleries* and rooftops. Graceful fanlights crowned the doors. What had begun as a modest French farmhouse had blossomed into the *antebellum* mansion of flawless beauty and grandeur.

THE GALLERY HOUSE

The tiny French Cajun cottage, with its front porch protected by an overhanging roof, was the original gallery house. As the Cajun cottage evolved, it was enlarged and a second-story gallery was added on the front. As it was further embellished, it developed into the full-blown Greek revival that characterized many Southern mansions. Shadows-on-the-Teche is an excellent example. Some of the magnificent antebellum mansions that have survived to the present time are Shadows-on-the-Teche, 1830, New Iberia, Louisiana; Oak Alley, 1836, St. James Parish, Louisiana; San Francisco, 1849, Lower Mississippi, Louisiana;

Antebellum mansion

Figure 1.24. Shadows-on-the-Teche (1830), New Iberia, Louisiana. A fabled and beautiful southern Greek revival mansion. (Photograph by Gleason, courtesy of the National Trust for Historic Preservation, Washington, D.C.)

Dunlieth, 1847, Natchez, Mississippi; and Houmas, circa 1840s, New Orleans, Louisiana.

THE FRENCH TOWN HOUSE

The galleries of the French town house faced away from the street onto a private courtyard. The ground floor was used for shops or utilitarian purposes; the family quarters were above. Lacy cast-iron balconies facing the street were added in the nineteenth century, which gave the Old Quarter of New Orleans a flavor of French architecture found nowhere else in America.

Over the years, houses reminiscent of French city houses, manors, and cottages have been adapted in America, but many of these homes lack the quality and charm inherent in their originals. In more recent years, many French houses of distinctive style have been designed, which are finding favor in residential areas and are appropriate for contemporary living.

The following are the general characteristics of four French styles:

Louisiana French

□ High, raised basement to protect from floods and dampness

□ High, steep, hip roof, with or without dormers

□ Tall, decorative chimney on each end

□ French windows and shutters

□ Porch with one-story columns

□ Lacy ironwork

Louisiana French—raised basement

Figure 1.25. Dunlieth (1847), Natchez, Mississippi. Two-story columns surround this southern mansion of exceptional beauty. (Courtesy of the State of Mississippi Department of Economic Development.)

French city house

French manor

French cottage

Dutch farmhouse

French City House

□ Formal, dignified, bisymmetrical design

□ High, hip roof

□ Windows breaking line of eaves

□ Delicate stucco

□ Lacy ironwork (frequently)

French Manor House

□ Style a combination of simple château and glorified farmhouse; usually built like shallow horseshoe around three sides of courtyard

□ *Dovecote* roofs on wings

□ *Mansard roof* with dormers on central structure

□ French windows on main floor

□ Beautifully symmetrical

□ Brick painted in delicate colors

French Cottage

□ Low, hipped roof

□ Asymmetrical design

□ Arch over doorway (frequently)

□ French windows

THE DUTCH HOUSE

By 1650 Dutch settlements were well established throughout the regions of Manhattan Island (which the Dutch settlers named New Amsterdam), New Jersey, and Delaware. Although Dutch domination was brief, Albany, New York, still reflects *Flemish* influence in the few remaining houses with *stepped gables*. Dutch houses built in the countryside were usually constructed of fieldstone and typically had high, rectangular gable ends with a long, sweeping roofline extending over a full-length porch. The early Dutch gambrel had a breaking just below the ridgeline; later it was dropped to its final (lower) position. Three notable examples of the Dutch house in America are Van Cortlandt Manor, Croton-on-Hudson, New York, begun in 1665, now authentically restored; Van Rensselaer Manor, 1650, Hudson River, opposite Albany; and Dyckman House Farmhouse, 1783, New York, New York.

THE GERMAN HOUSE

German colonists who settled in Pennsylvania built snug homes of fieldstone with 2-ft-thick walls. The typical roof was steeply pitched, but the gambrel was sometimes used. A distinguishing feature found in some German houses was a sheltering hood between the first and second stories, which was known as a "pent" roof. Examples of stone houses built by the Pennsylvania Germans, mistakenly referred to as Pennsylvania Dutch (Deutsch) are Ingham Manor, circa 1750, Bucks County, Pennsylvania, and Thompson-Neeley House, 1701, Washington Crossing, Pennsylvania.

Pennsylvania German stone house with sheltering hood

Figure 1.26 (*facing page, top*). Van Cortlandt Manor, a restored revolutionary war estate in Croton-on-Hudson, New York. Built of fieldstone with characteristic Dutch rectangular gables, and long, sweeping roofline extending over full-length porch. (Courtesy of Sleepy Hollow Restorations, Tarrytown, New York.)

Figure 1.27 (*facing page, bottom*). Thompson-Neeley House (1701), Washington Crossing, Pennsylvania. An example of a Pennsylvania Dutch home. (Courtesy of the Washington Crossing Foundation.)

THE SWEDISH HOUSE

Swedish colonists who settled in the Delaware Valley in 1638 introduced the log cabin to America, although it was also familiar to the German settlers. Log construction, however, was borrowed to only a limited extent on the eastern seaboard. With the opening of new wilderness areas for colonization, particularly the westward movement, the log cabin became the standard dwelling. Swedish colonists also built stone houses, often with gambrel roofs, large end-chimneys, and dormers. Three of the few authenticated early Swedish houses extant are John Morton Homestead (log), 1654, New Prospect Park, Pennsylvania; Hendrickson House, 1690, Delaware Valley, Pennsylvania; and Keith House, 1722, Graeme Park, Pennsylvania.

The Victorian era (circa 1845–1900)

Architecture of the industrial age coincided with the reign of Queen Victoria and bears her name. Nostalgia for buildings of the past pervaded America during this time, expressing itself in an unprecedented panoply of architectural styles. The revival of interest in Victorian architecture led to years of harsh criticism. The style has long been maligned and held in disrepute, having been referred to as the "battle of the styles," among other derogatory terms.

In recent years, however, many authorities have regarded Victorian architecture as inventive, full of vigor and diversity, and representative of a coherent and unified course of development. To-

ROOF TYPES

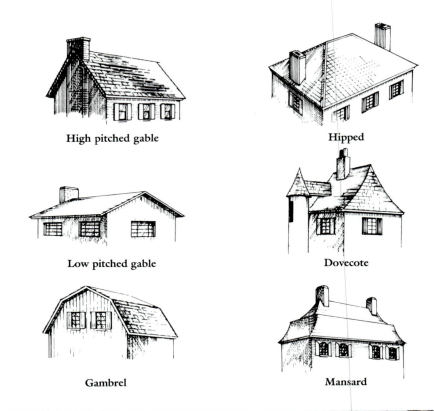

High pitched gable   Hipped

Low pitched gable   Dovecote

Gambrel   Mansard

Figure 1.28. Keith House (1722), Graeme Park, Montgomery County, Pennsylvania. Representative of the work of Swedish artisans, who built this structure from native fieldstone. (Courtesy of the Pennsylvania Historical and Museum Commission.)

day, many people believe that architecture of the nineteenth century is particularly American and is the most significant style in our nation's history. Americans throughout the country have re-discovered these picturesque yet long-neglected dwellings, and have remodeled or restored them for their own use. Children once again are sliding down the sturdy stair rails and looking out from fairytale cupolas. The Victorian house has come once more into its own.

During the second half of the nineteenth century, through a rapid succession of overlapping modes, four major architectural styles emerged: Gothic, *Italianate,* mansard, and Queen Anne.

THE GOTHIC REVIVAL (1840s–1850s)

Andrew Jackson Downing (1803–1892) is considered the father of the Gothic revival in America. Since stone—the material used in English Gothic—was costly and stonemasons were few, Downing

Carpenter Gothic

translated the English stone Gothic into wood, and the style became known as "carpenter Gothic." Thousands of these houses, many of which are still standing, were built throughout the country in the 1840s and 1850s.

The following are the characteristic features of the carpenter Gothic house:

- Broken, picturesque exterior, planned from inside out

- Steep gables

- Wood sheathing, often board and batten (vertical, overlapping boards)

- Porches leading to informal gardens

- Lofty windows, often pointed

- Bargeboard or vergeboard (shaped wooden edging) under gables

- "Gingerbread" decoration in gables (from stone *tracery,* which consisted of ornate patterns in the pointed arches of Gothic architecture)

One famous Gothic structure from the period is Lyndhurst, which was built during 1838 to 1841 in Tarrytown, New York, and overlooks the Hudson River.

THE ITALIANATE STYLE (1830s–1920s)

In the 1830s, America's admiration for the Italian arts resulted in popularity for the modified Italian *villa.* Used for both urban and suburban dwellings, including town houses, the Italianate style re-

Figure 1.29. Lyndhurst (1838–1841), Tarrytown, New York. America's most distinguished Gothic revival mansion. (Photograph by Frohman, courtesy of the National Trust for Historic Preservation, Washington, D.C.)

Italianate

mained popular for 100 years and left a lasting imprint on American architecture.
The following are the general characteristics of the early Italianate style:

□ Stately structures with vertical emphasis

□ Free arrangement of blocks and wings

□ Easy access to outdoor *terraces*

□ Wide overhanging roof with heavy and often fanciful brackets under cornice; hence called "Hudson River bracketed"

□ High windows, often arched

□ Structure topped by a square tower, built for pleasure rather than for utility

A later development was a cube-shaped house, but the tower—called a cupola, belvedere, or observatory—continued as the most distinctive feature. An adaptation of the Italianate was the town house or row house, which in the eastern cities was often known as the "brownstone" house.

THE MANSARD OR GENERAL GRANT STYLE (1850s–1870s)

The mansard roof (also called the General Grant style after Ulysses S. Grant), which originated in France, was the

answer to many architectural problems. The roof was adaptable, took a variety of shapes and sizes, and was used on many structures.

The mansard house is characterized by the following:

□ Handsome structure with tall French windows opening onto deep porches

□ Crowned by mansard roof with massive cornices; frequently topped by iron cresting

Mansard

THE QUEEN ANNE STYLE (1870s–1880s)

The most whimsical of the Victorian era's *eclectic* styles was the so-called Queen Anne. This style had no relationship to Queen Anne and was a deliberate imitation of many defunct architectural styles. The Queen Anne style, however, has some identifying characteristics:

Queen Anne style

□ Sharp gables ornamented with applied wood detail and plaster *festoons*

□ Generally low, stocky basic shape, although variable height and sometimes built on grand scale

□ Fishscale shingles common (in the form of overlapping fish scales)

□ Porches often circular with *colonnettes* and turned railings

□ Windows grouped in banks, with upper panes often colored

□ Most distinctive feature: circular tower extending from ground to floor, with circular bay windows on each floor

In the 1880s and 1890s, a revival of Old World styles left a legacy of Victorian extravagance in many areas of the country. Two areas displaying particular examples are the Hudson River region and Newport, Rhode Island. During the late nineteenth century, some Americans developed a mania for building castles along the Hudson River, which was called the "American Rhine." Although this enthusiasm was partly inspired by the flamboyance of Victorian architecture, the greatest influence came from world-traveling Americans, who desired to imitate the castle-lined Rhine in Europe. On nearly every eminence was erected a Greek temple, an Italian villa, a medieval fortress, a Tudor manor house, or an Oriental dwelling. Many of these structures have been victims of twentieth-century "progress." Others, through the

Figure 1.30 (*facing page*). Whitmore Mansion (1898), Nephi, Utah. An example of the unusual Queen Anne style. (Courtesy of Don and Darlene Bendoski, proprietors.)

concerted efforts of many dedicated individuals and organizations, remain today as monuments to Victorian architecture. Among those structures remaining are Lyndhurst, 1835, America's most distinguished Gothic revival mansion (see Figure 1.29); Alana, 1872, a majestic Persian castle; Sunnyside, 1785, the home of Washington Irving and an extravagant structure and literary shrine; and Edgemont, mid-nineteenth century, a great Gothic structure.

More than any other area in America, Newport, Rhode Island, exhibits the conspicuous wealth of the Victorian era. There, during the last half of the nineteenth century, occurred the greatest concentration of palatial residences (called "cottages"), built in a variety of Old World styles.

Four of the best known of these mansions are The Breakers, 1892 to 1895, an Italian villa and an outstanding American residence (see Figure 1.31); Marble House, 1892, a French mansion in the neoclassic style (see Figure 1.32); The Elms, 1901, a beautiful French château built in America; and Château-sur-Mer, 1852, considered an excellent example of Victorian architecture in this country.

Preserving our architectural heritage

Only during the last 15 or 20 years has the preservation of our architectural heritage generated widespread interest. Some earlier, reconstructed villages—notably Colonial Williamsburg, Sturbridge Village, and Strawbery Banke—have for some Americans created a nostalgic curiosity about the legacy of our nation. Many houses, some of which are featured in this text, have been authentically restored and made available to the public. Hundreds of homes have been preserved, but thousands have been destroyed. Magnificent structures built to stand for over a hundred years have fallen before the bulldozer, after a life of less than a third of their time.

Figure 1.31 (*top*). The Breakers (1892–1895), in the foreground of an aerial view of the Cliff Walk, which depicts the concentration of palatial residences in Newport, Rhode Island, at the turn of the century. (Photograph by John T. Hopf, courtesy of the Newport County Chamber of Commerce.)

Figure 1.32 (*bottom*). Marble House (1892), Newport, Rhode Island. A lavish mansion modeled after the Petit Trianon in Versailles. (Photograph by John T. Hopf, courtesy of the Newport County Chamber of Commerce.)

Since the years when colonial architecture was developed and refined, its popularity has never ceased throughout the United States, especially with respect to the small home. Although building materials may vary in different areas, this need not alter the inherent charm found in the original styles. Because colonial styles depend so little on ornamentation and so much on proportion and scale for their beauty, they must be expertly designed and built. Colonial houses are appropriate for many areas of the country, and their well-proportioned design will never become dated.

Enthusiasts of American architectural history, those interested in America's cultural heritage, and casual observers can view houses from every period today. A considerable number of these houses are in their original form; others have been restored. Many are furnished in the authentic style of the time in which they were built, and are open to the public.

Perhaps the most important towns surviving today with much of their early architecture extant are Ipswich and Salem, Massachusetts; Portsmouth, New Hampshire; Newport, Rhode Island; Charleston, South Carolina; Natchez, Mississippi; and New Orleans, Louisiana. Ipswich probably has the most seventeenth-century houses. Salem is well known for its imposing federal period mansions. Many designed by McIntire border the famed Chestnut street, once reputed to be the "handsomest street in America." Newport, once known as the "Athens of the New World," claims the distinction of having more prerevolutionary buildings (about 300) than any other community in the United States. In Portsmouth, however, the most complete

and well-preserved record remains. The houses range from simple structures with weathered siding and shingles to large, elaborately designed and decorated houses of the Georgian and early federal periods. Charleston, South Carolina, has preserved more of the beauty of its rich historical background than perhaps any colonial city in the continent. In no other city in the United States are there so many superbly built and exquisitely decorated southern-style homes. Once every year, the Charleston Historic Foundation sponsors Open-House Days, during which many private homes are open to the public. During March of each year, Natchez, Mississippi, a romantic antebellum city, recreates the charm of plantation living by opening some 30 of its great houses to the public.

In the past, people interested in old structures were sometimes looked on as eccentric and somewhat anomalous. This attitude is changing, however. Throughout the country, organizations have been established to locate, research, and preserve old buildings in local communities. The concern of these organizations is not limited to impressive public buildings and distinguished mansions; their interest extends to all structures—old mills, candy factories, even whole neighborhoods—provided these buildings have documented historic value. Many of these organized groups are made up of young people, who are finding in their architectural heritage a sense of permanency and a connection to the past.

The National Trust for Historic Preservation in Washington, D.C., founded in 1949, is the largest organization in the country that is devoted to the preservation of historic buildings, districts, and neighborhoods. A private entity sustained by public and private contributions, the National Trust maintains historic buildings as museums, disseminates information about preservation to property owners and to the public at large, and assists in a variety of preservation, restoration, and rehabilitation efforts around the country. Local chap-

ters have been organized in cities and counties throughout the country, and many sites have recently been designated as historic landmarks for preservation and restoration.

The Victorian Society of America, founded in the late sixties, has local chapters from coast to coast. Members of this organization are dedicated to the preservation of the architecture and decorative arts of the nineteenth and early twentieth centuries. Their efforts are predicated on the belief that the Victorian era was the most typically American era in our country's history.

The present trend of preserving America's past is now well established and should gain momentum as time progresses. Although thousands of impressive, historic buildings have needlessly been destroyed, the many others remaining can and should be saved.

CHAPTER TWO

*The
Modern House
and
Future Trends*

During the 1880s, the United States rebelled against nineteenth-century eclecticism and enslavement to the past—a reaction that was first seen in Europe. The originators of this movement in the United States were Frank Lloyd Wright—who became what many consider America's greatest architect—and a group of Chicago architects, led by Louis Sullivan. Through experimentation with the new materials and technology that were developed during the industrial revolution, they made rapid architectural progress.

The modern house

In 1892, Wright broke with Sullivan and set up his own practice. His work was soon recognized in Europe, and by the turn of the century he was well known in the Chicago area. His innovative techniques eventually won acclaim throughout the United States. During the first half of the twentieth century, Wright was the dominant force in American architecture. In 1894, he formulated the following fundamental principles of what he called "organic architecture":

□ The house must be integrated with the site in a harmonious relationship.

□ The structural materials must be frankly revealed.

□ Planning must be done from the inside out, with spatial flexibility and with the fireplace the heart of the house.

□ The house must have horizontal emphasis, asymmetrical composition, and a minimum of applied decoration.

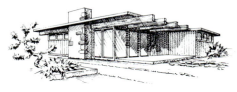

Modern

Falling Water, built in 1936 at Bear Run, Pennsylvania, is Wright's most famous house and illustrates the architect's firm principles.

The international house

During the second decade of the twentieth century, efforts were being made in the United States to assimilate new materials and techniques in the develop-

Figure 2.1 (*facing page*). An earth-sheltered house, planned for maximum energy conservation. The greenhouse provides passive solar energy. The floor plan is shown at right. (Courtesy of Milliner Construction, Inc., Frederick, Maryland.)

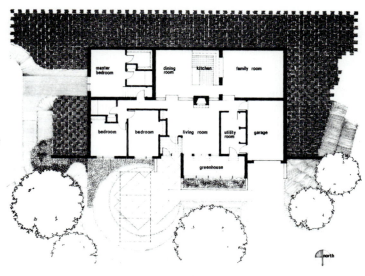

Figure 2.2. Falling Water (1936), Bear Run, Pennsylvania. The best-known house among those designed by Frank Lloyd Wright. (Photograph by Michael Tedison, courtesy of the Western Pennsylvania Conservancy.)

ment of a new type of architecture. This architectural form, which became known as the *international style,* was based on the teachings of the *Bauhaus.* Headed by Walter Gropius, the Bauhaus was a school of art and architecture begun in 1919 in Weimar, Germany, for the purpose of unifying art and technology. The Bauhaus style concentrated on applying practical artisanship to solve industrial problems, and was characterized by an economy of design and geometric proportion. The school, however, met with vigorous opposition from the German government. It was moved twice and finally closed in 1933. In the meantime,

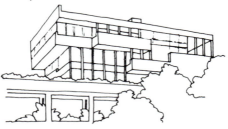

The international style

Gropius and other members of the Bauhaus came to America, where they gave impetus to the new movement.

Villa Savoye in Poissy, France, designed by Le Corbusier and built during 1929 to 1931, displays the beginnings of modern sculptural architecture and the international style. Villa Savoye is considered a great residential building of the twentieth century.

The international style, a term that American architects Philip Johnson and Henry-Russell Hitchcock coined, reached its apogee in the 1950s and established for a generation of architects a discipline based on functionalism and purity of line. The formula set down for the new international style had many features of the earlier modern style of Frank Lloyd Wright. Whereas the organic (or modern) house was integrated with its sur-

Figure 2.3. Villa Savoye (1929–1931), Poissy, France, designed by Le Corbusier. Raised on free-standing columns, the stark white, flat-roofed structure seems to float in space. (Photograph by Miriam Stimpson.)

roundings, the international house, with its flat roof, stark white masonry walls (resulting from the use of reinforced concrete), and large windows, stood out in direct contrast to its natural environment.

Some notable homes in the international style are Lovell House, by Richard Neutra, Los Angeles, 1929; Charles Eames Case Study House, Santa Monica, California, 1949; Edith Farnsworth House, by Ludwig Miës van der Rohe, Plano, Illinois, built 1949 to 1951; Walter Gropius House, Lincoln, Massachusetts, 1938; Philip Johnson House, New Canaan, Connecticut, 1949; and Douglas House, by Richard Meier, Harbor Springs, Michigan, 1975.

By the late 1960s, postmodern architecture had begun to borrow from the early modernists, whose principles were combined with new, creative designs and modern technology. Since then, the modern house in America has been freely experimental and innovative as architects meet the challenges of inflation, land shortages, and energy conservation.

Although categorizing the modern house into a standard list of characteristics is difficult, the following features generally apply:

□ Basically plain design; ornamentation generally geometric or abstract

□ Frank use of materials such as wood, stone, brick, concrete, stucco, metal, plastic, and glass

□ Line emphasis horizontal (as seen in early modern), vertical, diagonal, or curved

□ Asymmetrical composition usually dominant

□ Continuous wall surfaces, often combined with large openings and large panes of glass

□ Open floor plan

□ Roofs flat (as seen in early modern), domed, pitched, or in a variety of forms including solar paneling

□ Great freedom of architectural expression

The Japanese house

The Japanese house has contributed much to the modern style of architecture in America, particularly to the mass-produced **prefabricated** house. The classic Japanese house was usually constructed of wood, and although many of the houses built today use concrete, steel, masonry, and stucco, they still retain the classic Japanese form. In recent years, many California architects have adapted Japanese ideas to meet American needs.

The following are general characteristics of the Japanese house:

□ Wood construction (frequently)

□ Unpretentious facade with frequent retaining walls

□ Sloping, protective overhangs with hipped and gable roof

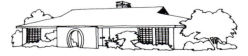

Japanese house

□ Natural stone foundation supporting posts and roof

□ Close connection to outdoors; garden (often several small gardens) part of house

□ Open planning with **fusuma screen** partitions

□ Materials left in natural state

□ Predominance of horizontal lines

□ Avoidance of symmetry

□ Honest expression of basic structure

□ Feeling of serenity and refinement

□ Universal use of uniform module 3-by-6-ft **tatami mat** (here translated into 4-by-8-ft gypsum board)

Present trends

A recent survey of population shifts shows that since the peak of metropolitan growth, which occurred in the mid-1970s, a definite move to small communities has occurred. This survey, done by Professor Harley Johansen, University of Idaho, and Professor Glen Fuguitt, University of Wisconsin, is the first systematic analysis of American villages (population 2500 or less) done on a national scale since the late 1920s. The findings of the survey are published in *The Changing Rural Village in America: Demographic and Economic Trends Since 1950.*

The latest home ownership survey (1983) by the U.S. League of Savings Institutions shows that condominiums are not the wave of the future. Although still favored by retirees, condominums are in excess supply. When lower interest rates and prices provided the opportunity, the baby boom generation chose single-family houses on their own lots. Condominiums in most cases were considered as temporary accommodations.

Despite a nationwide trend in the early seventies toward simplification to provide affordable housing, most people still want the amenities they have come to expect in today's housing, particularly in the kitchen, the bathroom, and the master bedroom.

MARKET DEMANDS

Because of inflation, high interest rates, the need for energy conservation, smaller families, and changes in life-styles, a number of significant changes in the demands of the building market have recently occurred:

□ Buyers are better educated than in the past and are asking more questions.

□ Important to buyers is the optimum balance of value and cost—a concept known in the building market as "value effectiveness." In other words, people want their money's worth when buying a home.

□ Buyers are interested in saving energy.

□ Buyers place a high value on prestigious locations.

□ Living units must suit a variety of life-styles.

□ Buyers place a high priority on security.

□ Buyers want homes with low maintenance, labor-saving devices, and water-saving appliances, especially dishwashers, toilets, and shower heads.

TRENDS IN HOME DESIGN

To anticipate market needs, architects and builders are forecasting that in the near future:

□ Fewer single-family homes will be built in conventional subdivisions.

□ Living spaces in both attached and detached housing will be smaller than those to which Americans are accustomed.

□ Volume will be used to make spaces more flexible and to give them a larger appearance.

□ Although rooms will be fewer, they will be larger and will have more flexibility.

□ Floor plans will be influenced by changing life-styles and will be more expandable.

□ More industrialization and factory-made parts will be used, with on-site building techniques joining with pre-fabricators.

□ Buyers will have more options, such as the capacity to add or subtract walls, and to choose or refuse luxury appliances.

□ Security will be given a high priority.

□ New product advances will be used to save labor, cut down on maintenance, promote luxury and convenience, save energy, and save space (but retain the appearance of space).

Options for prospective home owners in the 1980s

A wide variety of options are available for the prospective home owner today. He or she can choose a custom-designed, predesigned, or factory-built home, a tract home, a **condominium,** an apartment, an older home to remodel, or a motor home. Each of these options has various advantages and disadvantages. The buyer's household size, life-style, and economic capability will determine what the choice will be.

Although increasingly fewer buyers are able to build the home of their dreams, some people *are* able to plan and build single-family detached houses. Those people have three building options: (1) the custom-designed plan, (2) the predesigned plan, and (3) the factory-built (prefabricated) package. The buyer should carefully examine each option to determine which one most closely meets his or her household's physical and economic needs. Problems involved in building will be solved differently, depending on which building option the buyer chooses. Before making the final decision to build a home, the buyer must accept that many problems may arise. Building a home requires much planning, numerous decisions, and infinite patience, but the final product can bring many rewards.

THE CUSTOM-DESIGNED HOUSE

The buyer who chooses a custom-designed plan first works out a personalized floor plan, indicating room arrangement, traffic lanes, storage, wall space, doors, and windows. When the floor plan has been finalized, the buyer hires an architect, who makes rough drawings for the buyer's approval. After approval is obtained, the architect prepares the final working drawings. He or she helps the buyer to select materials and obtain contract bids, and acts as liaison between buyer and builder. The architect also oversees the construction to ensure that the house is built according to the buyer's specifications. A custom-designed plan is the most expensive procedure, but is followed in the construction of much upper middle-class and prestigious housing.

Two alternatives to working with a professional architect are available. One is to hire an architectural designer. Here, the quality of work is often comparable to that of the professional architect, but the fee is less. The other alternative for the buyer is to let a local architect at a reputable building firm draw up his or her plans and supervise the building. Most lumber companies have such drafters on their staff, and the charge for their services is minimal if the buyer purchases materials through the company.

The primary problem in custom design is cost. When people are building for the first time, they are seldom prepared to cope with the unexpected costs that inevitably arise. Too often they have an unrealistic notion of what their desired home will cost, and getting a firm estimate on the finished project is almost impossible today. A great amount of planning and research is the best assurance of satisfaction. A wise house plan for a young family is one that is potentially expandable. A basement or an upstairs can be roughed in (the necessary construction for walls, floors, and ceilings installed) and converted to usable space at a later time. If planned initially, walls can be added later to the main floor with a minimum of expense.

THE PREDESIGNED HOME PLAN

Some buyers consider the cost of an architect prohibitive and choose a predesigned plan instead. Thousands of plans are available today, and a set of complete working drawings is moderately priced, depending on the designer and the size of the home. These drawings can be purchased directly from the plan service, from the individual designer, or through building magazines.

The problem with a stock plan is that the buyer may not find one that exactly fits his or her needs. The buyer should study many plans carefully to find the one that most closely approximates his or her personalized plan. Making minor alterations to the predesigned plan is possible, and the cost savings will justify making some personal compromises. Some plans include a complete materials list, detailing the quantity and size of lumber, doors, windows, and many other items that will be used in construction.

After selecting a plan, the buyer hires a contractor and discusses with him or her any minor changes that are desired. Any modifications can usually be accomplished with little or no extra expense if they are done during the planning stage. Once building has begun, however, any construction change becomes expensive, not only in this type of plan but also in

any plan. When the details have been worked out, the project should proceed much the same as with a custom-designed house, except that an architect will not do the supervising unless the buyer makes special arrangements for this service. Developing the competency to do the supervising personally may be time well spent for the buyer. His or her concern with every detail will compensate for any lack of technical know-how.

THE FACTORY-BUILT (PREFABRICATED) HOUSE

The use of industrialized building techniques is no newcomer to the United States. Many of the early settlers built their cabins from panelized parts shipped from England. Since that time, technology has come a long way, and today a well-constructed factory-produced house cannot be distinguished from its *counterpart* of traditional construction. Unfortunately, the term *prefab* has for too long carried the stigma of inexpensive, inferior housing. As a result, people have often regarded this house as one to be built only as a last resort. Public resistance to factory-built homes is rapidly changing, however, due to improvements in design and construction and the high cost of traditional building methods. Many people are now purchasing and enjoying this

Figure 2.4. A basic one-story factory-built house in compact styling is planned for efficiency, economy, and expansibility. (Courtesy of Capital Industries.)

Figure 2.5. A classic 1½-story Cape Cod style factory-built house. A basic affordable home designed to grow with the family. (Courtesy of National Homes.)

Assembling a modular home at the site

Exterior

Interior

type of house, and some industry sources predict that factories will soon be producing half the nation's housing.

Factory-built houses come in three basic types: (1) the **modular house**, consisting of various elements made and put together at the factory and shipped for immediate assembly on a permanent site, (2) the *component unit*, a precut house in which all materials are cut, sized, and labeled in sequence for fast erection, and (3) the *mobile home*, also a modular house, but put together and shipped in one or more units to be placed on a temporary foundation, which in the vast majority of cases becomes permanent.

Buying a factory-built home has a number of benefits. Because these homes are built in quantity, less waste occurs, quality can be controlled, which many manufacturers claim produces a higher-quality home, and inspection is done at less cost. All these factors add up to better homes for less money. Another item to be considered is *time*. People often take months—even years—to de-

cide to buy or build a home, but when the decision is made, they want instant results. The factory-built house can be ready for occupancy in a fraction of the time it takes to construct a house by conventional methods. Moreover, the conventional route to building is fraught with uncertainties and hazards. Scarcity of available skilled labor, along with vandalism and pilferage, may contribute to delay and to unexpected expense. A definite price established at the outset for the factory-built house precludes the latter. In addition to these benefits, factory-built homes can be just as energy efficient as their site-built counterparts.

Mobile homes began as makeshift shelters in the housing shortage days of the 1940s. The term *mobile home* is a misnomer, since these homes spend only 1 percent of their time on the move. The Mobile Home Manufacturers Association calls a mobile home a "transportable structure built on a chassis and designed to be used as a dwelling unit with or without a permanent foundation when connected with the required utilities."

When mobile homes were first put on the market, they were looked on as the poor relations of housing, and mobile home parks were a dreaded neighborhood liability. Today their role in the housing market is of increased importance. Radical changes have taken place in the homes themselves and in the

Figure 2.6. Thoughtful placement on the site and use of exterior elements and planting can comfortably integrate the mobile home into a traditional neighborhood.

attitudes that many people have about them. In general, the public today is becoming better informed on housing at all levels, and a growing awareness of and a demand for better quality and design are bringing about improvements in the mobile home. Evidence of these changes is seen not only in the recent alliance between industry and architecture but also in an increased sophistication in technology and in a growing belief that good design need not be costly.

With skyrocketing prices, the need for manufactured housing has increased, the greatest demand coming from the young and the old. In the 1970s, the largest number of mobile homes was purchased by people under 33 and over 55 years of age. With the present increase in the number of people between 20 and 34, and between 55 and 74, the demand is increasing dramatically. With a lessening of the concern that mobile parks are harmful to the aesthetic environment, mobile home subdivisions promise to increase. They will be better planned and surrounded by attractive gardens that the occupants may own and maintain.

The change in public attitude toward mobile homes in recent years has brought about new zoning that has helped to move them out of trailer parks and into subdivisions. New government deregulations have removed costly financing—making it possible for mobile homes to be financed almost the same as on-site houses. With these advantages, and with the poor image eliminated, the mobile home should be a practical alternative and a leader in affordable houses in the future.

SHELL FRAMING

One concept that is having moderate success is shell framing, in which the builder constructs, on the owner's foundation, a bare frame with doors and windows. Finishing of the roofs, interior walls, plumbing, electricity, and all inside work are left to the owner. The result of this type of construction depends on the ingenuity and business acumen of the owner.

THE TRACT HOME

The term *tract house* refers to a house that is one of a group of dwellings in which only a few alternative plans are used. Mass production allows the builder to offer such a house at a price considerably less than a custom-built one. If the location of the tract is wisely chosen with future area growth in mind, and the house well designed and constructed, the value of a tract house should keep pace with inflation and should bring a higher price than the buyer initially paid, should he or she wish to sell later. A completed tract home is offered at a set price "as is." If the buyer contracts the builder before construction has begun, however, making minor changes is possible, at little or no extra cost. The buyer is also permitted to select paint colors and to have some choice in the selection of appliances.

During the 1950s and 1960s, tract developments created neighborhoods in which row upon row of look-alike houses presented an atmosphere of total anonymity. Individual families were hard put to give their homes a distinct person-

Figure 2.7. Town house condominiums. Attractive two-story multifamily town houses provide convenient living for a variety of life-styles. (Courtesy of Kinateder and Smart Associates.)

ality. This trend is being reversed today as more and more planned communities with houses of varying styles are clustered to take advantage of natural surroundings and to create a feeling of individual living. Today, however, the tract house to a great extent is being replaced by the condominium.

THE CONDOMINIUM

Another alternative in the choice of a home is the condominium or town house apartment. *Condominium* is a Latin word dating back to the sixth century, meaning "joint dominion" or "joint ownership." Such an arrangement does not specify a type of housing, however; it is a financial governance commitment that may involve any type of housing. The occupant is the sole owner of his or her own apartment or housing unit in a multi-

family project, but shares with other co-owners common areas and elements of the property, such as gardens, swimming pools, and lobbies. All owners share in making the rules and in governing the project; in many places they also share the responsibility for enforcing the rules.

The *co-op* is a variation of the condominium. In the co-op, the resident owns a share in the corporation that owns the building. Co-op residents have a long-term proprietary lease on their units, but must get approval for a would-be buyer from the board of directors. Condominium owners may sell to whomever they wish and have their own mortgage on their individual unit. Co-op

tenants might share the mortgage of the entire project.

Once thought of as places for weekend retreats, condominiums are now being used year-round. Many refinements have been added, but the main advantages seem to be good security and freedom from maintenance worries. All mechanical conveniences that contribute to creature comforts, such as utility centers, electrical apparatus, heating, and air conditioning, are taken care of. Some disadvantages are present, however. Yards are usually small, and storage space is often limited. Because of the necessary cooperative nature of these communities in solving common neighborhood problems that arise, living happily in such close proximity is often difficult for families with children. Nevertheless, many first-time home buyers—singles (young or elderly), elderly couples, busy professionals who may or may not walk to work, small families with one or both parents, couples whose grown children have left home, and many others—find the condominium the best answer to their housing needs and the best buy per square foot.

Condominiums are designed in two basic styles: the conventional *row house,* or town house, design and the *cluster.* Town house condominiums are usually two or three stories and are made up of similar attached units. *Cluster planning,* which has more of the appearance of the single-family dwelling, represents a more enlightened attitude about today's environment. Detached and attached single-family houses are clustered around cul-de-sacs with a central recreation area, and cluster groups are isolated from each other by green belts.

THE APARTMENT

In the past, many people—particularly newly married and mature couples—have chosen the apartment as their home. Apartment dwellers pay a monthly rent, which sometimes includes the cost of utilities and the use of laundry facilities. Renters are free from obligations outside of the apartment itself, and privacy is usually a sought-after advantage. Apartment living for families with children, however, is usually not the most desirable, since many apartment houses do not allow children. Moreover, apartments throughout the country are being converted into condominiums and co-ops which may eventually make the traditional apartment a thing of the past.

Figure 2.8. Clustered condominiums have the charm and individuality of custom-built homes, plus the advantages of a planned community. (Courtesy of the Irvin A. Blietz Organization.)

THE MOTOR HOME

The motor home is usually a temporary dwelling and is most often used for vacation living. Originally considered only as an economical way to provide food and lodging while traveling, today's motor home is a recreational vehicle that offers comforts, conveniences, and luxuries that have a great appeal to a wide segment of the population.

The biggest advantage of a motor home over other types of recreational vehicles is that the unit is completely self-sufficient and self-contained. Varying in length from 20 to 27 ft, the unit has electricity, gas, and water, without requiring connections to external sources, although such connections may be used and are available. Shower stalls and fresh-water flush toilets with waste-holding tanks are standard equipment, and campgrounds located throughout the country operate dumping stations. An efficient heating system makes comfort in cold weather possible. Compact, well-planned space provides room for food preparation and storage, dining, sleeping, clothing storage, and relaxation, with a surprising amount of comfort, privacy, and space for movement.

Motor homes constructed by reputable companies are built to rigid national codes and federal standards. Their electrical, plumbing, and heating systems meet codes established by the National Recreational Vehicle Industry Association. For many young couples, this type of dwelling can be an economical temporary home while attending college or while saving for a permanent home. An established part of the American scene, the motor home will likely continue in the foreseeable future.

Figure 2.9. This 31-ft motor home features oak cabinets, large coach windows, and a full galley with optional microwave. (Courtesy of Winnebago Industries, Inc.)

The Energy-efficient house

A principal challenge facing architects and builders in the eighties is the conservation of energy. In meeting this challenge, the heat from the sun, or solar energy, is being successfully harnessed and used to supplement dwindling and progressively more expensive energy supplies.

THE SOLAR HOUSE

Solar houses come in a variety of guises and may be large or small, but all have one common attribute: they are built to capture the sun's energy and conserve conventional fuel. Solar energy is used by way of two major systems: *passive* and *active*.

THE PASSIVE SOLAR ENERGY SYSTEM

The passive system is a nonmechanical method that relies on the house itself to absorb and store the sun's heat. The system uses indoor thermal masses of air, found in garden rooms, greenhouses, and indoor pools, and masses of masonry such as walls and floors where heat from the sun makes direct penetration. In each case, heat is absorbed during the day and is radiated at night.

The *envelope* house, a self-cooling and self-heating unit, is a new concept in passive thermal regulation. By this method, the house is encircled by a continuously circulated envelope of air. Excess heat is stored in a layer of insulated earth beneath the house. An integral part of the envelope house is the greenhouse, which acts as the solar collector. This system works in any climate and can be adapted to any style of house.

Waterwall space heating is a passive method in which a water-filled panel installed between the wall studs acts as a solar-powered radiator that stores and releases the sun's heat. Many innovations are being tried, in which simple applications that do not require any moving

Figure 2.10 (*top*). A passive solar energy exterior. The lean-to greenhouse is designed to fit against the house, extend living space, and serve as a passive solar collector to help reduce fuel bills. (Photograph by Robert Perron, courtesy of Lord and Burnham.)

Figure 2.11 (*bottom*). A passive solar energy interior. The solarium is weather tight, totally insulated, and ideally suited to serve as an energy-efficient solar collector. (Photograph by Robert Perron, courtesy of Lord and Burnham.)

Figure 2.12. Decade Eighty Solar House, an active solar energy structure, is high-lighted by a copper roof of which solar collectors are an integral part. Dozens of technical features and design innovations create a comfortable and convenient solar home. (Courtesy of the Copper Development Association, Inc.)

Figure 2.13. Both active and passive solar energy systems are used in this charming gambrel. The roof panels provide active solar energy, and the solarium provides passive solar energy. (Courtesy of Timberpeg.)

parts work very well. The passive solar energy system has a number of advantages over the active system: (1) it allows more design freedom, (2) it is simpler to operate, (3) it is silent, (4) it is more economical.

THE ACTIVE SOLAR ENERGY SYSTEM

The active system relies entirely on mechanical means—collector panels, fans, pumps, and a storage area—to trap the heat and distribute it throughout the house. Some disadvantages of active solar at the present time are: (1) the collector panels are expensive, (2) the panels limit the design of the house, and (3) the indispensable photovoltaic cells, used to generate electricity from solar energy, are at present in a semi-experimental stage and need perfecting for the residential market.

THE EARTH-SHELTERED HOUSE

The idea of homes inside the earth dates back to prehistoric times, when earth dwellings protected humans from the elements. The earth is a natural temperature moderator that keeps temperatures fairly constant, and the dark and dampness formerly associated with earth-sheltered living have been overcome by today's sophisticated waterproofing and lighting (see Figure 2.1). Although the earth-sheltered house has many possibilities and holds great promise for the future, it is still in the experimental stage and has some definite disadvantages. This type of dwelling requires a large tract of land, the floor plan requires particular attention, and at the present time its use is severely hampered by building code restrictions.

Looking to the future

Experimentation in housing since World War II has produced houses with a wide variety of plans and ideas. The **Geodesic dome** offers practical possibilities. Winged rooflines, concrete frames, unconventional structures called "pop architecture," and other alternatives to traditional construction are being designed.

The following statement, made in the mid-1970s by George Romney, the former secretary of housing and urban development, is still pertinent today:

Figure 2.14 (*above, left*). **A geodesic dome exterior. An innovative concept in living, the 2100-sq-ft dome has a loft and may be built with two or three levels. (Courtesy of Geodesic Structures, Inc.)**

Figure 2.15 (*above, right*). **A geodesic dome interior. The first-level walls are nearly vertical, making furniture arrangement easy. Generous windows add to the feeling of spaciousness. (Courtesy of Geodesic Structures, Inc.)**

In the decades ahead, the public interest and indeed our national survival require us to assign our housing and urban goals a high priority—at least comparable to the priority we gave our space program in the decade just ended. Let us set priorities. Let us set timetables. Let us commit resources. Let us build homes and cities and a new America. If we do, we can fulfill the promise of America for ourselves and all mankind.

The bicentennial of our nation, which had a great impact on many areas of American life, engendered in architecture a wave of traditionalism that will likely be evidenced for some time into the future. Many of the familiar facades of several decades ago, such as those discussed and illustrated in Chapter 1, are returning. Some will have modern adaptations; others will be faithfully reproduced from homes of our heritage. For many Americans, the traditional home has always been a favorite, but today young people are discovering these houses for the first time. Young people, more than any other segment of the population, are buying and restoring old houses and are discovering in them the charm and permanence that they have been seeking. This presages a resurgence of development in established inner-city neighborhoods and in close-in areas with extensive remodeling of the town house that had its demise in the early years of the twentieth century. Nevertheless, the *contemporary* style is, and will continue to be, the favorite house for many families of all ages and in all economic brackets. The current objective, which is to provide adequate housing for everyone, is not geared to any particular style but will be regulated by demand.

Forward-looking architects and developers, in shaping homes for the future, believe that if we are to house our people, the status quo cannot prevail. They forecast that in the future, changing life-styles will be satisfied in smaller living spaces. With rising land costs, detached houses will be fewer, smaller, and will be built up instead of out, often with a rental unit to pay off the mortgage (although the latter will likely create zoning problems). More two-, three-, and four-plex houses will be massed together to give the image of semi-detached houses. Owners will be willing to share this type of mass housing if it is in a pleasant location and has good design, attractive features, and a personal identity to satisfy the American dream of private ownership.

The single-family detached home will continue as an important part of the American way of life, and is the choice of a large percentage of the American people. This choice was determined in the 1983 national home-shoppers' survey of 3000 home buyers in nine representative areas throughout the United States (see Figure 2.16). Although findings varied in different parts of the country and involved people with varying incomes, the overall result showed the following preferences: the traditional detached single-family house, 39 percent; the town house on leased land, 27 percent; the factory-built house, 23 percent; the apartment conversion, 8 percent; and the mobile home, 3 percent.

However Americans are housed in the future, former Secretary of the Interior Stewart Udall's statement has relevance:

The only reasonable course for the United States is to begin a transition to a lifestyle and economy which emphasizes thrift and efficiency. If the country is prudent, it will seize an opportunity for creative change. This challenge can permanently alter our architecture, the design of our cities and the personal lives of each individual.
—from *The Energy Balloon* (McGraw-Hill)

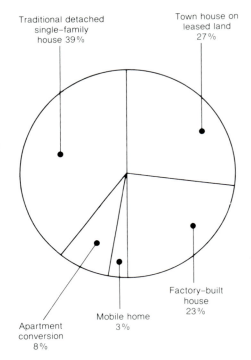

Traditional detached single–family house 39%

Town house on leased land 27%

Factory–built house 23%

Mobile home 3%

Apartment conversion 8%

Figure 2.16. Results of 1983 home-shoppers' survey. (Courtesy of *Builder* magazine, copyright Handley-Wood, Inc.)

CHAPTER THREE

Floor
Plans

Houses are built to live in and not to look on; therefore, let use be preferred before uniformity, except where both may be had.
—SIR FRANCIS BACON, 1612

*O*ne of life's great challenges is creating a desirable home. The need for adequate shelter is only the beginning. The worthy endeavor of creating a refuge, an environment in which to promote the growth and development of a household—not only physically but also intellectually, morally, and spiritually—merits dedicated study and application.

Fundamental requirements for an efficient and attractive home

The ultimate goal when planning a home should be the integration of the basic requirements for an efficient and attractive home: function, economy, beauty, and individuality.

Figure 3.1. Open planning expands visual space and allows for casual living. The high ceiling and open balcony, which direct the eye upward, and the vista to the garden, which provides a link to the outside, add to the feeling of spaciousness. (Courtesy of Timberpeg.)

FUNCTION

To be livable, a house should fulfill its intended function: to satisfy the needs of the people for which it is designed. The prospective owner may therefore want to carefully consider many things long before the plan of the house is begun or a purchase has been made. Members of each household should ask themselves numerous questions concerning their life-style. With deep and costly regrets, many owners have sold their homes because they had been influenced by others' advice rather than by their own everyday living concerns. This pitfall may be avoided if the home owner carefully and accurately assesses his or her household's needs—now and in the near future.

Selecting the site is probably the most important—and the most difficult—decision of the entire project. Before making the selection, the prospective home owner should have the general plan of the house in mind. Not until the site has been decided on, however, should that plan be finalized. If the prospective home owner is planning to build, many factors are to be considered before the building site is purchased. Such things as schools, transportation, availability of police and fire protection, the neighborhood, water, power, sewage disposal, garbage collection, and taxes should be investigated.

The prospective owner should avoid making a bad judgment in the *type* of site he or she selects. The safest topography is a gently sloping lot that provides good natural drainage and allows sewer lines to be connected easily. A steep lot may cost less initially but will most likely require expensive retaining walls, and other hidden costs are possible. The prospective owner should also become familiar with building restrictions in the area.

ECONOMY

A home is probably the largest single investment a buyer will ever make. Receiving the best value possible for every dollar spent is, therefore, highly important for the owner. The owner should study costs on paper and should look carefully at his or her resources, abilities, time, and energies. The initial cost of buying a home is only the beginning; payments must continue. According to most home-financing agencies, the monthly payment should not exceed 25 percent of monthly *take-home* pay. The percentage may vary in different parts of the country, but 25 percent is the amount generally approved.

The three enclosures below, each requiring the same amount of wall surface, illustrate the way in which the price per square foot increases as the space deviates from the square.

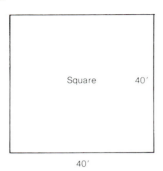

= 160 ft wall surface
= 1600 sq ft floor space

= 160 ft wall surface
= 1200 sq ft floor space

(A loss of 400 sq ft of floor space with the same wall surface)

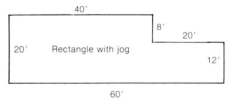

= 160 ft wall surface
= 1040 sq ft floor space

(A loss of 160 sq ft of floor space plus the extra expense of the jog)

Before the overall expense of the house is determined, the buyer may wish to investigate ways of limiting building costs. A reputable architect or builder can be helpful, but in most cases the buyer should take the initiative and assume most of the responsibility for keeping costs down. The following suggestions concerning methods and materials can help minimize building costs and upkeep, and can add to the resale value of the house:

Beginning with a good design can pay for itself in good living and can increase the value of the house over the years. The services of a good architect are invaluable, but if the buyer cannot afford one, he or she may want to select a good stock plan that an architect has designed. A simple house plan can maximize space and minimize cost. Most houses are based on one of six basic plans: the rectangle, and the H, U, T, L, and E. Of these plans, the rectangle, the L, and the U are the most common. Regarding cost, the nearer to a square shape the exterior walls are built, the less will be the cost per square foot. Cost does not increase in direct proportion to a home's square footage; jogs and angles are expensive. Two stories cost proportionally less than a low, rambling plan, since the roof and foundation can serve twice the space, heating can be more centralized, and the second story provides extra *insulation* against summer heat and winter cold. A unified theme is important; unnecessary mixing of materials should be avoided. Any building material, no matter how old or new, should be used appropriately. Simplicity is the key to a well-designed home. Insulation should be adequate. In areas where wood is readily available, the buyer might consider installing a wood- or coal-burning stove to cut heating costs. In some areas, however, burning coal may create a pollution problem. Locating the house to take the best advantage of the climate can save on heating and air-conditioning bills. The winter sun should strike long walls and large windows, but large areas of glass

Figure 3.2. A wood- and coal-burning stove can be a big money and energy saver as well as an attractive feature. (Courtesy of Suburban Manufacturing Company.)

should not face the afternoon sun in the summer. Passive solar energy systems might be incorporated. A wise location of the house can reduce the cost of utilities. The costs of connecting water, gas, and electricity to the main line depend on the distance from the house to the road.

Centralized plumbing can save money. Bathrooms can be placed back to back or one above the other. Kitchen and utility room plumbing can be located to take advantage of the same major drains.

The structure should use indigenous materials that are plentiful. Flawed materials will cost less, and character can often be gained by making a feature out of a fault.

Standard milled items should be used. Standard doors, window frames, cabinets, stairways, mantels, and all manner

Figure 3.3. A wood-burning stove adds a relaxing focal point and country charm to this family room. (Courtesy of Armstrong World Industries.)

of wood trim are available and well designed at factory-built prices. Standard windows in place of sliding glass doors can hold down costs. In some areas, plastic plumbing pipe can be used instead of copper pipe. Full-wall-height closet doors will eliminate door head and trim.

Before making the final decision on any item that goes into the completed house, the buyer might consider the upkeep over a long period of time. Some things that are the most costly initially are the most economical in the long run. For example, the best heating plant for a particular house, in its particular locality, is the most economical. Brick, in some areas, may cost more than frame construction or facades, but it never needs painting, and the resale value is usually higher than that of wood. A lifetime roof will cost considerably more than one of plain cedar shingles, but the latter may need repainting every few years, may have to be replaced several times during the life of the house, and is a fire hazard. Hardwood *balusters* are more costly than

pine, but pine balusters are easily broken, and the replacement may soon add up to more than the cost of the hardwood.

The owner may wish to negotiate with his or her builder to leave some tasks to do personally, such as painting, finishing cabinetry, and laying flooring. Planning for expansion can save money when more space becomes necessary, and can enhance the resale value of the house. Once the design is completed and construction has begun, making further changes should be avoided, since they are expensive at this stage.

BEAUTY

A house, to be a satisfactory home, should appear pleasing to those who live in it and ought to have a certain intrinsic beauty. What is beauty, and what makes a home appear beautiful?

Beauty has been described as that quality which pleases the senses and lifts the spirits. Authorities in the interior design field generally agree that beauty in any object is achieved through the application of the principles of design and a skillful use of the elements, unified by a

EXPANDING A SMALL HOUSE

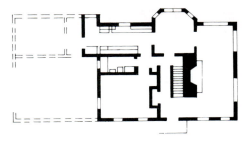

Add walls to the main floor

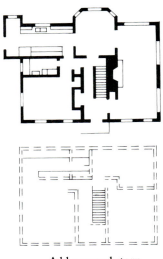

Add a second story

basic theme. Any house designed with these principles and elements in mind, regardless of the style, ought to appear pleasing and have resale value.

INDIVIDUALITY

Individuality is an elusive quality, particularly in a house. It develops slowly and naturally with the personality of the household. In custom-built homes, this development is not difficult, but in look-alike subdivisions and in mobile home areas, the challenge for each owner is to give his or her dwelling that personal mark which makes it different.

The floor plan

Too few prospective home owners are aware of the impact that the physical home environment has on people's lives. In the plan of a house, an impressive facade should be far down the list of requirements. The internal considerations are more important. Well-arranged floor space should be given top priority.

To have a home in which many household activities can be carried on with a minimum of frustration should be a major concern of the home owner. Having the valuable space he or she needs is possible even on a limited budget—if there is a willingness to forego expensive frills. Building a house with a good plan costs no more than one with a poor plan, and it may cost less. Although the responsibility for the final design is the architect's, the owner should carefully study his or her own needs and habits to help the architect plan a house that will be right for the household.

Time and experience have proven that basic elements in the general plan of a house are conducive to the smooth working of a home and contribute immeasura-

Figure 3.4. In keeping with the trend of combining various functions, a dividing peninsula serves both kitchen and dining areas while providing privacy for the dining area's wide range of activities. (Courtesy of Wilsonart Products.)

bly to the daily enjoyment of household life. Some of these features are good traffic patterns that preserve privacy and save wear and tear, a private dining area in which relationships can be strengthened daily, a fireplace around which to gather in camaraderie, and a place to retreat to be alone or to work at hobbies. With the advent of modern architecture, however, the message was that the traditional pattern of the house plan was outdated. "Now," the modernists said, "we will have functional houses." Out went the entrance hall, the separate dining room, and the pantry—and the open plan came into vogue. Glass curtains came down, masonry walls were replaced with great areas of exposed glass, and the "fishbowl" era was in full swing.

After several decades, however, this open plan, so strongly advocated, widely adopted, and suggestive of family togetherness, did not prove the most desirable arrangement. Many families abandoned such houses and purchased and restored older homes that more closely met their needs. Togetherness is important but should not be at the

expense of privacy. All household members need both, and if a house is to be a successful home, it must be responsive to the needs of the individuals who live there.

Aware of the dissatisfaction of many home owners, *House and Garden* magazine and the National Association of Home Builders conducted in 1964 a nationwide survey in which they asked homemakers what they wanted in their homes. The response was gratifying, and requests from homemakers across the country were amazingly similar. Included in these requests were the return of the entrance hall, the separate dining room, the living room off bounds to children's activities, and the old-fashioned pantry. Unanimously requested was the removal of the laundry from the kitchen. Architects and builders were quick to respond. New floor plans soon appeared, in which these and other features that for several decades had been eliminated were again incorporated, along with other improvements, into house plans. In recent years, however, skyrocketing building costs and interest rates, along with dramatic changes in the family structure, have

ARCHITECTURAL SYMBOLS

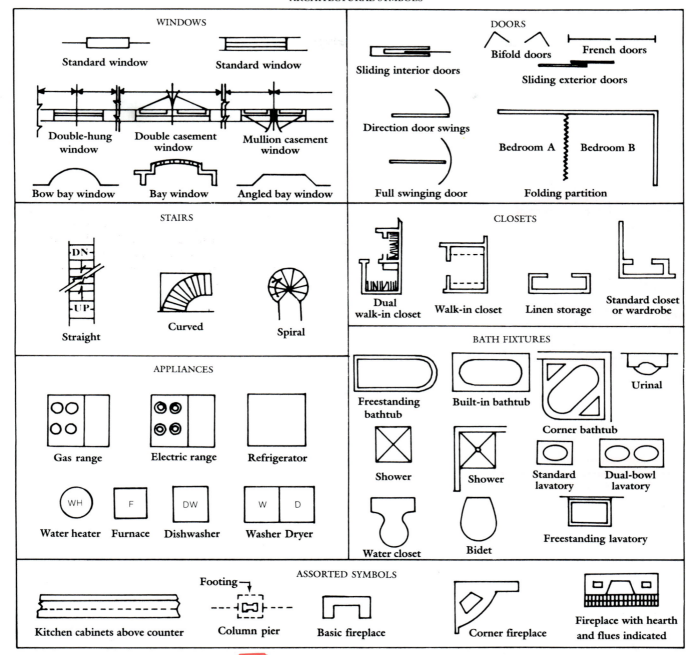

WINDOWS

Standard window

Standard window

Double-hung window

Double casement window

Mullion casement window

Bow bay window

Bay window

Angled bay window

DOORS

Sliding interior doors

Bifold doors

French doors

Sliding exterior doors

Direction door swings

Bedroom A   Bedroom B

Full swinging door

Folding partition

STAIRS

DN
UP
Straight

Curved

Spiral

CLOSETS

Dual walk-in closet

Walk-in closet

Linen storage

Standard closet or wardrobe

APPLIANCES

Gas range

Electric range

Refrigerator

WH — Water heater

F — Furnace

DW — Dishwasher

W D — Washer Dryer

BATH FIXTURES

Freestanding bathtub

Built-in bathtub

Corner bathtub

Urinal

Shower

Shower

Standard lavatory

Dual-bowl lavatory

Water closet

Bidet

Freestanding lavatory

ASSORTED SYMBOLS

Kitchen cabinets above counter

Footing — Column pier

Basic fireplace

Corner fireplace

Fireplace with hearth and flues indicated

forced people to live in smaller spaces, making multipurpose areas a necessity.

The prospective homeowner who is planning to build, either working with an architect or from a predesigned plan, should be able to read and understand an architect's working drawing of a floor plan. This drawing is referred to as the *blueprint,* since the old, outdated printing method used white lines on a bright blue ground. The standard today, however, is to use blue lines on a white ground. To understand the blueprint, the home owner should become familiar with basic architectural symbols, which include room dimensions, closets, openings, stairways, bathroom fixtures, kitchen appliances, and heating. With this knowledge, he or she can intelligently examine the blueprint while "moving" from room to room. Although this examination does not provide a three-dimensional understanding, it will reveal any objectionable features, which can be changed before the plan is finalized.

Although individual differences in life-style should be taken into account when planning a home, basic time-tested features should also be considered if the home is to function efficiently. The following features and considerations deserve serious study.

FUNDAMENTAL REQUIREMENTS FOR AN EFFECTIVE FLOOR PLAN

WELL-DEFINED BASIC AREAS

Working areas for cooking, washing dishes, laundering, ironing, sewing, hobbies, and so forth should be conveniently located with well-arranged space and adequate lighting.

Informal eating areas for quick snacks and informal family meals should be conveniently located in or near the kitchen. More formal dining areas need privacy from the front door, with provision made to shut the eating area off from the clutter of the kitchen. A pleasant atmosphere and effective lighting are important. This room can serve a number of purposes when not being used for dining, such as studying, sewing, and playing games.

Informal family and recreation rooms should be convenient to the kitchen, to the outside, and to the bedroom wing. More formal areas should be placed away from major traffic lanes and should be designed for privacy and relaxation.

Sleeping and dressing areas should be located for quiet and privacy with easy access to bathrooms.

EFFICIENT TRAFFIC LANES

Traffic lanes should be adequate but not wasteful. A central entrance hall should channel traffic to all areas of the house. The kitchen should have easy access to the front door, back door, utility room, service area, garage, and all areas of the house. The utility area should have direct access to the outside service area whenever possible. At least one living area should have easy access to the outside living area. An access door—other than the large garage doors near the front of the house—leading directly into the

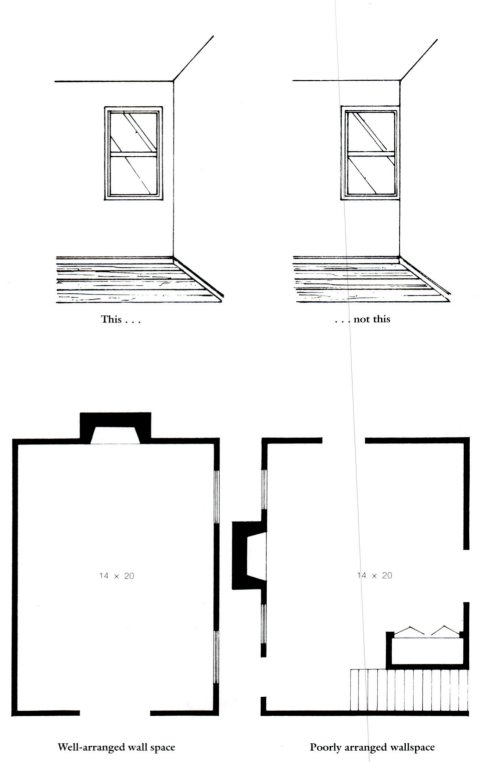

This . . .   . . . not this

Well-arranged wall space   Poorly arranged wallspace

14 × 20   14 × 20

kitchen is a valuable feature. All major traffic lanes should be routed to avoid going through any room to reach another. (One possible exception is the family room.) Diagonal traffic lanes should particularly be avoided.

WELL-PLACED OPENINGS

Doors should be conveniently located to preserve wall space, and windows should should be placed for easy draping.

WELL-ARRANGED WALL SPACE

Wall space should accommodate large and necessary pieces of furniture.

AMPLE STORAGE SPACE

Sufficient storage space should be conveniently located throughout the house and in the garage.

OTHER CONSIDERATIONS

Plumbing should be economically located wherever possible, such as kitchen and utility room in close proximity, bathrooms back to back, and plumbing in a second story placed directly above plumbing on the ground floor. A wash basin and toilet should be placed near the back door whenever possible.

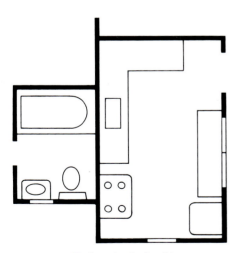

Back-to-back plumbing

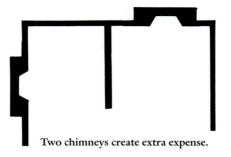

Two chimneys create extra expense.

Two fireplaces can be combined to share the same chimney.

A fireplace should be conveniently located for the arrangement of a private conversation area. If the house has two fireplaces, they could be arranged to take advantage of the same chimney.

An area that can be used as a workshop or hobby shop is a useful feature. A room that can be used as a study is also an important consideration. A dining area can serve double duty, and even a small bedroom can be equipped with bookshelves, a study desk, and a lamp.

EXAMPLES OF DETACHED FLOOR PLANS

The simplest floor plan is the rectangle. The further the plan departs from this shape, the more complicated and costly it becomes. Each jog and each additional roof angle means added expense, and thus more dollars per square foot of floor space.

The following three economically and efficiently arranged floor plans are (1) the rectangular plan, (2) the two-story plan, and (3) the L-shaped plan. Each plan should be carefully studied for well-arranged features and possible improvements.

THE RECTANGULAR PLAN

The rectangular plan is economical and readily adapted to both traditional and contemporary exteriors. The plan shown is unusually well arranged and meets all the necessary requirements.

The desirable features of the rectangular plan are as follows:

▫ An ample entrance hall routes traffic to all areas of the house.

▫ Basic areas are well defined and conveniently located. Plumbing is back to back in the bedroom wing and in the work area.

▫ Large windows looking onto a private garden create a pleasing indoor-outdoor relationship.

▫ The family room has easy access to the outside.

▫ Access from the kitchen and utility rooms to the outdoors and to the garage is convenient.

▫ The garage faces away from the street.

▫ The access door opens from the front yard into the garage.

▫ Ample space is provided for informal and formal eating.

▫ Fireplaces in the living room and family room use the same chimney.

▫ Storage is adequate and well placed.

▫ Openings are placed for convenience.

▫ Wall space is adequate throughout.

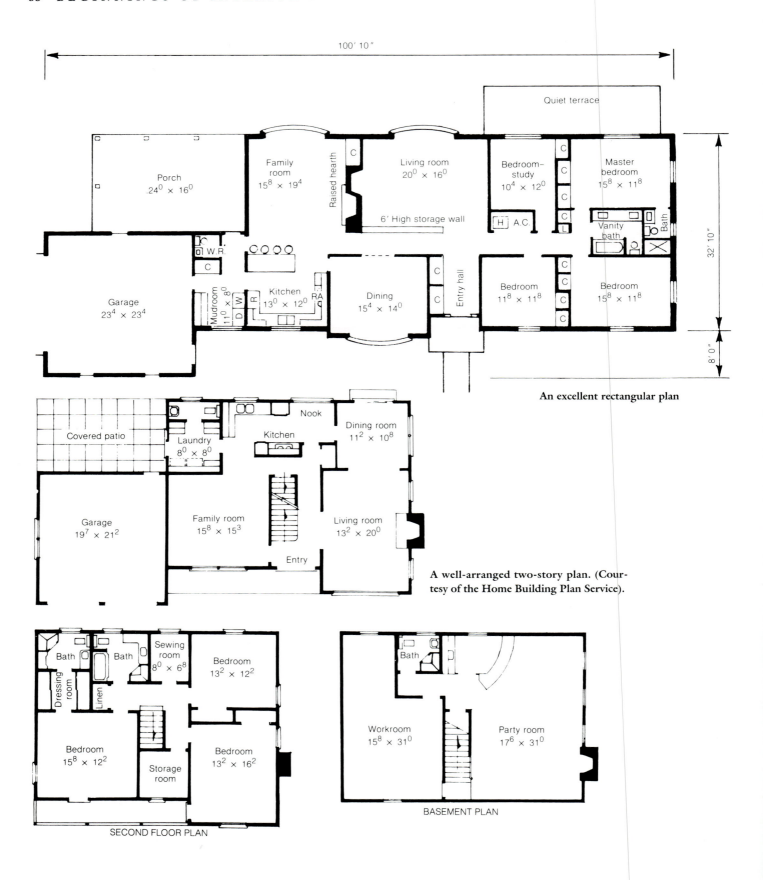

An excellent rectangular plan

A well-arranged two-story plan. (Courtesy of the Home Building Plan Service).

SECOND FLOOR PLAN

BASEMENT PLAN

Living room
20 × 13

Eating bar

S

R

O

Family room–kitchen
27⁶ × 13

Entrance

C

C

Dining
12 × 11

Service

B

W

D

WH

W

F

Garage
20 × 20

Bedroom
12 × 10

W/R   W/R   Lin

C

Bath

Bath

Storage

Bedroom
12 × 11

W/R

W/R   Dress   W/R

Bedroom
11 × 13³

Bedroom
13 × 12

An efficient L-shaped plan

THE TWO-STORY PLAN

This excellent two-story plan will allow for versatile living. The full basement may be roughed in and finished at a later date.

The desirable features of the two-story plan are as follows:

□ A rectangular plan eliminates most unnecessary jogs.

□ All basic areas are well defined for convenient living.

□ An entry hall channels traffic throughout the house.

□ Traffic lanes are economical and permit easy access wherever necessary and privacy wherever desirable.

□ Doors and windows are well placed.

□ Plumbing is back to back on each floor, and second-story and basement plumbing are directly above and below the main floor plumbing.

An undesirable feature is that the front of the garage has no access door. This could easily be added at the right.

THE L-SHAPED PLAN

This excellent L-shaped four-bedroom plan will guarantee the enjoyment of comfortable and gracious living.

The desirable features of the L-shaped plan are as follows:

□ The exterior can be traditional or contemporary. If the lot is wide enough, the garage may have a side opening.

□ The plan incorporates the basic requirements for a well-arranged home.

□ A central entrance hall routes traffic directly to the living, sleeping, and work areas without cross-circulation.

□ Large glass doors opening onto the private garden, away from the street, give an indoor-outdoor openness.

□ The family room is conveniently combined with the kitchen for informal activities.

□ The garage has an access door.

□ The service area is between the kitchen and the half-bath, where it is out of the main line of traffic and yet convenient to the kitchen and the outside.

□ The bedroom wing is away from work and living areas.

□ The family bath and private bath are back to back.

□ Closet space is well placed in the bedrooms, and three closets open to the main entrance hall.

□ The bar in the family room is handy for quick snacks, and the separate dining room invites more formal meals.

□ Rooms are well planned with well-placed openings and ample wall space, with the exception of the two front bedrooms, which each have an added window for cross-ventilation.

A poorly arranged floor plan

A POORLY ARRANGED FLOOR PLAN

Careful examination and comparison of the following two floor plans should aid the student in reading and critically evaluating a plan.

Because of the poor arrangement of space in this plan, the price per square footage would be unnecessarily costly, and living would be inconvenient and frustrating.

The undesirable features of the plan are as follows:

□ The house has too many costly jogs.

□ Traffic lanes are not planned.

□ No space is provided for an entrance way, which makes the living room a major traffic lane.

□ Traffic from the poorly located front door would prevent a private conversation area around the fireplace.

□ No privacy is provided in eating areas.

□ The garage is too far from the kitchen, which would be inconvenient when transporting groceries.

□ To reach the half-bath from the kitchen, crossing a bedroom is necessary.

□ Bathrooms are not economically located.

□ The washer and dryer are in the kitchen—a location that is usually objectionable.

□ The window in the small corner bedroom is abutting the wall. The windows in the living room are too small and would not provide sufficient light.

□ No storage is provided in the garage.

A WELL-ARRANGED FLOOR PLAN

Compare this well-organized, easy-to-live-in, and economically designed plan with the previous plan. This plan has more living space and could be built for the same amount or less money than the poorly arranged plan.

The improved features of the plan are as follows:

□ Eight costly jogs have been eliminated.

□ A family room and a separate dining room have been added.

82'

Bedroom 1
$15^2 \times 12^2$

Bath

Bath

Family room
$19^6 \times 16^2$

Kitchen
$11^6 \times 16^2$

Laundry

Storage
$20^8 \times 6^8$

A well-arranged floor plan

Bedroom 2
$12^2 \times 11^2$

Bedroom 3
$12^2 \times 11^2$

Entry

Living room
$22^2 \times 15^2$

Lav

Dining room
$11^8 \times 15^2$

Garage
$20^8 \times 21^6$

28'2"

▫ Traffic lanes are well planned with (1) an entrance way directing traffic throughout the house, allowing privacy for living and dining rooms, (2) an outside entrance into the family room, (3) an access door into the front of the garage and from the back of the garage to the backyard, and (4) convenient traffic lanes from the kitchen to the outside.

▫ Plumbing is centralized; bathrooms, and the kitchen and utilities, are back to back.

▫ Washer and dryer are out of the kitchen but are nearby in a utility area.

▫ The U-shaped kitchen is compact and efficiently arranged.

▫ Windows provide sufficient light and are located to permit easy draping.

▫ Convenient storage is planned in the garage.

▫ Two fireplaces use the same chimney.

The arrangement of floor space over the years has fluctuated between two basic schemes: the *closed plan* and the *open plan.* The closed plan, as seen in the preceding illustrations, provides separate rooms for specific activities and allows more individual privacy. Many people, particularly large families, prefer this plan.

THE OPEN PLAN

In the open plan, space for various activities flows from one area to another and is not broken by wall barriers. One advantage of this plan is that it seems to

Figure 3.5. Open planning makes limited space appear much larger and allows for freedom of movement and furniture arrangement. Here, kitchen, dining, and living areas share well utilized space. The open balcony and ceiling window contribute to the capacious feeling of the room. (Courtesy of Armstrong World Industries.)

expand space, which may be left entirely open or partially isolated by freestanding partitions. This plan has particular appeal to an informal life-style.

Open planning has been used in this spacious U-shaped design to visually enlarge two areas. The living and dining rooms are combined, and for additional space the master bedroom can be opened. Visual space is further provided by sliding glass patio doors. The kitchen and family rooms are also one open unit for informal living.

THE ATRIUM PLAN

Another house plan of importance is the *atrium plan.* Used by the ancient Romans, the atrium has become a desirable feature in many contemporary homes. It can be completely enclosed as the central focus of the entire house, or can be built within a U shape or to one side. With the increasing importance of solar energy, the atrium or sun room is gaining in popularity, since it is essential to passive solar houses.

CONDOMINIUMS FOR DIFFERENT LIFE-STYLES

Architects are currently designing high-density housing units that will accommodate a variety of life-styles and appeal to a diversity of tastes. In all cases, the main concerns are efficient use of space, privacy, security, and energy conservation. Units in clustered condominiums are planned much like single detached houses. Floor plans in town houses vary from large two-level multiroom units to compact one-room flats. The following are three compact town house condominiums designed for different life-styles.

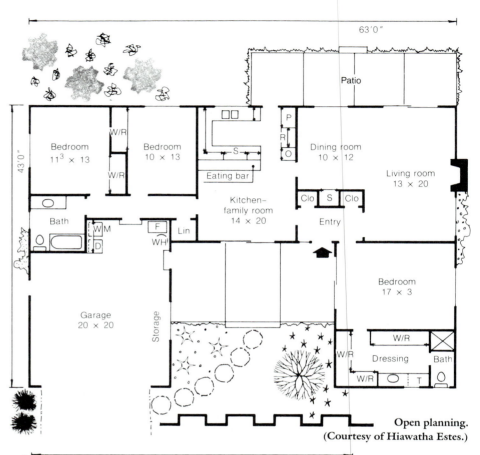

Open planning.
(Courtesy of Hiawatha Estes.)

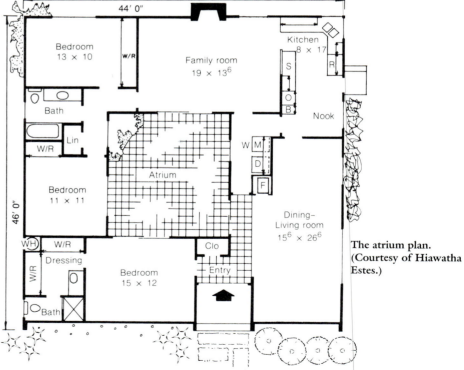

The atrium plan.
(Courtesy of Hiawatha Estes.)

The one-bedroom unit has a conventional plan for a tandem buyer. Well-arranged space is convenient and adequate for a couple or for a single person. A tandem arrangement is one in which individual units are placed side by side or one behind the other.

The compact studio shows how to make the most of limited space. The living room includes above-the-safe storage, the dining table can be used for work or hobby space, a queen-sized bed folds away during the day, and the bathroom is compartmentalized.

The mingles unit has two separate but equal living spaces. The unit has mirror-image sleeping and living spaces and equal-sized baths, with shared kitchen and dining areas sandwiched between. Access is by a single-entry unit.

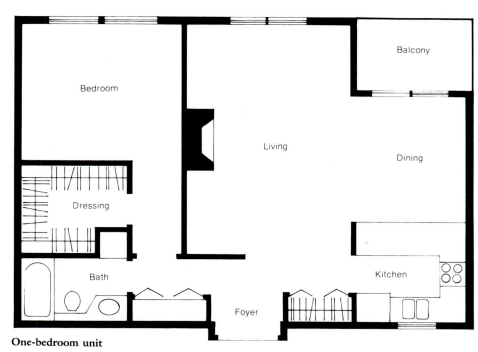

One-bedroom unit

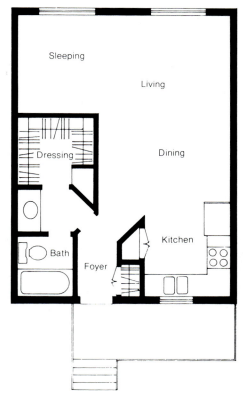

Compact studio

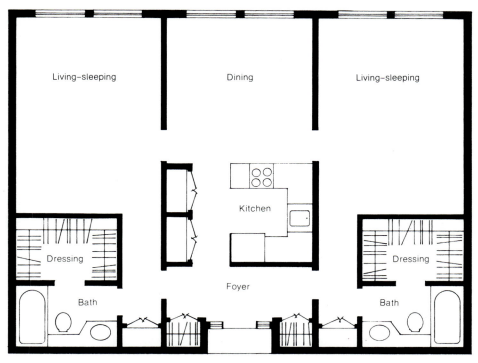

Mingles unit

ASSIGNMENT

In the following assignment, you will demonstrate competency in selecting an economical and efficiently designed floor plan.

Select a floor plan that meets the requirements set forth in the text, keeping in mind that this plan must be for a *year-round family dwelling*. Do not attempt to draw a plan, since this requires special training and skill that are beyond the scope of this course. Submit your plan, mounted on black or white paper, with an accompanying critique that considers all of the features discussed under "Fundamental Requirements for an Effective Floor Plan."

In addition to the critique, the total cost of the house you have chosen should be computed by multiplying the total number of square feet by the *current* cost per square foot in the student's particular area. If the plan has a basement or a second story or both, the costs should be checked with a builder or an architect. Costs vary in different sections of the country and almost from month to month.

CHAPTER FOUR

Design Theory and Application

Poverty is a poor excuse for ugliness, and one can never get rich enough to purchase good taste.
—ALICE MERRILL HORNE

*P*eople are not born with that illusive element called "good taste"; it is a capability for **aesthetic** judgment that develops over years of learning and experience. Anyone can express personal preference, but necessary to acquiring good aesthetic judgment is a knowledge of the elements and principles of design. This knowledge can serve as a basis for understanding the qualities of design and for visual appreciation and intelligent selection. Although acquiring this knowledge informally or through exposure is possible, more formal training is usually required. Once the basic principles are established, new media and modern technology can be applied in original and creative ways to produce appropriate

solutions to current situations. To the person trained to discriminate between good and poor design, the use of innovative forms and proportions can not only be favorable but can also be desirable. Attempting the latter without first having an understanding of the basic principles of design, however, would be folly.

Basic guidelines for design

Good design has no absolute formula. Although the successful employment of aesthetic principles—scale and proportion, rhythm, balance, harmony, and emphasis—will enhance the interior designer's skill, these principles may change over extended periods of time. Honesty and simplicity are important ingredients in good design, along with consideration for the design's function and its relationship to the environment and to people. Whatever the design, its basic intention should be to enrich people's lives and enhance the human experience. Good design is a long-term investment; it may not be inexpensive, but it is worth the cost. Mediocre design will always be mediocre, and good design will always be good, no matter what the change in fashion. The best design should be demanded and expected in all areas.

For the student who anticipates a career in interior design, certain guidelines can help in acquiring the capability to choose design of lasting beauty and enjoyment. A knowledge of the principles and elements of design is fundamental. Deliberate application of these principles will enable them to become part of the aspiring designer's consciousness. Careful and constant observation of objects in nature: light and shadow, shape and texture, and pattern and color can develop personal awareness. These elements should be viewed not only in and of themselves, but also with respect to how they interrelate. Looking for balance, scale and proportion, rhythm, and emphasis in nature can help to develop a sense of the harmony these principles produce.

Study and research will enable the student of interior design to become knowledgeable about interiors of historical and contemporary styles. Also of benefit is critically examining periodicals, visiting furniture stores and decorating

Figure 4.1. Skillful use of texture, pattern, line, form, space, color, and lighting has created a room of contemporary elegance that is enticing but uncluttered. (Courtesy of Collins and Aikman Corporation.)

DESIGN IN NATURE

Gradation

Asymmetrical balance

Bisymmetrical balance

studios, and asking questions. A knowledge of accessories is important, particularly with regard to small items that are appropriate for each style of furniture, as well as their use for enhancing rooms.

Fashion is not a good criterion of design. Like fashion in clothes, fashion in home furnishings may often become outdated. Individual taste is influenced by national trends and events, such as the 1976 bicentennial, and over the years world fairs have had a great effect on public taste. Novel ideas, materials, and designs that have been vividly presented have determined, in varying degrees, future trends in fashion, domestic architecture, and home furnishings.

Applying knowledge of what constitutes good design will enable home purchases to be made discriminatingly. Each purchase, no matter how small, is of utmost importance. Whether the purchase is a crystal goblet, a chair, or a house, good taste is not determined by cost alone. Ultimately, taste is a sense of what is appropriate to a particular life-style, and the success of interior design depends on the choice of ingredients and the way in which they are blended together.

Basic design

Webster defines design as "the arrangement of details which make up a work of art." As defined in the *Encyclopaedia Britannica,* design is "the arrangement of lines or forms which make up the plan of a work of art with especial regard to the proportions, structure, movement, and beauty of line of the whole."

In any well-planned and executed design—whether a silver spoon, a rug, or a complete house—the principles of design will have been carefully considered. Before discussing design principles, however, a necessary step is to become familiar with the two basic types of design: structural and decorative.

STRUCTURAL DESIGN

Structural design relates to the size and shape of an object; the design is an integral part of the structure itself. For example, the ancient pyramids of Egypt are a structural design because they expose the stone blocks from which they were made. Contemporary architecture, both inside and out, frankly reveals the materials that make up the basic structure, such as wood or metal beams, brick, stone, and concrete. The design of modern furniture is seen in the form itself, such as the metal frame of the Barcelona chair and the molded plastic of a *pedestal* table.

The attributes essential to successful structural design are simplicity, good proportion, appropriateness of materials used, and suitability.

Simplicity. Whether the structure itself is to stand as the finished product or is only the supporting element for decoration, it should be kept simple. If the basic structure—a house, a room, or an accessory—is badly designed, the finished product will not be pleasant. For example, a room with too many or poorly placed openings, arches, and niches will seldom be pleasing until some elimination or camouflaging has been accomplished.

Good proportion. Any object that is structurally well proportioned will be intrinsically pleasing, whether it remains plain or is appropriately decorated. A well-designed room is a pleasure to decorate; one that is badly proportioned is difficult to correct. An upholstered chair with armrests that overpower the rest of the design must often be completely rebuilt to make it pleasing.

STRUCTURAL AND
DECORATIVE DESIGN

Decorative

Structural

Decorative

Structural

Appropriateness of materials. Different materials lend themselves to different objects and construction methods. Glass may be blown and intricately decorated by skilled craftspeople, and molded plastic chairs may be turned out by an assembly-line method. Interchanging the procedures for the above materials, however, is not feasible.

Suitability. The purpose for which any item is intended should immediately be recognizable. A lamp of structural design should look like an object for giving light and not like a **Dresden** doll holding an umbrella. A salad bowl should look like an article to contain something and not like a depressed bouquet of flowers.

DECORATIVE DESIGN

Decorative design relates to the ornamentation of the basic structure, which may be achieved through the selection and placement of color, line, and texture. For example, the exterior surfaces of the East Indian temples are completely covered with embellishment. The over-elaboration of the Victorian house usually buried the basic structure. Furniture may be handsomely carved to add charm and dignity, but sometimes decoration is unnecessary and may even destroy rather than enhance the basic structure.

Decorative design falls into four classifications:

☐ Naturalistic, realistic, or photographic, in which the motif is reproduced from nature in its natural form

☐ Conventional or stylistic, in which the motif is taken from nature but is adapted to suit the shape or purpose of the object to be decorated

☐ Abstract, in which recognizable elements are transformed into nonrepresentational design

☐ Geometric, in which the design is made up of geometric motifs, such as stripes, plaids, and zigzags

TYPES OF DECORATIVE DESIGN

Naturalistic

Conventional

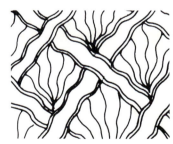

Abstract

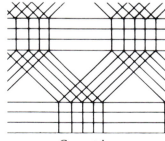

Geometric

The attributes essential to successful decorative design are appropriateness, placement, and proportion.

Any decoration that is added to the basic structure should accent its shape and beauty. For example, vertical *fluting* on a supporting column will make it seem higher, but crossbars will appear to cut the height and reduce its dignity. Classic figures on a *Wedgwood* vase will emphasize its rounded contour, but harsh lines will destroy its beauty.

The embellishment of any item should be placed with purpose in mind. *Bas-relief* on the seat of a chair is inappropriate, but such carving on a wall plaque is desirable.

The amount of surface decoration should be placed with great care, and the basic structure should be kept in mind. The Greek proportions of 3:5, 4:7, and 5:8 are wise to follow (see the section on proportion and scale). It is usually unwise to embellish exactly half the surface of an object.

Elements of design

Design consists of the following elements: texture, pattern, line, form or mass, space, color, and lighting. The following discussion should help to clarify the nature of these elements.

TEXTURE

Texture refers to the surface quality of objects—the quality that not only can be seen and touched but also can be sensed through memory. For example, the roughness of sandstone, the softness of a deep pile rug, the smoothness of glass, and the shininess of growing leaves all produce a peculiar sensation because of previous association with these textures. Texture adds much to the visual interest of the environment and has been important in the dwellings of all people through the centuries. Cave dwellers enjoyed the feel of animal skins under their feet. The early Greeks delighted in the smoothness and beauty of mosaic floors. The people of Persia have always taken pride in the fine texture of their

DECORATIVE DETAILS

Griffin　　Antefix

Wheat　　Honeysuckle　　Strapwork

Rinceau

Swag　　Lozenge

Arabesque　　Lunette

Acanthus

Urn　　Palmette band

Festoon　　Husks

Cornucopia

Modillion　　Linenfold

Tudor rose

Rosette　　Volute

Cartouche　　Escutcheon

Guilloche　　Shell carving

Quatrefoil　　Trefoil

Lotus　　Fret

Diaper work　　Laurel leaf

Dentil molding　　Spool bead

(Courtesy of the Seng Company.)

Figure 4.2. A study in texture. The three-dimensional abstract design that simulates a sculptured Inca sunburst, the tweedy armchair, the wicker baskets, and the standing screen with a bold geometric design create a unified and informal composition. (Courtesy of Warren Muller Dolobowsky.)

Figure 4.3. A variety of compatible textures create this informal environment: rough plaster walls, sisal rug, gleaming copper, soft vinyl, earthen pottery, and primitive patterns. (Design by Thomas E. Dyer, courtesy of Naugahyde Fabric by Uniroyal.)

Figure 4.4. Texture and pattern create this informal country French dining room: rough plaster walls, masonry tile floor, simple distressed furniture, tweed hooked rug, plaid upholstery, nubby woven drapery, and stoneware and brass accessories. (Courtesy of Heritage Furniture Company.)

hand-knotted rugs, and the Japanese enjoy the freshness of grass mats. Modern interiors particularly depend on texture for variety and interest, and most often the natural surface of materials such as rough barn wood is maintained. In traditional interiors, the surface of wood materials is usually modified by sanding, staining, and polishing. The dominant texture of a room is largely established by architectural background. For example, a room paneled in fine-grained and polished wood, or papered in a traditional wall covering, will require furniture woods and fabrics with a smoother texture than that which a room paneled with natural coarse-grained wood or constructed of masonry will require.

Throughout history, smooth, highly polished surfaces, lustrous metals, and fabrics of satin, silk, and fine linen have been symbolic of opulence, wealth, and high status, and rough, hand-hewn textures and homespun fabrics have characterized

the homes of peasants and lower economic classes. Today this is no longer so. Many people of affluence prefer the handcrafted look, which may likely cost as much as the more refined look. Regardless of the style, a knowledgeable use of texture is a sure way to bring character to a room.

PATTERN

Pattern, as opposed to plain design, is the simplest way to designate surface enrichment. Pattern is created by the use of line, form, space, light, and color. Too much pattern can make a room too "busy" and uncomfortable, and a room that is devoid of pattern may be stark and

Figure 4.5. Texture is an important element in establishing this formal mood. Smooth plastered walls, a handsome oriental rug, fine-grained mahogany furniture, appropriate eighteenth-century design fabrics, silver, and fine china make up this elegant, traditional dining room. (Courtesy of Hickory Chair Company.)

dull and may lack character. The total arrangement of the various components of a room creates an overall pattern, but the more obvious patterns are seen in fabric and wallpaper, and should be appropriate to the general feeling of the room. The use of pattern in fabrics is discussed in Chapter 6.

LINE

Line is the direction of an art creation and is particularly dominant in contemporary art and interiors. The feeling of a composition—a room—is established by the lines that give it motion or repose. Skillful use of line is therefore of utmost importance.

Line can seemingly alter the proportion of an object or of an entire room. For example, assume that two identical rectangles are divided, one vertically and the other horizontally. The eye travels upward along the vertical line, and the area is made to seem higher. Along the

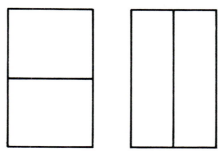

When two identical rectangles are divided differently—one horizontally and one vertically—the proportion seems to change.

Figure 4.6. Although the vertical line dominates this guest bedroom, other lines are pleasantly employed throughout the room. Horizontal line is seen in the underblinds, chest, beds, deck chair, and floors. Diagonal line is evident in the ratten chest, chair, and pillows, and curved line is seen in the beds, chair, pottery, and light fixtures. (Courtesy of Juan Montoya Design Corporation.)

horizontally divided area, the eye is directed across making the rectangle appear wider. Each kind of line has a particular psychological effect on a room. To achieve the desired result, the interior designer should keep in mind the distinct effects of each line.

Vertical lines tend to give height, strength, and dignity. These lines are seen in the exterior of a building, particularly where columns are used, and in the interior, where upright architectural members are conspicuous, in high pieces of furniture, and in the long, straight folds of drapery.

Horizontal lines give a feeling of repose, solidity, and strength. These lines are seen in cornices, **dadoes,** bookshelves, and long, low pieces of straight-lined furniture. Falling Water, a famous Frank Lloyd Wright house, is an excellent example of horizontal architecture.

Figure 4.7. The predominantly straight horizontal lines and rectilinear forms of this conversation area are relieved by the round table and the diagonal lines of the painting and plants. (Courtesy of Thayer Coggin.)

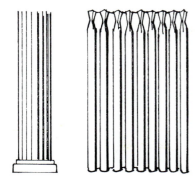

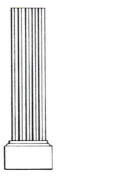

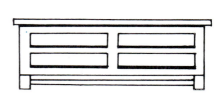

Vertical lines add height and dignity.

Vertical lines emphasize and enhance the basic structure.

Zigzag lines detract from the basic structure.

Horizontal lines give a feeling of repose.

Diagonal lines are lines of movement.

Curved lines add grace and delicacy.

Figure 4.8 (*facing page, top*). In this large-scaled room, in which line is a predominant element, the diagonal line in the upholstery fabric dominates. (Courtesy of Drexel Heritage Furnishings.)

Figure 4.9 (*facing page, bottom*). Monotony of curved lines in this conversation grouping is avoided by the straight lines in the floor, windows, sofa base, and rectangular accessory base. (Courtesy of Thayer Coggin.)

Diagonal lines give a room a feeling of action. They are evident in slanting ceilings, staircases, Gothic arches, and so forth. Too many diagonals may give a room a feeling of unrest.

Curved lines have a graceful, delicate effect on a room. They are found in doorway arches, drapery *swags,* rounded and curved furniture, and so forth. The *Taj Mahal* is a supreme example of graceful architecture.

Too much line movement in a room tends toward instability. Furniture should be static, and curves should be restrained. A room completely decorated in curved lines is tiresome, and too many horizontal lines may become overpowering. A careful balance of line is essential to the feeling of comfort and harmony in a room.

FORM OR MASS

The contour of an object is represented by its shape, which is made up of lines. When a two-dimensional shape takes on a third dimension, it becomes form or mass. In the planning of interiors, mass is perceived as objects of furniture that require space and that may be moved to various locations. The arrangement of form within the room—furniture arrangement—is discussed in Chapter 10.

Too much variety in form and shape may produce a room with a feeling of confusion, and a lack of variety may result in monotony. The transition from one object to another as the eye moves about the room should be easy and pleasurable. The emphasis created when a curved object is placed against a rectangular panel, however, may produce a plesant diversion. For example, a pair of ornately carved Belter chairs against a plain paneled wall in a modern room can provide unexpected and agreeable relief to the otherwise severe lines of the room.

SPACE

Space is perhaps the most important element of domestic architecture. Well-planned and well-organized space makes for a smooth-working home. Pleasant rooms free of clutter, with an occasional empty corner, can aid in producing a highly desirable feeling of tranquility. The arrangement of space within the interior framework of the house is discussed in Chapters 3 and 10.

COLOR

Color, the most important and least costly of all the elements of design, is considered in detail in Chapter 5.

LIGHT

One section in this chapter considers the various aspects of artificial lighting, an important element of interior design. The effects of artificial lighting on color are discussed in Chapter 5.

Principles of design

Over 2000 years ago, the Greeks established a system of proportion, and its basic principles remain valid today. Through these principles, to which the human spirit has responded positively over the years, decisions are still made and design elements are effectively combined. Understanding these principles is one means for an interior designer to achieve excellence, whether the design involves a painting, a room, or an entire house. Although some successful contemporary designs violate these time-tested principles, understanding them is central to the interior designer's creativity and is essential for every beginning designer.

The principles of design are proportion and scale, balance, rhythm, emphasis, and harmony.

PROPORTION AND SCALE

==Proportion encompasses both the relationship of one part of an object to the other parts or to the whole,== and the relationship of one object to another—both aspects involving shape. Proportion has been a major concern to creative minds through the ages. The early Greeks discovered the secret of good proportion and set down rules that students of design have accepted and incorporated in their art compositions for centuries. The ==Greeks found that the square was the least pleasant proportion for an enclosure and that the rectangle was better.== Their standard for good proportion was a rectangle or oblong with its sides in a ratio of 2:3. ==This shape is called the== *golden rectangle*. The *golden section* involves the division of a line or form in such a way that the ratio of the smaller portion to the larger is the same as the larger to the whole. The progression 2, 3, 5, 8, 13, 21, 34, and so on, in which each number is the sum of the two preceding numbers, will provide a close approximation to this relationship. For example, 2:3 is roughly the same ratio as 3:5, 5:8 is roughly the same ratio as 8:13, and so forth. Other pleasant space relationships are 3:5, 4:7, or 5:8. By multiplying any of these combinations of figures, the interior designer can plan larger areas with similar relationships.

Perhaps the most important application of these proportions in house planning and furnishing lies in the relationship of sizes or areas. These proportions can be applied when planning the dimensions of a room or when selecting a piece of furniture for a particular area. For example, if the length of the living room measures 25 ft, a desirable width would be 15 ft. This measurement is determined

SCALE

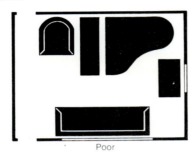

Poor

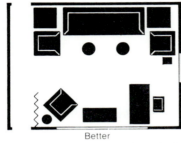

Better

Furniture should be in the right scale for a room.

by using the following process. Since the length of the living room (25 ft) is divisible by 5, the 3:5 ratio may be used. If $\frac{width}{length} = \frac{3}{5} = \frac{W}{25}$, then W would equal 15. In another example, a piece of furniture that is 4 ft long would be a good size to place against a 7-ft wall space. These dimensions have the desirable ratio of 4:7.

Another Greek discovery was that the division of a line somewhere between one half and one third its length is the most pleasing. This division is still retained as a *golden mean* and can be applied when planning any wall composition, such as the height for a mantel, tying back drapery, or hanging pictures, mirrors, or **wall sconces.** The Greeks also discovered that odd numbers are more pleasing than even ones. A group of 3 objects to 3 is more pleasing than 2:2 or 4:4, and 2:3 is better than 2:4.

PERCEPTION

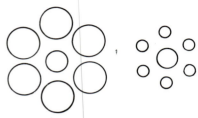

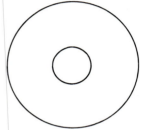

The center circles in the above diagrams are identical. The apparent change in size is due to the difference of the surrounding circles.

The center circles above are identical. The apparent change is due to the difference in size of the surrounding area.

Scale refers to the overall size or parts of an object compared with other objects, regardless of shape. A house is large but may be large or small in scale. A table is a smaller item but may be large or small in scale. The correct use of scale and proportion is important to the success of a house and its furnishings. Yet, since scale is a relative quality, mathematical correctness is not the solution, because weight and measurement will not always produce a feeling of rightness. For example, two love seats may have the identical overall dimensions, yet may not look the same or be right together if one has heavier arms and shorter legs than the other.

Good scale and proportion should begin with the choice of the house on the

GREEK PROPORTIONS

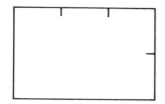

The golden rectangle. The Greek standard for good proportion is a rectangle with its sides in a ratio of 2:3.

The golden section. 3:5 is roughly the same ratio as 5:8.

4:7 is a pleasing proportion.

The Parthenon at Athens—based on a mathematical ratio of 1:1.6—fits almost precisely into a golden rectangle. Because of the frequency with which it occurs in the arts, the golden rectangle has mystified experts for centuries.

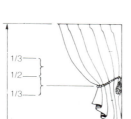

The golden mean. The division of a line somewhere between one half and one third is the most pleasing.

Figure 4.10. The overall dimension of the two table groupings are identical, yet their apparent size is markedly dissimilar because of the great difference in scale and proportion. (*A*, courtesy of Baker Furniture; *B*, courtesy of Wood and Hogan.)

A

B

lot and should be taken into account until the last accessory is chosen and put into place. A tiny house on a spacious lot will look lost, and a large house will look cramped and uncomfortable on too small a plot of ground. The size of trees and shrubs should be chosen with the overall plan in mind.

The material used in construction should be in scale with the house itself. For example, a Cape Cod cottage would not look right made of large cinder block.

The architectural features on the exterior of the house should carefully be designed and located. Because the door is the focal point of the facade, perfect scale is of utmost importance. The windows also should carefully be scaled and well placed, or the overall effect will not be pleasing.

An object is perceived in relation to the area around it. Objects that are too large will crowd a small room and will make it appear smaller; furniture that is too small will seem even smaller in an oversized room. When surrounded by small-scaled furniture a large piece of furniture will appear larger than when surrounded by large-scaled pieces. A small table with spindly legs placed at the end of a heavy sofa or chair will look out of place, and a large-scaled table placed near a dainty chair will not be pleasing.

Accessories such as mirrors, pictures, and lamps should be scaled for the items with which they are to be used. A lamp should not overpower a table, nor should it be so small that it looks ridiculous. The lamp shade should be the correct scale for the base.

Not only form but also color, texture, and pattern are important in the consideration of scale and proportion. Coarse textures, large patterns, and bold colors will cause the object on which they are used to appear larger than an object with smooth textures, small patterns, and soft, light colors. Whatever attracts the eye seems larger. Through the skillful use of these and other principles, the apparent

size and proportion of rooms and objects may be altered. The *decor* of a room succeeds largely on the knowledgeable use of the principles of design.

BALANCE

Balance is that quality in a room which gives a sense of equilibrium and repose. It is a sense of weight as the eye perceives it. The three types of balance are *bisymmetrical, asymmetrical,* and *radial.*

Bisymmetrical or formal balance is that in which identical objects are arranged similarly on each side of an imaginary line. Traditional decorating employs a predominance of this type of balance. Most composition needs some bisymmetry.

Asymmetrical, informal, occult, or optical balance is more subtle than bisymmetrical. It requires more thought and imagination, but once achieved, remains interesting for a longer time. In this type of balance, objects of different sizes, shapes, and colors may be used in an infinite number of ways. Two small objects may balance one large one, a small, shiny object may balance a larger, dull one, a spot of bright color may balance a large area of neutral, and a large object moved closer to a central point may balance a smaller one pushed farther away. No measurement will indicate at what point these different items should be placed. The point at which balance is achieved must be sensed. Contemporary interiors are predominantly asymmetrical in balance.

Radial balance is that in which all the elements of the design radiate from a central point. This balance is most often seen in a room in which chairs surround a round dining table or a coffee table.

The architectural background, which includes doors, windows, paneling, and fireplaces, should be arranged so that the room has a feeling of equilibrium. Opposite walls should have a comfortable feeling of balance through the pleasant distribution of high, low, large, and small objects. Most rooms need both bisymmetrical and asymmetrical balance. Radial balance, which requires more space, is less often used.

BALANCE

Bisymmetrical

Asymmetrical

Radial

angle

curves

combination of line & space

Figure 4.11. Radial balance is seen in this attractive arrangement that artfully combines horizontal, vertical, curved, and diagonal lines. (Courtesy of Thayer Coggin.)

RHYTHM

Rhythm is an intangible component of a composition. Rhythm to most people suggests a flowing quality, but in interiors is something that assists the eye in moving easily about a room from one area to another. This principle can be achieved through *repetition, gradation, opposition, transition,* and *radiation.*

Repetition is rhythm established by repeating color, pattern, texture, line, or form. For example, a color in the upholstery fabric of a sofa can be repeated on a chair seat, or a pair of identical chairs, tables, or lamps can be placed in a room, thus introducing rhythm by repetition and providing unity.

Gradation or progression is rhythm produced by the succession of the size of an object from large to small or of a color from dark to light.

Opposition is found in a composition wherever lines come together at right angles (as in the corners of a square window frame), where a straight fireplace lintel meets an upright support, or wherever a horizontal line of furniture meets a vertical architectural member.

Transition is rhythm found in a curved line that carries the eye easily over an architectural element, such as an arched window, or around an item of furnishing, such as drapery swags or a circular chair.

Radiation is a method of rhythm in which lines extend outward from a central axis. This pattern is usually found in the accessories of a room, such as in lighting fixtures or in a bouquet of flowers.

TYPES OF RHYTHM

Gradation

Repetition

Transition

Opposition

Radiation

EMPHASIS

Emphasis in a room refers to the focal point or center of interest. In every well-planned room, one feature should repeatedly draw the eye. This emphasis, or focal point, can bring a feeling of order and unity into a room, and all other groupings should be subordinated to it. A common focal point is the fireplace, which radiates warmth and hospitality and is a natural site for a main seating arrangement. In the absence of a fireplace, a dominant architectural feature—such as a wall of books or a beautiful window—can be emphasized. When an architectural point of interest is lacking, one should be created by decorative means. A well-displayed art collection, a striking mural, a handsome, important piece of furniture, or a colorful rug are only some of the items that can become the dominant point in a room and can make an attractive decorative axis for a furniture grouping. Whatever the choice, the focal point should be important but not overpowering, and should be linked to the other furnishings of the room through color, scale, and general theme.

The following elements will assist the interior designer in creating, emphasizing, or enhancing a point of interest:

Color is probably the most important element by which a grouping may be brought into immediate focus. This element should be used artfully in achieving the right amount of emphasis. The use of colors that are too demanding should be avoided.

Comfortable furniture should be placed in a friendly, inward-facing arrangement, focusing on the point of emphasis. A convenient opening should be left so that the relationship to the rest of the room is inviting.

Lighting can be used to tie the group together, to dramatize, to attract attention, and to create a focal point.

Accessories should be chosen with discrimination. When well chosen and artistically arranged, accessories can give importance and individuality to a room in a unique way.

EMPHASIS

The fireplace in a room becomes the natural focal point. The television placed in the same wall makes good use of the convenient furniture arrangement.

A corner window with a pleasant view can be the room's focal point.

HARMONY OR UNITY

Harmony, or unity, is an essential ingredient in any well-designed room. A unifying theme—a *common denominator*—should run through all the component parts and blend them together.

In every room, the interior architecture should be the determining factor. Just as exterior and interior architecture should be consistent, the furnishings of a room should also be in harmony with the background. For example, molded plastic chairs do not belong against formal eighteenth-century paneling, nor is a classic Louis XVI chair pleasing against a heavy block wall. A surprising juxtaposition of seemingly unrelated objects may occasionally add relief, but this practice requires sophisticated judgment.

Furniture in the room should seem to belong there. Whether the room is large or small, furniture should be scaled accordingly. Whether the architectural background is strong—perhaps with exposed beams and masonry construction—or more formal and refined, the furniture should reflect the same feeling.

Colors should be appropriate to the style of furnishings: formal eighteenth-century French furnishings call for delicate colors, and modern furnishings are usually more effective with bold colors and striking contrasts.

Fabrics should be in harmony with the furniture in color, texture, and design. Heavy, homespun texture is generally not suitable for a Louis XV chair, nor is silk damask usually at home on rough-hewn ranch oak.

Windows should be decorated with fabric that is right for the theme of the room and that is hung appropriately for the style of decor. For example, ruffled cottage curtains are out of place in an oriental-style house, and silk damask swags are inappropriate for a rustic cottage.

Floor coverings should carefully be chosen. Many floor coverings are extremely versatile and can go anywhere. Rugs, such as many Persian orientals, are at home in any decor. Shags, which were originally considered only for modern-style rooms, are now acceptable in most types of rooms. Wall-to-wall carpeting, however, should be chosen with theme and purpose in mind. A heavily textured tweed is not appropriate for a room with formal Italian furniture, nor is a plush, white, wall-to-wall carpet appropriate for a family room. Hard floor covering should also be selected with purpose and style in mind.

Accessories should be chosen to fit pleasantly into a room. If an accessory is not beautiful, useful, or meaningful to the person using it, it does not belong.

The final touches added to a room reveal individual personality more readily than any other item of furnishing, and should not be overlooked in creating rooms of beauty and interest. Items that are essentially good, however, can lose their charm when not well used. For example, a gracefully scrolled wrought-iron wall sconce can add much to a room of Spanish or Mediterranean styling, but would look heavy and out of place in a pastel room with delicate furnishings.

Consistency or harmony is best achieved by carrying out a basic theme or style. The basic style, however, should not be followed slavishly; rather, the effort should be to maintain a general feeling of unity throughout, whether the feeling is one of formality, casual elegance, or an informal country atmosphere. Within this overall theme, an occasional surprise to give variety and interest can provide charm and individuality.

Artificial lighting

LIGHTING FOR FUNCTION AND BEAUTY

As an essential element of interior design for both function and beauty, lighting merits special consideration from the initial planning of the house until the last accessory is in place. The lighting needs of each room can most satisfactorily be determined by drawing a floor plan and indicating the location of all built-in overhead and wall fixtures, switches, and flexible outlets for portable lamps.

Light for function is lighting for specific activities. This category includes task lighting of all kinds, and the lighting needs of each activity require special attention. Lighting for safety is also an important consideration. Stairways, hallways, basements, attics, porches, and patios all present hazards if not provided with adequate and strategically placed lighting.

Besides lighting for particular tasks and for safety, lighting for other household activities deserves thoughtful planning. For example, conversation, dining, and television watching require only a low level of *diffused* light. In areas where a large group gathers, light should be at a high enough level to enable the group to see clearly about the room, yet should not be so brilliant that it is aesthetically unpleasant.

Light for beauty is a magic tool, and the ways in which today's versatile lighting can be used in beautifying a room are limited only by the extent of the interior designer's ingenuity. Through the art of decorative lighting, space can be modified, structural elements can be emphasized or subordinated, color and texture can be enhanced, plants, paintings, and other art objects can be brought into focus, and an atmosphere of cool formality or warm intimacy can be imparted to a room. To accomplish this, the interior designer should have an understanding of both the aesthetics and tech-

niques of lighting. In most rooms, incorporating a variety of lighting is desirable, since comfort, beauty, and general mood are influenced by the source, amount, and quality of illumination. *Fluorescent lighting* can successfully be used for ambient lighting, and *incandescent lighting* can effectively be used for specific locations and decorative accents. When mixing incandescent and fluorescent lighting, a warm white or warm white deluxe fluorescent should be used. Built-in lighting can be direct or indirect, warm or cool, harsh or soft, bright or dim. When supplemented by strategically placed hanging fixtures and an occasional floor or table lamp, harshness, glare, and strong contrasts of light can be avoided, and beauty achieved.

BASIC LIGHTING TERMINOLOGY

The term *lamp* is a generic name for a man-made source of light. A lighting unit consisting of a lamp with a shade or reflector (or both) enclosing a light is also called a lamp. The light source within the unit is the globe or bulb. A *luminaire,* which is a complete lighting unit such as a ceiling fixture, wall bracket, portable lamp, or a built-in or an applied unit, is also referred to as a lamp. Although light is the illumination or density of luminous flux on a surface, a complete fixture is sometimes referred to as simply a light.

TYPES OF LIGHTING

The three main types of lighting are (1) ambient (or general), (2) task, and (3) accent. A fourth type—mood lighting—can fall within the accent and ambient categories.

AMBIENT (OR GENERAL) LIGHTING

Ambient lighting spreads an overall luminosity and reduces harsh contrasts between pools of concentrated light. Ambient lighting can be produced by large area light sources, by a number of small sources focused to ceilings, walls,

Ambient lighting

and drapery, by direct or indirect light, and by chandeliers, downlights, and reflected light from open-top lamps. Soft general lighting may be relaxing, but too much indirect or reflected light can be harsh and uninviting. When recessed lighting is used for general illumination, lamps with aluminum reflectors will provide almost twice as much light as ordinary "white cans."

TASK LIGHTING

Task lighting is functional and is localized for a particular activity such as sewing, reading, writing, preparing food, and grooming. Task lighting is usually located near the activity and should be aimed to avoid glare and distributed evenly over the working surface to reduce shadows to a minimum. Most tasks of a concentrated nature, especially when prolonged, require a high level of illumination, which

Task lighting

Figure 4.12. Ambient (or general) lighting in this living room is provided by ceiling lamps that light the entire room and reduce sharp contrasts between task lights. (Courtesy of General Electric Company.)

Figure 4.13. Task lighting for grooming is amply furnished by a well-placed soffit. (Courtesy of General Electric Company.)

can be achieved by the use of pendants, recessed lights, pole- or track-mounted fixtures, and shielded fluorescent tubes either hanging, placed under shelves or cabinets, or wall mounted above and on each side of a mirror. Placement, shade design, socket location, and shielding all contribute to controlling glare and supplying good quality light, and the choice of lamps or tubes will determine the quantity of light (see Table 4.1).

ACCENT LIGHTING

Accent lighting uses a concentrated beam of light to focus on a particular object or area. A highly flexible lighting tool, accent lighting can be placed at any angle and can be precisely controlled to provide the desired amount of intensity and color to emphasize one area and subordinate others. This type of lighting can separate one area from another, highlight a treasured item, establish a focal point, and create a touch of drama. Accent lighting, which is often combined with ambient lighting, can be produced by recessed, surface-mounted, track-mounted, or portable fixtures.

Accent lighting

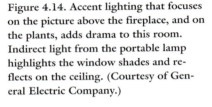

Figure 4.14. Accent lighting that focuses on the picture above the fireplace, and on the plants, adds drama to this room. Indirect light from the portable lamp highlights the window shades and reflects on the ceiling. (Courtesy of General Electric Company.)

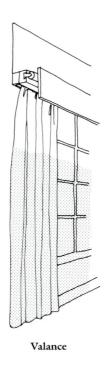

Valance

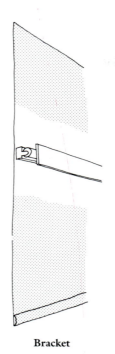

Bracket

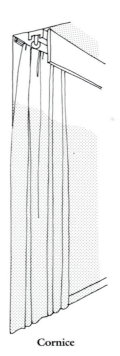

Cornice

Base

METHODS OF ARTIFICIAL LIGHTING

The two basic methods of artificial lighting are (1) structural (or architectural) and (2) portable (or nonarchitectural).

STRUCTURAL (OR ARCHITECTURAL) LIGHTING

Structural lighting is closely correlated with the architecture of the room and should be included in the original plan of the house as an integral part of the structural design. This method supplies lighting for both function and beauty, is unobtrusive, and is particularly good for contemporary rooms. The flexibility of structural lighting, however, can be fairly limited, considering the various functions that can take place in a room. The following are a number of ways in which structural lighting is used:

Valance lighting is used over windows. A horizontal fluorescent tube is placed behind a valance board, and the light reflects off the ceiling and also shines on the drapery, thus producing both direct (downlight) and indirect (uplight) lighting.

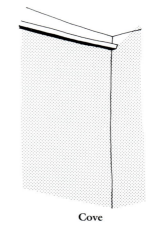

Canopy

Cove

Bracket lighting is similar to valance lighting, but is placed either high on the wall for general wall lighting or low for specific tasks such as washing dishes, cooking, or reading in bed. When used in living areas, the length of the bracket should relate to the furniture grouping that it serves.

Cornice lighting is usually installed at the ceiling and directs the light downward only. This lighting can give a dramatic effect to drapery, wall covering, and pictures. When used over a window, it eliminates the black mirror effect at night.

Cove lighting placed near the ceiling directs all the light upward and gives a feeling of height (see Figure 4.21).

Canopy lighting is a canopy overhang that provides general illumination. This lighting is most applicable to bath and dressing rooms, but may be used for a particular purpose in other rooms.

Figure 4.15. Bracket lighting is used to illuminate the walls and to cast light on the ceiling. The lighting is also reflected throughout the room. (Courtesy of General Electric Company.)

Figure 4.16. Cornice lighting, which directs the light downward only, gives a dramatic effect to this room. The standing screen is emphasized, and the picture is brought into contrast. (Courtesy of General Electric Company.)

Soffit lighting consists of enclosed light attached to the ceiling and is designed to provide a high level of light directly below. Excellent for bathrooms, this lighting is also effective in niches such as over built-in desks and sofas.

Luminous ceilings consist of recessed light diffused through ceiling panels, and are used primarily in kitchens, utility areas, and bathrooms.

Luminous wall panels, another recessed type of lighting, can be used purely for function or to create a variety of dramatic effects.

Downlights are recessed lights that may spotlight a definite object or may produce general lighting when used in sufficient numbers (see Figure 4.12). The "eyeball" type is adjustable and can be focused in any direction. Downlight is also produced by ceiling-mounted and track lights.

Base lighting is used in dark hallways and in the base of steps as a safety device.

PORTABLE (OR NONARCHITECTURAL) LIGHTING

Although the wiring for ceiling and wall lighting must be part of the original plans of the house, the fixtures themselves are not considered structural. Nonarchitectural lighting, which consists of ceiling and wall-hung fixtures and portable lamps, is designed today to complement the decor of any style and to accommodate any room.

Ceiling fixtures when carefully chosen can add an important accent to any interior. **Chandeliers** should be scaled to the room. Those hung in 8-ft-high dining rooms should be suspended approximately 30 in. above the table and raised 3 in. for each additional foot of ceiling height. Chandeliers must be high enough for clearance if they are hung in rooms in which people move about. Ceiling-mounted contemporary chandeliers need to be related to the ceiling plane. They may be simple and purely functional, or a gleaming shower of crystal. **Pendant chandeliers** may be chosen from a galaxy

Lighted soffits provide high-level light wherever needed.

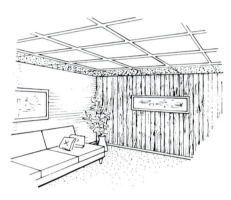

Luminous ceilings provide a skylight effect.

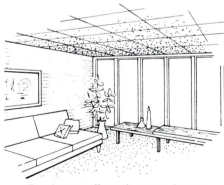

Luminous wall panels create pleasant vistas.

of designs and can be hung singly or clustered depending on the purposes they serve and the area in which they are used.

Track lighting consists of a track that can be mounted vertically, horizontally, or suspended, and comes in a broad array of scale, form, and finish. Fixtures clip anywhere along the track to create a precisely designed optical system with a vast range of lighting effects. Fixtures, however, should be hung 4 ft apart to avoid a cluttered look, and tracks should be restricted to high ceilings or semiconcealed spaces. Layout configurations are infinite, and choice can be made from an abundance of fixtures that are economical, easily installed, and highly energy effective. Track lighting is a total lighting system that is virtually unlimited in flexibility and versatility to meet the needs of both contemporary and future homes. Other ceiling-hung lights may be shielded in a surface-mounted outlet box that directs light to a specific area, or may be attached singly to swivel individually.

Wall lights or **sconces** have returned to popularity, and when carefully chosen and located, they can contribute to the mood and charm of most areas (see Figure 4.5). In small rooms, they can substitute for lamps that require floor space or a table.

Nonarchitectural and portable lamps (both table and floor types) are the oldest forms of interior lighting. They provide the most flexible lighting in the home and can give decorative qualities to a room that no other medium can provide. Although they often function as a secondary light source, portable lamps are conspicuous when equipped with translucent shades, and their placement in the room is important. They should be positioned as part of a furniture grouping, near an electrical outlet, and out of the line of traffic.

Figure 4.17. A luminous ceiling casts a diffused light throughout the room and illuminates shadows, which makes this lighting particularly desirable for kitchens. (Courtesy of General Electric Company.)

Lamps may be purely functional, purely decorative, or a combination of both. Lamps for function should be chosen with the definite task in mind. For example, a table lamp used for reading is most effective when the bottom of the shade is at the eye level of the person seated—38 in. to 42 in. above the floor. Generally, the shade should be at least 16 in. across the bottom so that the lamp will shed light on more than just the reading area and thereby prevent eyestrain caused by a sudden change from light to dark. The shade should be lined with white to provide maximum light and should cover the bulb and fixture to avoid glare. For the best light diffusion, a soft white bulb should be used. An opal glass diffuser bowl will also improve the quality of light, and a flat dishlike diffuser can soften and mask direct light from horizontal bulbs.

A lamp used primarily for decoration should be chosen with an eye to scale and style to ensure that it enhances the room. Overelaboration in both base and shade should be avoided. A lamp used for decoration should usually be of low wattage, especially if it is exposed to a direct view.

Figure 4.18. The famous Frisbi chandelier, a favorite among many interior designers and architects. The design consists of only one lamp, but it casts three kinds of light: reflected, diffused, and direct. (Courtesy of Atelier International Lighting.)

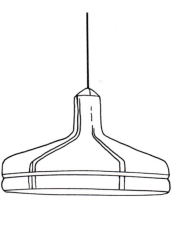

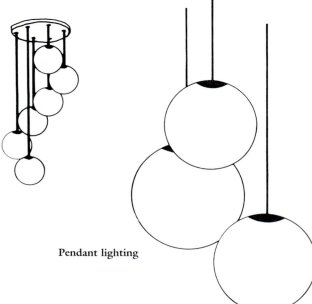

Pendant lighting

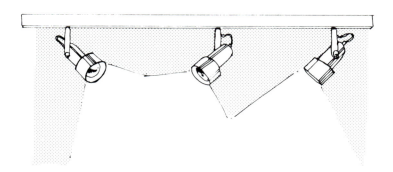

Track lighting

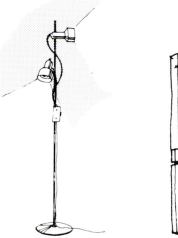

Vertical track lighting

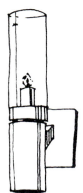

Wall light or bracket

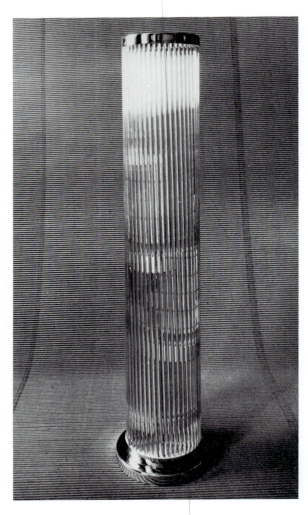

Figure 4.19 (*above, left*). This beautifully crafted contemporary acrylic table lamp can add grace, beauty, and a cosmopolitan effect to any room. (Courtesy of Lang Levine Studios.)

Figure 4.20 (*above, right*). This innovative floor lamp, made of acrylic and superbly finished metal, can enhance any contemporary room. (Courtesy of Lang Levine Studios.)

LIGHTING SOURCES

Artificial light is produced in three ways: (1) combustion, (2) incandescence, and (3) fluorescence (or *luminescence*).

COMBUSTION

Combustion is the oldest-known method of producing light. Fire used by ancient tribes, oil lamps, wax candles, and gaslights are all methods of combustion. Candles are still widely used, but only as supplementary lighting. Their main value is in the soft glow that sheds a flattering light and bestows an atmosphere of warmth and intimacy.

INCANDESCENCE

Incandescent light comes from the familiar light bulb, in which is sealed a tungsten *filament* that glows when heated. Incandescent lights are the smallest, the most adaptable, and the most easily controlled. They do not flicker or hum, and cause little interference with radio or television. Although not the most efficient light source, incandescence is the basis of the most effective accent and task lighting, since it permits precise optical control (see drawings).

REPRESENTATIVE INCANDESCENT SHAPES

General service

Decorative

Reflectorized

DIFFUSERS

Bowl

Shallow dish

FLUORESCENT TUBES

Straight tube

Circline tube

U-shaped tube

Circlete tube

FLUORESCENT SHAPES

Outdoor light

Security light

Bug light

Night light

FLUORESCENCE (OR LUMINESCENCE)

Fluorescent light, the luminescent light most often used in homes, is produced in a glass tube that is lined with a fluorescent coating, filled with mercury vapor and argon, and sealed at the ends by cathodes. When gases are activated by an electric current, ultraviolet rays stimulate the phosphorous bulb coating, which in turn emits visible light. Fluorescent lamps emit less heat, use less energy, and last longer than incandescent lamps. Their sources are also larger and create broader areas of light. The most commonly used cool white lamp produces a cold light, which many people consider unflattering. Tubes are available in other fluorescent colors, however, including warm white and warm white deluxe, which blend with incandescent light and create a more inviting atmosphere. Fluorescent tubes are made straight, U-shaped, circline, and circlete (see drawings).

DIRECT AND INDIRECT LIGHTING

Direct lighting is light that is thrown directly onto a particular area, resulting in shadows and sharp contrasts between dark and light. Downlights of all kinds yield direct lighting. They may have an ambient glare over a large area or may be concentrated on a specific object.

Indirect lighting is lighting directed from a hidden source onto the ceiling or another surface, which reflects the light back into the room. Indirect lighting tends to expand space visually, and when reflected from the ceiling provides general illumination, which causes few if any shadows. Like the sun at midday, however, indirect lighting tends to be flat and in most cases needs to be supplemented by portable lamps. Indirect lighting can also be used to dramatize a particular area or object and to create a soft and exotic mood. Concealed floor spotlights

Indirect lighting can add a dramatic touch.

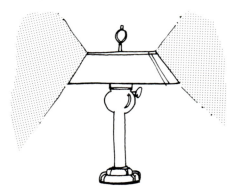

Direct and indirect lighting

placed behind grilled windows or directed upward on a plant can create fantastic shadows.

Direct and indirect lighting can be produced by portable lamps with open tops, particularly those with *opaque* shades that direct the light both upward and downward. Some fixtures are specially equipped to direct most of the light upward, some direct most light downward, and still others distribute the light more evenly.

SWITCHES AND OUTLETS

The convenient location of switches and outlets is essential and should be indicated on the blueprint and the electrical plan of the house. Each room requires a light switch—which may or may not control both built-in and portable lamps—conveniently placed on the latch side of each access door to provide immediate illumination on entering and to serve as a reminder to turn it off when leaving. Switches are also necessary at both ends of hallways and at the top and bottom of stairways. Where task lighting is necessary, switches should be placed within easy reach.

Outlets placed at regular intervals, approximately 3 to 12 ft apart between doorways and floor-length windows, will decrease the need for hazardous extension cords. Throughout the house, outlets should be ample and suitably installed for specific tasks, for appliances in kitchen and utility areas, and for electrical equipment in bathrooms. Where heavy mechanical devices are power driven, special heavy-duty outlets should be provided. Outdoor outlets should be weatherproofed, ground fault interruptible, and safely situated.

LIGHTING FOR SPECIFIC AREAS

Through the art of creative lighting, aided by today's new and wondrous technology, one can bring light to everyday activities and can endow various areas of a house with safety, efficiency, beauty, and individuality.

The entrance hall, as the keynote to the decor of a home, should provide a cordial air of hospitality in which lighting plays an important role. During the day, the entry hall should be bright enough to allow a reasonable transition from the bright outdoors to the darker interior. Illumination need not be a high level at night, but should be strong enough to enable entering guests to see and be seen. Pendants or chandeliers, hung high enough to avoid collisions with tall persons, plus suitably placed wall sconces that diffuse light and direct it both up and down, will provide adequate lighting and a pleasant atmosphere. Staircases should be well lighted so that treads and risers can clearly be distinguished. The entrance is an ideal place to try a dramatic lighting effect such as an accented art object, a lighted wall panel, or an exotically uplighted plant.

Living rooms need soft general lighting supplemented by special area lighting. Both direct and indirect lighting are desirable, although an excess of indirect lighting may result in a washed-out appearance. Well-chosen lamps, at necessary locations, will add a feeling of comfort and hospitality. A low-hung pendant light can pull a furniture grouping together and can provide an inviting area for people to gather and relax. When accented by downlights, built-in shelving, display cases, and art objects help to personalize a room and can establish the room's focal point.

Family and recreation rooms, which accommodate a variety of activities, require particularly flexible lighting. General lighting is essential, with area and task lighting supplied for specific activities.

Dining areas deserve versatile lighting that can be adjusted for a variety of functions in addition to formal and casual dining, such as studying, sewing, and playing games. A low-level background light can be provided by wall sconces or recessed downlights. A chandelier or pendant, using incandescent globes and hung over the table, will add sparkle to silver and glass at formal meals. Dimmer controls will allow for a change of mood, and added light from candles will shed a glow that is flattering to skin tones. If the dining space is part of or open to other areas, ingenious lighting can successfully set it apart.

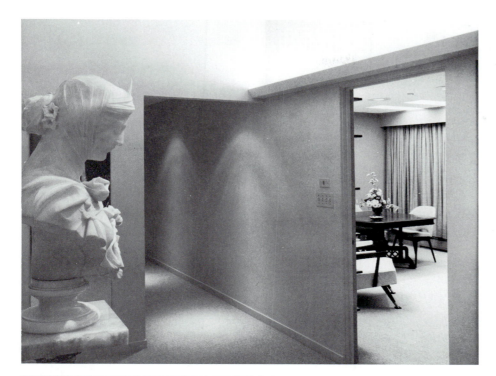

Figure 4.21. Cove lighting supplies a pleasant allover glow in this entrance hall. Recessed downlights accent the statue and add interest to the plain wall. (Courtesy of General Electric Company.)

Figure 4.22. Strategically placed soffits in this utility room provide an abundance of task lighting for laundry, ironing, linen storage, and sewing. (Courtesy of General Electric Company.)

Figure 4.23 (*above, left*). A cornice above the window drapery casts the light downward. Direct and indirect illumination from portable lamps provides light for nighttime reading and reflects light on wall and ceiling. (Courtesy of General Electric Company.)

Figure 4.24 (*above, right*). A well-designed ceiling fixture housing two circline fluorescent lamps provides ambient lighting for this bedroom. The bedside lamp with opaque shade gives extra light for reading. (Courtesy of General Electric Company.)

Kitchens and utility rooms should have generous overall lighting for safety and efficiency. **Perimeter lighting,** completely shielded close-to-ceiling fixtures, recessed downlights, or an illuminated ceiling will give adequate general light and will eliminate shadows. Recessed or shielded fluorescent tubes over work areas will help to prevent accidents, speed up food preparation, and enhance the decor. Warm white or warm white deluxe tubes will give red objects and meat a pleasing color.

Bedrooms should have general lighting with appropriate task lights for reading, desk work, grooming, and other activities, depending on the uses of the room. Simple pull-down lights are handy and can be pushed out of the way when not in use. Dim circulation lighting for safety at night is a basic requirement.

Bathrooms require shadowless lighting for shaving and grooming, which can be supplied by light from overhead and from both sides of a mirror, and by light reflected upward from a light-colored basin or counter top (see Figure 4.13). Mirror lighting is usually sufficient to illuminate an average-sized bath or powder room.

Halls need overall illumination for safe passage. The fixture may be recessed in or hung from the ceiling, attached to walls, built in near the baseboard, or supplied by a combination of two or more of these methods.

Outdoor lighting is worthy of special attention. Since the front door conveys the first impression of a home, it might be set off by fixtures that have eye appeal, conform to the style of the house, and are weatherproof. A recessed door is attractive with a downlighting. When artistically lighted, patios, terraces, walks, and gardens can be enjoyed from the inside at night, and will seem to expand interior space.

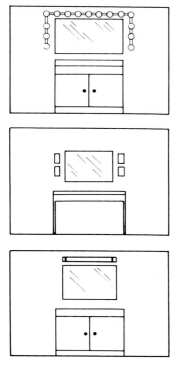

Bathroom light for grooming

LIGHTING FOR ENERGY CONSERVATION

Knowledgeable planning and purchasing can give a home sufficient lighting and still save watts and dollars. The following guidelines can help to conserve energy in lighting:

Lighting should fit specific needs. Since task areas such as kitchen counters require more light than nonworking areas such as circulation space, lighting should be chosen accordingly. Sufficient light is important, but using more light than necessary wastes electrical energy. Dimmers are useful in adjusting light levels.

Fixtures should be energy effective. Light should be placed where it is needed instead of trapped or scattered wastefully. Fixtures that can be adjusted and moved when necessary are a wise choice. Track lighting has great flexibility and permits the light to be directed where it is wanted. A reflectorized lamp is good for accent or task lighting. Low-voltage spotlights are especially effective where a tightly controlled beam is required.

Light sources should be efficient. Light output is measured in *lumens* or *footcandles* per watt, and each type of light source varies in efficiency according to wattage and color. Fluorescent lamps use as much as 80 percent less energy, produce 3 to 5 times as much light, and last 20 times longer than incandescent lamps. Three-way incandescent lamps allow for selectivity in the amount of light needed. Where appearance is not a consideration, as in garages and basements, industrial reflectors are an economical option. Ceilings, walls, floors, and furniture should have light-colored finishes. Rooms done in dark colors that absorb light may require much more lighting than those done in light-reflecting colors. Keeping reflectors, diffusers, and lamps clean will help to maintain lighting equipment. Lights should be turned off when not needed.

TABLE 4.1. *Recommended ranges of light levels for some activities*

ACTIVITY	PROLONGED DURATION	INCANDESCENT	FLUORESCENT
Craft work	Moderate to high	75–200 w	30–55 w
Dining	Low	40–60 w	16–22 w
Entertaining	Low to high	40–200 w	16–55 w
Grooming	High	150–200 w	40–55 w
Hand sewing	High	150–200 w	40–55 w
Ironing	High	150–200 w	40–55 w
Kitchen and laundry	High	150–200 w	40–55 w
Machine sewing	High	150–200 w	40–55 w
Reading musical scores	Moderate to high	75–200 w	30–55 w
Reading	High	150–200 w	40–55 w
Television viewing	Low to moderate	40–100 w	16–44 w
Writing	Moderate	75–100 w	30–44 w

ASSIGNMENT

The following is an assignment aimed at promoting your awareness of the many principles and elements involved in the complete design of a room.

Select a *clear, colored* picture of a living room. The view should be complete—not just a corner view. The picture should be mounted on white paper, allowing a margin sufficiently wide for answering Question 1. The answers to the remaining questions should be written below the picture.

1 Point out the following by drawing a line from the correct object or objects in the picture to your explanation in the margin:

An example of structural design

An example of decorative design

The use of the golden mean (explain briefly)

A vertical line

A horizontal line

A curved line

A diagonal line

An example of bisymmetrical balance (explain briefly)

An example of asymmetrical balance (explain briefly)

Rhythm by repetition

Rhythm by gradation

Rhythm by opposition

Rhythm by transition

Rhythm by radiation

2 Is there a predominance of one line, or are lines pleasingly distributed?

3 Are the elements of the room more strong or more delicate—or is neither effect predominant?

4 What kinds of designs are used in the fabrics in the room (e.g., naturalistic, conventional, abstract, geometric)? If the fabrics have no design, point out two specific textures used.

5 What is the focal point of the room? Point out four ways through which elements were used to bring this area into focus (see the section on emphasis).

6 Does the room have a feeling of unity and harmony? Examine the room carefully: backgrounds, furniture, fabrics, and accessories. Point out six specific elements of the room that contribute to the overall feeling of unity (see the section on harmony).

7 Does lighting appear to be adequate? Are lighting fixtures and lamps artfully and conveniently located?

You should make comments specifically related to your picture. Selection and presentation will be considered in evaluating this project.

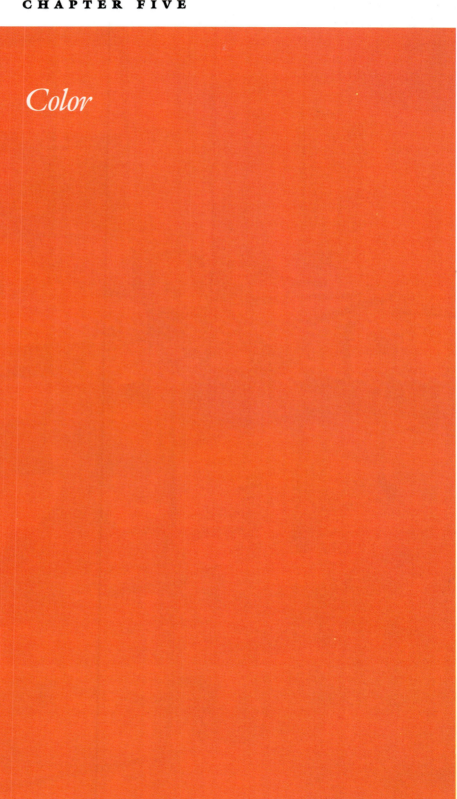

CHAPTER FIVE

Color

Color, like music, is an international language. Throughout the world, birds, animals, trees, flowers, jewels, signals, and many other things are identified by their coloring. The red-breasted robin, the green pine tree, and the blue sapphire look much the same wherever they are found. A red signal is recognized everywhere as a warning of danger, a green signal as an assurance of safety.

Color has always had symbolic importance. In early China, yellow had religious significance and remains today the imperial color. In early Greece and Rome, red was believed to have protective powers. Purple was the imperial color of the ancients and was restricted to

the use of nobility—hence the term *royal purple.* When the remains of Charlemagne (742–814) were disinterred in the middle of the twelfth century, the coffin contained robes of sumptuous purple velvet. To the present time, purple is identified with royalty.

Among English-speaking people, many colors signify certain character traits. For example, yellow connotes deceit and cowardice, and blue is related to honesty and wisdom. Numerous expressions using color names that have specific meanings are commonly used and understood. When someone has the blues, the interpretation is that the person is depressed. When someone has a green thumb, the meaning is that he or she has an unusual ability to make plants grow.

Color in history

Color has revealed much about the civilizations of people in both primitive tribes and highly developed cultures, but perhaps the greatest value of color is its power to create beauty. Since the dawn of history, humans have toiled to bring beauty into their environment through the use of color. The ancient Egyptians

adorned the walls of tombs and temples with brilliant hues of blue, tangerine, green, and *carmine.* The great temples and dwellings of Greece and Rome were decorated with colored marble floors, brightly painted walls and ceilings, and rich tapestries and silks. The great cathedrals of medieval Europe, with their gloriously colored stained-glass windows, brought beauty into the drab lives of a downtrodden people and remain today as a supreme creative achievement of Western culture.

All through history, color has significantly reflected the spirit of the age. During the Italian Renaissance, the vibrant reds, greens, golds, and blues used by the master artists were carried into the sumptuous villas of the reigning families in Italy and later into the great palaces of France and Germany. With the *rococo* extravagance of Louis XV in France, where feminine tastes had a great influence, colors became less vibrant. During the latter part of the eighteenth century, when Marie Antoinette dominated the court of Louis XVI, colors became even more delicate and softly

Figure 5.1. The beautifully developed triad color scheme in this traditional eighteenth-century room is established by the lively fabric of the love seat. The dark blue wall gives a contemporary feeling and adds drama. (Courtesy of the James River Collection, Hickory Chair Company.)

pastel. Throughout the late seventeenth and eighteenth centuries, a period when France dominated the arts of the Western world, delicate French colors were in vogue wherever beauty and luxury were cherished.

The eighteenth century in England was one of great elegance. Colors were rich, showing a strong Chinese influence in the use of much red and gold. Toward the latter part of the century, the excavation of Pompeii inspired the Brothers Adam to introduce the neoclassic look into England. Colors became more delicate, with Adam green (a sharp, light green) being the favorite.

The long Victorian era was a period of eclecticism known for its abundance of "things." Colors were predominantly dull reds, greens, browns, and mauves, which prompted the era to be referred to as the Mauve Decades.

During the opening decades of the twentieth century, the revolutionary ideas of art nouveau introduced plant forms and flamelike shapes reflected in languid, sinuous curves and delicate pastels. The influence of modern art was then reflected in the introduction of garish colors, which in the twenties were replaced by subdued tones; the monochromatic room then became the vogue. Sleek surfaces and strong contrasts became high fashion, with black, gray, silver, brown, beige, and white as favorite colors.

Typical of the thirties was the all-white interior, which gradually gave way to delicate pastels with bright accents. Preferred colors were cocoa brown with hyacinth blue, mustard yellow with gray, and prune with turquoise.

Light colors were preferred through the fifties. American interest then turned to Mexico, and a shift to bright colors with more contrast occurred. This shift paved the way for a shocking palette of color, which found favor with lovers of Spanish colonial and modern architecture and design. In the sixties, a renewed interest in English furnishings of the sixteenth and seventeenth centuries brought with it rich, blended color schemes employing blue, green, gold, and red.

The decade of the seventies witnessed a wide range of color fashions. The patriotism generated by the bicentennial produced a renewed interest in the ever-popular combination of red, white, and blue. These colors were prominently used not only for color schemes in many rooms of the house but also for clothing and for many areas of industry and the arts. The widespread use of these typically American colors promises to continue.

Concurrent with the predominant color trends are color fads that for a time become popular with certain groups of people. These fads may stay in vogue for only a short time and then be replaced by something entirely different, or they may remain popular for a long period. Several "in" fads may be present at the same time. During the early 1970s, for example, three extremes were equally fashionable. One used shiny black walls with strong colors throughout the room, another used a silvery look on everything, and still another was the allover white look. As the decade came to a close, bright colors again found favor.

The psychology of color

The knowledge of color and its relationship to people is basic to the interior designer, but its importance is also recognized in industry—in advertising, manufacturing, and packaging. The significance of color in the physical environment is generally established. Experiments have shown that workers function more efficiently in surroundings of pleasant colors than they do in drab environments. Young people in detention homes were found to respond more positively when walls that formerly had been dull were brightly colored.

Responding to the generally accepted notion that red will excite one to action and blue will calm one's nerves, some athletic directors have painted their players' dressing rooms in bright reds and oranges, and visitors' dressing rooms in pale blues. The directors claim that it works.

Emotional reactions associated with color are spontaneous. The reaction is often due to the *result* of a color rather than to the color itself, and the reaction produced may be positive or negative. "One such situation occurred in a meat market in Chicago, which, when painted a bright and cheerful yellow, lost business. A color consultant quickly informed the owner that the yellow walls caused a blue after-image. It gave meat a purplish cast, making it appear old and spoiled. The walls were repainted bluish green, creating a red after-image that enhanced the appearance of meat—and sales zoomed" (John Dreyfuss, *Los Angeles Times*).

These and other similar experiments, however, indicate the superficiality of the information on which popular assumptions about color are based. Serious research on the subject is inconclusive and often contradictory, and wide gaps between laboratory studies and their applications are frequent. Authorities in the field generally agree that color and emotion are closely related and that people react differently to color. They do not, however, agree on the emotional effects of color, nor do they know whether these emotional reactions are inherent or learned.

That people have definite color preferences is common knowledge. Every person generally has a favorite color to which he or she is invariably attracted and with which he or she feels most comfortable. Because of this, people should surround themselves with colors that are pleasurable to them, thus alleviating unnecessary mental discomfort.

The simplest psychological division of color results in two major areas or groups: warm and cool, with neutral in between. A line drawn through the standard color wheel will approximate the division between cool and warm colors.

A number of characteristics peculiar to these color groups should be understood and taken into consideration when choosing colors for decorative purposes.

Color groups

WARM COLORS

Warm colors of a strong intensity are generally

□ active

□ cheery

□ advancing

□ somewhat informal and tend to blend objects together (soften outlines)

If used in strong intensity in large areas, warm colors may cause psychological irritation.

COOL COLORS

Particularly in tints, cool colors are generally

□ restful

□ soothing

□ receding

□ somewhat formal and tend to make individual objects stand out (reinforce outlines)

Rooms done in cool colors may be too cool and unfriendly and may lack unity.

NEUTRAL COLORS

Colors falling midway between warm and cool are called neutrals. Neutral colors are important to every color scheme. A warm neutral is a tint, tone, or shade of a warm color, and a cool neutral is a tint, tone, or shade of a cool color. Warm neutrals are easier to work with than cool neutrals. Large background areas of warm neutral tones tend to produce the most livable and lasting color schemes.

In addition to the division of colors into warm and cool, each color contains peculiar properties that produce certain psychological effects.

Blue is cool and soothing, recalling sky, water, and ice, but it is difficult to mix and varies greatly under different lighting. More than any other color, blue is affected by the different materials it colors. Lacquer and glass, for example, have a reflective quality that intensifies blue. In deep pile carpet, blue has great depth. Nubby fabrics soften blue. Shiny materials make blue look frosted.

Green is nature's color and is serene and friendly. It is a good mixer, especially yellow green. White brings out green's best qualities. Green is a great favorite and when grayed, warmed, or cooled makes an excellent background.

Red is conspicuous wherever it appears, and since it it is lively and stimulating, it should be used with care. Red mixes well, and most rooms are enhanced by a touch of one of its tones.

Yellow is the sunlight color. High-noon yellows are the most revealing and

demanding, and merit careful attention. Gray yellows of earlier dawn are *foils* for more fragile colors—pinks, blues, pale greens. Warm afternoon yellow is a foil for rich, warm woods. Burnished yellows or brass give a cast of copper gilt and bring life into a room. All yellows are reflective, take on tones of other colors, and add flattering highlights.

Gold is the symbol of affluence and when used well adds style to most rooms. On large areas it may appear brassy or garish unless neutralized.

Pink is delicate and is flattering to almost everyone. Add a little yellow, leaning toward peach, and pink becomes warm. Add a little blue, leaning toward violet, and it becomes cool. Pink needs a stronger color for contrast. It blends well with grays, browns, and sharp blues. Combined with purples and lavenders, pink takes on a fresh look.

Violet can be a dramatic color. When pink is added, it becomes warm, and a touch of blue makes it cool. It combines well with both pink and blue.

Brown is warm, comfortable, and earthy. The homeyness of brown tones makes them universal favorites. Ranging from pale cream beige to deepest chocolate brown, these tones can be used together in a room to give infinite variety. Browns are easy to work with.

Gray is cool and formal in light tones. If light and slightly warmed, it makes an excellent background; if too heavy, it becomes oppressive. Grays are more difficult to work with than browns. In combinations of three or more, they tend to harmonize.

Off-white and off-black have the quality of making all colors in a room look cleaner and livelier. Warm off-white is unequaled as a mellow background color and works wonders in blending furniture of different woods and styles. Changes of light from day to night are kind to off-white and give it quiet vitality. Off-black (rich black brown) in furniture finishes, small areas of fabric, or accessories adds an important accent that makes other colors crisp and clear.

Color and pigment

Ever since Sir Isaac Newton, over 300 years ago, began a series of experiments that provided the foundation for our modern knowledge of color, people have been working to develop new color theories and systems. The different scientific approaches to color are many. The physicist works with colors in light, the chemist is mainly concerned with the production of pigments, and the psychologist's theories are based on visual perception and the effects of color on the emotions. The artist, and particularly the student of interior design, should have some understanding of all three approaches, although his or her main concern is with color in pigments.

The most practical approach to the understanding of color is from the viewpoint of personal experience. People are constantly surrounded by color, in light and in objects. The colors in objects are referred to as pigment colors, and the colors from the sun and from lamps are called light colors.

The process of combining primary colors (red, green, and blue) is said to be an "additive" one (i.e., the sensations produced by different wavelengths of light, or *spectral* colors, are added together). When pigments are mixed, how-

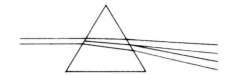

A beam of white light passing through a glass prism

ever, the resulting sensations differ from those of the spectral colors. In this case, the method is a "subtractive" one, since subtraction or absorption of the wavelengths of light occurs.

In reality, a ray of light is the source of all color, for without light, color does not exist. Color is light broken down into *electromagnetic* vibrations of varying wavelengths, which cause the viewer to see different colors. This phenomenon can be demonstrated by passing a beam of light through a glass prism. The beam divides into the colors of the spectrum, proving that white light contains these colors. The longest wavelength is perceived as red and the shortest as violet. Everyone has had the experience of seeing these rainbow colors in a variety of places. A bright beam of light striking a soap bubble or the *bevel* edge of a mirror reflects the spectrum hues.

Since the pigment colors are more commonly used, however, this text will limit its study primarily to these colors. What is meant by pigment in relation to color? Certain pigments are said to be combined to get certain colors, such as red and yellow to get orange, or blue and yellow to get green. Pigments are substances of various kinds that can be ground into fine powder and used for coloring dyes and paints. Before people learned how to produce pigments by chemical means, they were derived from animal, mineral, and vegetable sources. The *Mayans* in Central America extracted purple from shellfish. The highly prized Tyrian purple, which was used to color the robes of early Roman emperors, was obtained from shellfish found in the Mediterranean by the Phoenicians. Another important dye of the Near East was a red dye extracted from kermes, the dried bodies of scale insects.

The East Indians, who are usually credited with having first developed a thriving dyeing trade, were skilled in securing dyes from many plants, such as *madder* for red and *indigo* for blue. The ancient Chinese and Arabs were also familiar with natural sources of various pigments. For hundreds of years, nature was the only source of dyes, many of which did not hold up well. Modern technology has improved the sharpness of color and the fastness and durability of the dye.

A basic understanding of the derivation of color pigments is essential and rewarding to the interior designer. The history of color development constitutes a fascinating study in itself. Should the student wish to pursue the study of color further, many good books are available.

Color systems

A number of color theories, or systems, have been developed and are in use today. Some incorporate psychological as well as physical factors. A variety of color wheels have been developed, each based on a different group of basic colors. For example, the Ostwald color wheel, developed by Wilhelm Ostwald, is based on four principal hues: yellow, red, blue, and green, plus black and white; the Munsell begins with five hues: yellow, red, blue, green, and purple; and the Brewster uses the three primaries: yellow, red, and blue. This chapter will consider the Brewster and the Munsell theories.

THE BREWSTER SYSTEM

Developed by David Brewster, the Brewster system is the simplest and best known of all the color systems. (It is often referred to as Prang or the standard color wheel.) This is a pigment theory that employs the familiar color wheel based on three *primary* colors: yellow,

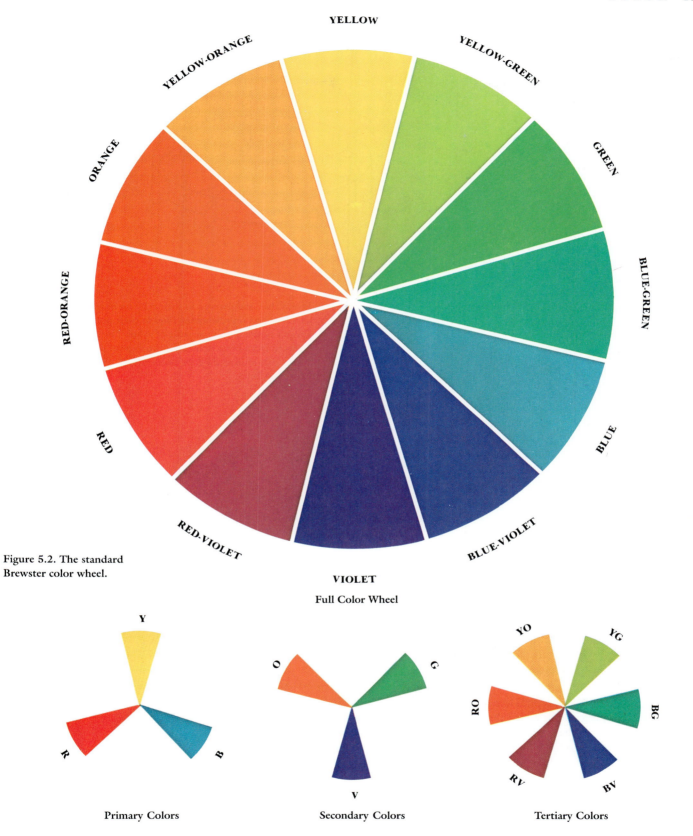

YELLOW

YELLOW-ORANGE

YELLOW-GREEN

ORANGE

GREEN

RED-ORANGE

BLUE-GREEN

RED

BLUE

RED-VIOLET

BLUE-VIOLET

VIOLET

Figure 5.2. The standard Brewster color wheel.

Full Color Wheel

Y

R

B

Primary Colors

O

G

V

Secondary Colors

YO

YG

RO

BG

RV

BV

Tertiary Colors

red, and blue. *Primary* means the colors cannot be mixed from other pigments, nor can they be broken down into component colors. Theoretically, with five tubes of paint—the three primaries, plus black and white—one could produce the entire range of colors, although the great degree of precision needed makes this almost impossible. By using the 3 primaries, however, the 12 colors of the complete wheel can be developed.

By adding equal amounts of any two of the primary colors, the result is a *secondary* color. The Brewster wheel has three such colors: green, which is produced by mixing yellow and blue, violet by mixing blue and red, and orange by mixing red and yellow. In each instance, the secondary color lies midway between the primary colors from which it is formed.

In similar fashion, *tertiary* or *intermediary* hues are composed by mixing equal amounts of a primary color and a secondary color. These hues are also situated midway between the two hues that produced them, and are identified by hyphenated names such as blue-green, red-orange, and red-violet. The last one, red-violet, is a combination of the two extreme hues of the spectrum. These 12 hues make up the full color wheel and include all of the spectrum colors plus red-violet. The Brewster color wheel is a simple and useful tool for the interior designer.

THE MUNSELL SYSTEM

The Munsell system of color notation is essentially a scientific concept of describing and analyzing color in terms of three attributes: hue, value, and chroma. The designation of each color is written as H v/c.

Hue is indicated by the capital letter H, followed by a fraction in which the numerator represents the value and the

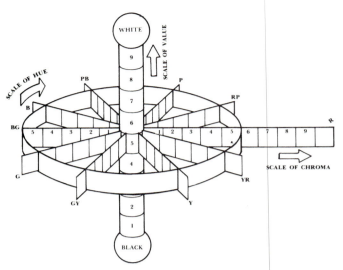

Hue, value, and chroma in their relation to one another. The circular band represents the hues in their proper sequences. The upright center axis is the scale of value. The paths pointing outward from the center show the steps of chroma, increasing in strength as indicated by the numerals. (Courtesy of Munsell Color Company, Inc.)

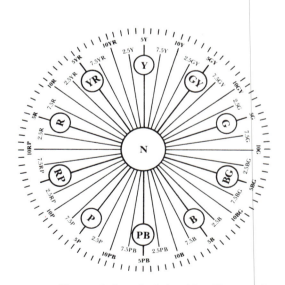

Hue symbols and relationships. Hue notations of the five principal and the five intermediate hue families are encircled. A breakdown into 100 hues is indicated by the outer circle of markings, and the breakdown of each hue family into four parts (2.5, 5, 7.5, and 10) indicates the 40 constant-hue charts appearing in the *Munsell Book of Color*. (Courtesy of Munsell Color Company, Inc.)

denominator indicates the chroma. In the diagram, hue is indicated by the circular band.

Value is indicated by the central axis, which shows nine visible steps, from darkest value at the bottom to lightest value at the top, with 5/ for middle gray. Pure black would be designated as 0/ and pure white as 10/.

The chroma notation is shown by the horizontal band extending outward from the value axis. It indicates the degree of departure of a given hue from a neutral gray of the same value. Since hues vary in their saturation strength, the number of chroma steps also varies. For example, yellow has the smallest number, and red has the greatest number. Since yellow is nearest to white, it is placed nearest the top of the color tree at step 8; thus, normal yellow is Y 8/chroma. Other hues are placed at their natural values' levels, such as 5 red in natural at R 4/. Thus, the value of 5R and step 4 on the value scale are equal, designated as R 4/c. Purple is the darkest hue and is normal at step 3 on the value scale: P 3/c. Thus the complete notation for a sample of vermilion might be 5R 4/14, which interpreted would mean 5R = pure red, 4/ = natural value, and /14 = strongest chroma (see drawing).

In the Munsell system, *chroma*, the Greek word for color, is used instead of intensity. In this system, the chromatic colors are based on the three primary colors, as is the case in the Brewster system, but they are divided into five principal hues: red, yellow, green, blue, and purple. The five intermediate colors that lie between these hues are yellow-red, green-yellow, blue-green, purple-blue, and red-purple, these being combinations of the five principal hues. Each of these ten hues is subdivided into four parts, indicated by the numerals 2.5, 5, 7.5, and 10. These hue names are symbolized by capitalized initials, such as R for red or YR for yellow-red. When finer subdivisions are required, these ten hues may again be combined, such as R-YR, which may be combined into still finer divisions.

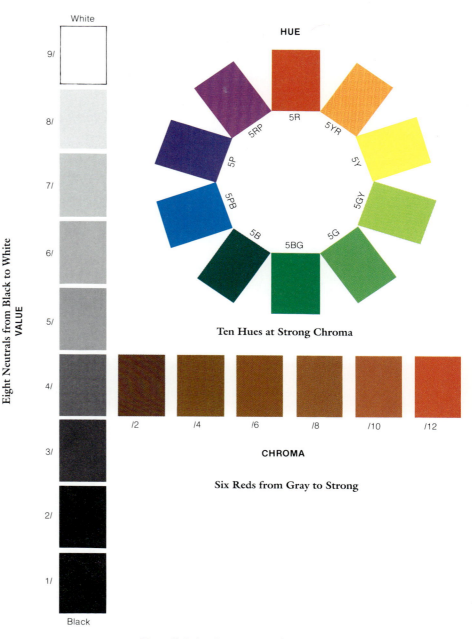

Ten Hues at Strong Chroma

CHROMA

Six Reds from Gray to Strong

Munsell Color System, including hue, value, and chroma relationships. The circular band represents the hues in their proper sequences. The upright, center axis is the scale of value. The paths pointing outward from the center show the steps of chroma increasing in strength, as indicated by the numerals. (Courtesy of Munsell Color Company, Inc.)

The segment lying between each of the ten color hues is divided into ten color steps (see drawing). In each case, the basic and intermediate color is in the center and is marked by the number 5, which indicates that it is the strongest degree of pure color of that particular hue. Each of the ten different hues, such as red, is designated by a number using the decimal system to indicate its degree of redness or intensity. For example, 2.5R has more red than 10RP, but both have much less red than 5R. Because this designation is done with the ten color segments, the Munsell color wheel has a total of 100 different colors.

By using the correct letters and numbers, one can describe any given hue and locate it on the color tree. Through this practical method, colors can be identified and standardized for professional purposes. This system of color notation is scientifically related to the Inter-Society Color Council, making it extremely useful in science and industry. This notation is also useful to the interior designer, since it enables him or her to communicate color information in a precise manner.

Color's three dimensions

The three dimensions of color have already been referred to in the Munsell notation. These major characteristics, basic to all colors, can accurately be measured and are essential in visualizing and describing any color. These qualities are hue, value, and intensity (or chroma).

HUE

Hue, or the color name, is that singular characteristic which sets each color apart from all the others. A color may be lightened or darkened, made more intense or less intense. If blue is the hue used, the result will be light blue, dark blue, bright blue, or gray-blue, but each will be of the same blue hue. In all, about 150 variations of full chroma of hue exist, of which only 24 basic hues of full chroma have enough variation to be of practical use.

When neighboring hues on the color wheel are mixed, they produce new hues that are harmonious and closely related. When hues opposite from each other on the color wheel are mixed, the result is a neutral hue. In beginning a color scheme for any room, one dominant hue should be a starting point against which all others colors are gauged. The choice of color is personal, but in each case the room's size, proportion, function, style, mood, and the exposure and amount of light should be taken into consideration. Since color frequently produces the first and most lasting impression on those entering a room, selecting and combining hues is probably the greatest challenge to the interior designer.

VALUE

Value is the degree of luminosity, or lightness and darkness of a hue in relation to black and white. Nine such gradations are easily visible to the eye (see Munsell drawing).

The value of any hue can be raised by adding white and lowered by adding black. When black or another darkening agent is added to a hue, the value is lowered, and the result is a *shade* of that particular hue. When white is added to a hue, the value is raised, and the result is a *tint*. Water added to watercolor paints will also make a tint. Many value steps may be created in any hue between normal value and black and white.

Tints, either clear or neutralized are most frequently used for large background areas such as walls and ceilings. When mixing tints, one should take into consideration that certain pigments are not perfect, that is, they contain other hues. For example, white contains blue and a little violet, orange contains too much red, and blue has some violet. Making a correction for these imperfections is therefore necessary to get a perfect tint of the desired hue. The chart on the following page points out the procedure for mixing tints by correcting imperfect pigments.

In addition to shades and tints, a third classification is *tone*. A tone is formed by adding both black and white to the hue

(*Facing page*) In the nine gradations of value from black to white, the small circles are identical in shade, demonstrating that the eye perceives color not in itself but in relation to its environment.

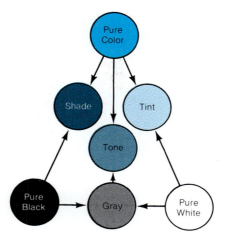

Although black and white pigments are not considered true colors, their addition to colored pigments produces tint, shades, and tones. Adding black to a pigment color produces a shade; adding white produces a tint. When gray (a mixture of black and white pigments is added to a color, a tone is produced. (Courtesy of General Electric Company.)

or a pigment of the color directly opposite from it on the standard color wheel. These grayed hues are extremely useful in working out color schemes in which muted colors are necessary to tone down the brighter hues. Any tint may become a tone with the addition of a touch of black or of some of the hue's complement.

Value may be applied in many ways when designing and furnishing a house. As an object is raised in value, apparent size increases. A fabric colored in low value will make a chair seem smaller than one in light or high value. Since light colors recede and dark colors advance, one may, with skill, alter the apparent size and proportion of individual items or of an entire room. In small rooms, light values will expand walls and ceilings. In long narrow rooms, colors in darker value will pull in end walls and will make the room appear shorter. Value may be used to conceal or emphasize objects. The use of sharp value contrast will emphasize an object. For example, the fine lines of a dark piece of furniture will be accentuated if placed against a

BASIC HUE	RESULTANT COLOR	CORRECTION	TINT
white + red	= light blue-pink	+ yellow	= red tint
white + yellow	= light violet-yellow	+ orange	= yellow tint
white + blue	= light violet-blue	+ yellow	= blue tint
white + green	= light blue-green	+ yellow	= green tint
white + orange	= light red-orange	+ yellow	= orange tint
white + violet	= light blue-violet	+ orange	= violet tint

Note: To get a clear tint of a color, yellow should be used to correct the color. When using yellow or purple, however, orange should be used to correct the color.

Figure 5.3. Space is visually expanded through the close coordination of color and skillful value distribution. Walls are emphasized through the use of light value. Medium value is used on the rugs and pillows. The dark value in the highly polished floors provides a suitable contrast in this contemporary apartment. (Courtesy of Clopay Corporation.)

Color can conceal and emphasize. The bright-colored shutters against the white siding create a definite contrast and call attention to the windows. The bright door attracts instant attention, and the windows and shutters blend into the walls of the house.

VALUE CAN ALTER THE APPARENT SIZE AND PROPORTION OF A ROOM.

Walls in light value tend to recede.

Walls in dark value tend to advance.

light background. The dark will seem darker, and the light background will seem lighter. A piece of furniture will seem unobtrusive if it is the same value as the background. Black and white have a strong visible effect on other colors when brought into juxtaposition. Black tends to make adjacent colors look richer. White reflects light into adjacent colors. Rooms that seem lifeless may often be given sparkle and interest by the addition of black, white, or both.

The manner in which tonal value is distributed throughout a room is of major importance. Each room usually contains three tonal values: light, medium, and dark, with varying amounts of each. The amounts of light and dark

INTENSITY (OR CHROMA)

Intensity, or chroma, is the degree of saturation of pure color. It describes the brightness or dullness and strength or weakness of the pure color that a hue contains. As any color may be raised and lowered in value by the addition of white or black, so the intensity may be strengthened by the addition of pure chroma or lessened by the addition of that color's complement, which is the color directly across from it on the standard color wheel. The more of the color's complement that is added, the less

should not be equal. In most cases, having large areas of light set off by small areas of dark is wise. When choosing paint, wallpaper, and fabrics, value should carefully be distributed if the end product is to be successful.

pure color the original hue contains. Two colors may have similar hue (both blue) and the same value (neither darker nor lighter), yet may be markedly different because of the different color strength or intensity.

A color is visually made more intense by adding more of the dominant hue to it. A color may be made to *appear* more intense by placing it against its complementary color, whether of the same intensity or neutralized. For example, a painting with predominantly orange hues will seem more orange if hung against a blue wall.

When two complementary colors are mixed in equal amounts, they tend to neutralize each other. Therefore, to decrease the intensity of a color, some of that color's complement, black, black and white, or another neutralizing agent should be added. The degrees of neutralization are many, the number varying with different hues. A color will *appear*

more neutral or less intense if placed against an object that is of the same hue but more saturated in chroma. For example, a muted green vase placed against a bright green background will appear even more muted.

When planning color schemes for rooms, one should keep in mind that strong chroma is conspicuous and size increasing. Furniture will seem larger and will fill up a room more if intense colors are used. Walls in strong chroma, as with dark value, will seem to advance and will make the room appear smaller. Since rooms are backgrounds for people, colors should not be too demanding. The psychological effect of too much intense color can be irritating and can have undesirable emotional effects. A wise choice, therefore, is to choose colors in

Figure 5.4. Sleek formality pervades this all-white kitchen. (Courtesy of Allmilmo Corporation.)

Figure 5.5 (*facing page*). When bright color is added, the room assumes a different aspect. Forms are emphasized and the room becomes less formal. (Courtesy of Allmilmo Corporation.)

Monochromatic
(one-color plan)

Analogous
(three- to six-color plan)

Direct complement
(two-color plan)

Split complement
(three-color plan)

softly neutralized tones for large background areas in most rooms in which people spend much time. Intense colors should be reserved for small areas and accents. A safe guide in planning a color scheme is the law of chromatic distribution: "The large areas should be covered in the most neutralized colors of the scheme. As the areas reduce in size, the chromatic intensity may be proportionally increased" (Whiton, *Interior Design and Decoration*).

Color is a great mood setter. Strong chroma tends to create a feeling of informality, and soft neutralized tones are more often reserved for a more formal atmosphere.

Color schemes

In general, all color schemes fall into two categories: related and contrasting. Within these categories the variations are endless. Related colors produce harmonious schemes that may be cool, warm, or a combination of both. Contrasting schemes have great variety and tend to be more exciting, particularly if strong chroma is used. In any scheme, black, white, or neutrals may be added without changing the scheme.

The three basic color schemes are monochromatic and achromatic, analogous, and complementary. Although professional interior designers seldom select a specific scheme initially, the final scheme often falls into one of these categories.

MONOCHROMATIC AND ACHROMATIC

Monochromatic color schemes are developed from a single hue but with a range of values and different degrees of intensity (see Figure 5.4). Unity is probably the most notable thing about this type of scheme, and if light values predominate, space will be expanded. A danger is that a one-color scheme may become monotonous; however, if one looks to nature, where monotony is never present, the guidelines are clearly apparent. By examining the petals of a rose, one may use the shadings from soft, delicate pink to deep red for a bedroom. The tones and tints of the green leaf and the variety of chroma in the brown bark of a tree can be combined in a room, using the subtle neutralized tones for large wall areas, slightly deeper tones for the carpet, medium tones for large furniture, and vivid chroma for accents.

Achromatic color schemes are those that possess no hue. They are made up entirely of black, gray, and white.

Striking textures in fabrics, woods, metals, and glass are necessary to bring life and interest into the monochromatic and achromatic schemes. When done well, these color schemes present a sophisticated and often dramatic effect that is particularly appropriate for modern rooms.

ANALOGOUS

Analogous, adjacent, or related color schemes are produced from any segment of colors that are in juxtaposition, but contain no more than half the colors on the standard color wheel. This color scheme has more interest, is more widely used, and is less difficult to achieve successfully than the monochromatic. Analogous color schemes are easy, natural, and comfortable to live with because they are found everywhere in nature. They may be warm, cool, or a combination of both. Harmony is easily established with analogous colors because they usually have one color in common. Yellow, for example, is the common factor in orange, yellow, and green, and by using the intermediate colors of yellow-orange and yellow-green, an interior designer may achieve a close relationship with a great variety of values and intensities. One dominant color should always be present.

COMPLEMENTARY

Complementary, or contrasting, color schemes are probably the most widely used of all the color schemes, since they have more variety. These may be developed in a number of different ways, but each one uses colors of contrasting hues. In each case, values and intensities may vary depending on the use and the amount of area to be covered. All con-

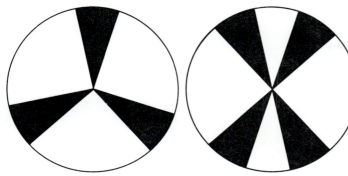 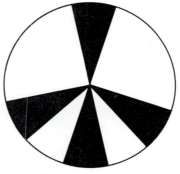

Triad complement
(three-color plan)

Double complement
(four-color plan)

Alternate complement
(four-color plan)

trasting hues placed side by side enhance each other, and if they are in the same intensity, each makes the other seem more intense. When added together, however, contrasting hues will subtract from each other, as in color neutralization. When equal amounts of two complementary colors are used, they produce a neutral. Complementary schemes will always have some warm and some cool colors, since they are opposite on the color wheel. These schemes are appropriate for either traditional or modern interiors. In strong chroma they are lively and vigorous; in grayed tones they may be subtle and restful. In each case, one dominant hue should set the mood.

The five types of complementary schemes are direct complement, split complement, triad complement, double complement, and alternate complement.

DIRECT COMPLEMENT

The direct complement is the simplest of the contrasting color schemes and is formed by using any two colors that lie directly opposite on the color wheel. In each case, one of the hues should dominate. Used in equal amounts and in strong intensity, complementary colors will clash, thus creating an unpleasant element in a room. The secondary color should therefore be neutralized or used in small areas.

SPLIT COMPLEMENT

The split complement is a three-color scheme composed of any hue plus the two hues that are next to its complement. For example, if yellow is selected as the dominant color, red-violet and blue-violet will be the complementary colors. These colors contrast less than the direct complement, which is violet. Red has been added to one and blue to the other, giving a softness to the scheme and at the same time adding variety and interest.

TRIAD COMPLEMENT

The triad complement is another three-color contrasting scheme (see Figure 5.1). The triad is made up of any three colors that are equidistant from one another on the color wheel. These colors may be sharp in contrast, using strong chroma such as the three primaries—red, yellow, blue, or red-orange, yellow-green, and blue-violet—or they may be neutralized, raised, or lowered in value to produce a tranquil scheme or any variant.

DOUBLE COMPLEMENT

The double complement is a four-color scheme in which two pairs of complementary colors are used. This scheme doubles the possible combinations of colors and offers a wide variety of decorative effects.

ALTERNATE COMPLEMENT

The alternative complement is another four-color scheme that combines the triad and the direct complement. The possibilities of creating interiors from this scheme are endless.

Creating livable color schemes

In addition to the three basic color schemes are many other methods of developing livable color schemes:

□ A scheme might begin with a favorite color, or a color desired for a particular room, and then include other colors that blend with it. Charts at paint dealers are helpful in determining harmonious colors.

□ Two or three bold colors might be selected as a base around which to build.

□ A neutral background can be accented by three or four harmonious colors (accented neutral).

□ A color scheme might be copied from a magazine or from a room in a furniture store.

□ A well-liked fabric, wallpaper, or rug might be a starting point. Following the law of chromatic distribution, one of the lightest, most neutral colors can be chosen for the room's background, and the other colors can be used on various objects in the room. The most intense colors should be reserved for accents.

□ A prized picture can determine the color scheme. The same procedures can be followed as with fabric.

□ Nature can provide an unlimited number of color schemes.

Figure 5.6. Color scheming from a fabric. The fabric on the sofa sets the room's color scheme, which is carried through to the warm tile floor, the wall, and the patterns of the chairs. (Courtesy of Pennsylvania House.)

Whatever method is followed, the result should be a livable color scheme appropriate for the particular room for which it was planned and for the people who will use it.

Other considerations in color application

THE EFFECT OF ADJACENT COLORS ON EACH OTHER

Perhaps most important to remember about color is that a color is not important in itself. What *is* important is what happens when different colors are brought together. The eye perceives color not in and of itself but in relation to its environment.

Physiologists have shown that people are not color-blind to one color only but to two or four, and that the eye is sensitive to colors not singly but in pairs. The familiar afterimage demonstrates this perception. If a person looks at any one color for about 30 seconds, then looks at a white page, he or she will see the complement of that color. Also, when the eye sees a colored object, it induces that color's complement in the environment. For example, when a green chair is placed against a light neutral background, the eye sees a tinge of red in that background.

When two primary colors are placed side by side, they appear tinted with the omitted primary, as red when placed near blue will take on a yellow tinge. When contrasting or complementary colors in strong chroma with the same value are used against each other, they will clash, producing a vibration that is fatiguing. When contrasting colors with strong differences in value are used side by side or one against the other, the colors will stand out but will not clash. Harmoniously blended colors of middle value

A chair in light value blends into a similar background.

A chair in light value placed against a dark background creates a more pronounced contrast.

A chair in dark value placed against a light background produces a contrast.

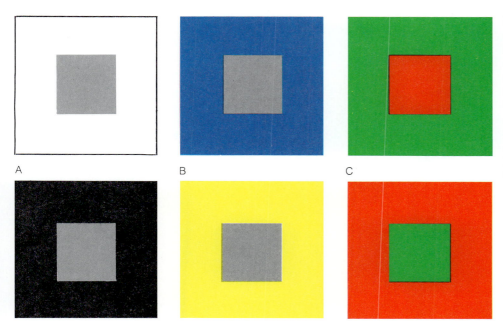

A

B

C

Figure 5.7. These diagrams illustrate the effect of adjacent colors: *A*, gray looks much darker against white than it does against black; *B*, a gray or neutral against a colored background appears to be tinted with the complement of the color; *C*, when placed side by side, complements of equal intensity create visual conflict. Complements of varying intensities enhance each other. (Courtesy of Large Lamp Department, General Electric Company.)

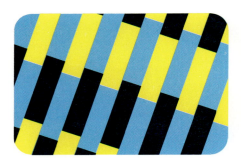

Figure 5.8. Chameleon effect. Colors of medium value and chroma will appear to change in the direction of the lighter, brighter colors—or the darker, duller colors—surrounding them. (Courtesy of Large Lamp Department, General Electric Company.)

Figure 5.9. Advancing and receding colors. Warm colors and light grays appear to advance toward the eye; cool colors and dark grays appear to recede. (Courtesy of Large Lamp Department, General Electric Company.)

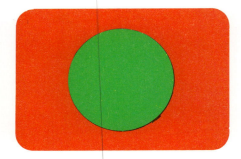

Figure 5.10. Clashing colors. Complementary colors of strong chroma and similar value will clash in juxtaposition, causing line vibration. (Courtesy of Large Lamp Department, General Electric Company.)

Figure 5.11. Complementary afterimage. Stare at the black dot just below center for 30 seconds, then look at the black dot in the white space at extreme right. Prolonged concentration on any color will reduce eye sensitivity to it, and the reverse (complementary) color, remaining unaffected, will dominate the afterimage for a brief period until balance is restored. (Courtesy of Large Lamp Department, General Electric Company.)

Figure 5.12. Additive spatial fusion. The green dot pattern in the shape of the United States will merge into solid gray when viewed from a distance of 6 to 8 ft. At that distance, the eye no longer distinguishes the individual colors. (Courtesy of Large Lamp Department, General Electric Company.)

used against each other will tend to blend together, and at a distance, the difference will become almost indiscernible (see Figure 5.12). The latter combination is the basis for most Japanese *shibui* color schemes.

The juxtaposition of colors affects not only hue but also value. The change of value may be seen when a gray circle is placed on a white background. As black is added to the background and becomes progressively darker, the gray circle appears progressively lighter, showing that colors may be made to appear either lighter or darker according to the tonal value of the adjoining or background color. When black and white are placed side by side, the white looks whiter and the black looks blacker. Colors that are closely blended will conceal an object, and colors that are contrasting will emphasize an object. These facts about color have numerous applications in decorating.

THE EFFECT OF NATURAL AND ARTIFICIAL LIGHT ON COLOR

Without light, color does not exist. Both natural and *artificial light* are important elements in any room composition. Light can be used to make rugs look deeper, fabrics more luxurious, metals exotic, and woods softer. The mood of the room can become dramatic or warm and intimate.

The first consideration in planning the color scheme for a room should be the quantity and quality of natural light that enters a room. The amount of natural light depends on the number, size, and placement of the windows. A room with few or small windows, and hence a small amount of light, should have light-re-

flecting colors. A room with large areas of glass may be more pleasant with a predominance of darker light-absorbing colors that will reduce glare. The following is the percentage of light reflected by some of the more common colors:

White	89%
Ivory	87%
Light gray	65%
Sky blue	65%
Intense yellow	62%
Light green	56%
Forest green	22%
Coconut brown	16%
Black	2%

To assure the necessary amount of natural light and still avoid glare, the color scheme for each room should be planned in relation to the reflective characteristics of the large elements in the room—particularly the backgrounds. For example, dark walls will absorb most of the light, and light walls will reflect most of the light. The effect of the floor covering will be the same. A dark carpet that has a *matte* finish will make a room much darker than a light-reflecting vinyl.

The quality of natural light depends on the direction from which it comes and on the time of day. Light from the north is cool. Light from the east is warmer than north light, but cooler than the warm afternoon light from the south and west. The quality of light varies not only from different points of the compass but also at different times during the day. Western light, during early hours of the day, is neutral, but in later afternoon it contains much red. Because of these differences, generally a wise choice is to use warmer colors in rooms with cool light and cooler colors in sunny rooms with south and west exposures. Because the quality of light also varies during the day, testing colors by carefully observing them during different hours is advisable.

Understanding the interrelationship of color and artificial light is necessary to achieve beautiful color schemes. *The color of artificial light is determined by* (1) the source of the light, (2) the surface that reflects it, (3) the type of diffusion, and (4) the amount of diffusion. *The color of an object is the result of* (1) the spectral qualities of the light source, (2) the reflective traits of the surface materials, (3) the level of illumination, and (4) the method of lighting. The following discusses the effects of the latter.

THE LIGHT SOURCE

The three sources of artificial light, combustion, incandescence, and fluorescence, have already been discussed in Chapter 4, with an emphasis on methods of lighting. This chapter is concerned with the light sources' effects on color. Ordinary incandescent light casts a warm glow, but can be varied by tinted globes. Fluorescent tubes come in white, warm, and cool tints. White light is the most natural and emphasizes cool colors. Warm light is most flattering to skin tones and is usually preferred in areas where lower levels of illumination are involved.

Review of the color wheel demonstrates that to gray or neutralize a color, some of its complement must be added, and to intensify a color, more of the basic hue must be added. Colored light will produce the same effect. Warm light accentuates warm colors and neutralizes cool colors. Cool light intensifies cool colors and deadens warm colors. Warm

Figure 5.13. A room in the natural light of day. (Courtesy of Louverdrape and Steve Chase Associates.)

Figure 5.14 (*facing page*). The same room as in Figure 5.13 is illuminated by artificial light. (Courtesy of Louverdrape and Steve Chase Associates.)

light is friendly and tends to unify objects. Cool light expands space, produces a crisp atmosphere, and tends to make individual objects stand out.

Not only single colors but also mixed colors take on a different look when subjected to artificial light. For example, a yellowish light will bring out the yellow in yellow-green and yellow-orange. A cool light will bring out the blue in blue-green and blue-violet. Under a warm light—regular incandescent or warm fluorescent—greens will tend to be unified, but blues, which may be pleasantly harmonious in natural light, are thoroughly undependable.

THE SURFACE THAT REFLECTS LIGHT

As with natural light, absorbing and reflective surfaces of the room should be planned and observed under artificial light.

THE LEVEL OF ILLUMINATION

The level of illumination will also affect the appearance of color. Quantity of light is measured in footcandles: one footcandle provides the amount of light produced by one candle at a distance of 1 ft. Experts have established minimum standards of illumination for various purposes, and these can be measured with a light meter. Many people have experienced the stimulating effect of color in a room when the light is bright, and the relaxing feeling when the light is low. Color, however, may become dull, lifeless, and dreary with insufficient light. As illumination increases, color becomes more vibrant.

THE METHODS OF LIGHTING

Color is also affected by the method of lighting: direct lighting, in which the light rays fall directly from the source onto the surface, or indirect lighting, in which the light is directed upward and is reflected from another surface, usually from the ceiling onto the area to be

lighted. The direct method is used for task lighting, but may also be effective in creating a warm glow over any area. An indirect light reflecting from a cove onto the ceiling produces an overall light resembling the light of midday. This method of lighting is practical for kitchens and work areas, but is unflattering for living areas, since it tends to give a feeling of flat monotony and when used alone may produce a commercial feeling. Portable lamps can give direct light, indirect light, or both, and with a diffused effect can produce soft shadows that alter colors, adding interest and attractiveness to a room. They can light any area for any purpose and can create decorative effects in a unique way.

Artificial light, when understood and used with skill, may alter, subdue, highlight, or dramatize the colors of a room in a way that no other decorative medium can. Because any situation has many variables, however, setting down definite rules for the use of light and color is impossible. In each instance, therefore, a necessary practice is to try each color in the environment in which it is to be used and to observe it during different hours of the day and after dark before making a final choice.

THE EFFECT OF TEXTURE ON COLOR

Color appears different when the texture is varied. Because smooth surfaces reflect light, fabrics with a deep, textured surface, such as pile carpet, velvet, and all manner of nubby weaves that cast tiny shadows, will appear darker than a smooth fabric that is dyed with the same hue and is of the same value and chroma. A rough textured wall may appear grayed or soiled under artificial light because of shadows cast from the uneven surface. A smooth, shiny surface will reflect light that can be used well. A dull or matte surface will absorb color, and if it is also dark, it may absorb all of the color.

THE EFFECT OF DISTANCE AND AREA ON COLOR

Near colors appear more brilliant and darker than the same colors at a greater distance. Brighter and darker colors used in large rooms will therefore seem less demanding than the same colors used in small rooms. Colors appear stronger in chroma when covering large areas. For example, a small color chip may be the exact color tone a person wants for a room, but when that tone is painted on four walls, it looks much darker, because the area of that color chip has been multiplied many thousands of times. When selecting a wall color from a small color chip, the choice should be one that is several tints lighter than the color desired for the completed room. A good approach is to paint a sizable area of color on walls in opposite corners of the room and then observe them in the light at different times of the day and night before making the complete application.

THE EFFECT OF COLOR ON TEMPERATURE

Some evidence indicates that color can alter the apparent temperature of a room. When used in large amounts, colors such as red, orange, yellow, and brown tend to make a room feel warm. Colors such as blue, lavender, and gray tend to make a room feel cooler.

SOME USES OF COLOR FOR THE INTERIOR

OFF-WHITE

A common notion among many untrained individuals is that off-white in itself is a specific color and goes with anything. This notion is far from the truth. Off-white is white tinted with a hue—any hue. To be compatible, however, off-whites must contain only the same hue. For example, off-white walls, ceilings, glass curtains, and fabrics, used in the same room, should be tinted with the same hue. Value and intensity may vary, but the hue must be the same. Warm off-whites are more easily blended than cool off-whites, recalling a basic characteristic of warm and cool colors.

FOR WOOD TRIM

The color of the wood trim is important to the general color scheme of the room. When painted it may be the same hue, value, and intensity as the wall, a darker shade of the wall hue, or a color that contrasts with the wall, if it is pleasantly related to some other major color in the room.

ON THE CEILING

The ceiling is the largest unused area of a room, and the color is important to the general feeling. If the objective is to have the wall and ceiling look the same, the ceiling should be a tint of the wall, since the reflection from the walls and floor tends to make the ceiling look several shades darker than it actually is. If the walls are papered, the ceiling may be a tint of the background or the lightest color in the paper. If walls are paneled in dark wood, the ceiling is best when painted a light tint of the wood color. If the wood trim is painted white, a white ceiling is advisable. When the ceiling is too high, a darker shade will make it appear lower.

A light ceiling expands space.

A dark ceiling feels lower.

WHEN SELECTING DRAPERY

The success of any room is largely dependent on the treatment of the windows, and the color used in the drapery fabric may make the windows the room's most conspicuous element. If the objective is to have a completely blended background effect, drapery fabric should be the same hue, value, and intensity as the wall. If a contrasting effect is desirable, the color should contrast with the wall but should relate well with the other colors used throughout the room. Glass curtains are usually most pleasing when they are off-white, blended to the drapery.

WHEN WALLS ARE PANELED

Where dark wood paneling is used, colors of intense chroma should be used about the room, since deep wood tones absorb color. If paneled walls are light, colors may be light—either blended or contrasted. If paneling is formal, colors should have a rich, formal look. If paneling is informal, colors should have the same feeling.

IN ALTERING APPARENT SIZE AND PROPORTION

An object that attracts the eye usually seems larger; therefore items of furniture may be made to appear larger if painted or upholstered with colors in strong chroma. A small room may be made to seem even smaller if demanding colors, which are space filling, are used on backgrounds and furniture. On the other hand, light, blended, and receding colors will expand a room and will seem to create more space. Through the skillful use of color, a room's dimensions may be altered significantly.

IN BRINGING BALANCE TO A ROOM

Since that which attracts the eye seems larger and therefore appears heavier, a small area of bright color will balance a large area of softly muted color, and a small area of dark color will balance a larger area of light color. For example, a small bouquet of bright flowers placed near one end of a long table will balance a large lamp of soft color placed near the other end. A small dark blue plate on a shelf will balance a much larger white one.

IN TRANSITION FROM ONE ROOM TO ANOTHER

Whenever two rooms adjoin, color and pattern should have a pleasant relationship. One or more colors should be carried from one room to the other, but not necessarily used in the same manner. For example, the accent color in the wallpaper of an entrance hall may be neutralized and used on the walls of the adjoining living room or may be emphasized in a piece of upholstery fabric. When dining and living rooms are open, walls, drapery, and floor coverings should be the same or closely related. Whenever one room may be seen from another, an easy transition of color should be used to give a feeling of unity.

Figure 5.15. Color transition. The oriental rug sets the color scheme for two adjoining rooms. Through skillful coordination of color and pattern in wallpaper and fabric, a subtle transition unites the two diverse rooms and results in overall sophistication. (Courtesy of David and Dash.)

IN PERIOD ROOMS

Particular styles and periods of furnishings have appropriate colors that reflect their character and set the feeling of authenticity (see Figure 5.1). Colors should be chosen with discrimination when decorating period rooms. Many excellent books are available that provide full information on the subject.

IN HUE DISTRIBUTION

The distribution of color has already been discussed under hue, value, and intensity, but a brief reiteration by way of emphasis seems appropriate. Color is the most unifying element available to the interior designer, and its skillful distribution is essential to the feeling of unity. Color distribution can be done in various ways.

First, value distribution should be planned. Each room should have some light, some dark, and some medium tones, used in varying amounts according to the effect desired. In most cases, the darkest tones are used in the smallest amounts, although in special rooms the reverse may be employed with dramatic results. When applying the law of chromatic distribution to a room, backgrounds will be in the most neutralized tones, large pieces of furniture will have more intensity, and accents, such as small chairs and accessories, will be in the strongest chroma. This procedure in distributing color produces rooms with a feeling of serenity and lasting comfort.

Second, most rooms should be planned around one dominant color. This color need not be repeated on all

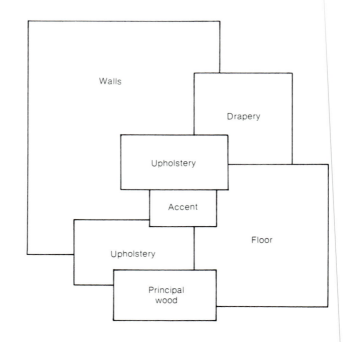

major pieces of furniture, but it should be repeated at least once to give a feeling of unity. Unity may also be achieved by using colors that have one hue common to all. For example, hues on the color wheel going clockwise from orange to blue-green all contain yellow and combine pleasantly together. The color that is common to all—yellow—will recede, and the other colors will stand out.

Although the preceding is the safest way to color scheme a room, deviating from these guidelines is possible and in some instances desirable. For example, dark walls can create a feeling of comfort, warmth, and security, and will unify the room's furnishings. A light floor will visually expand space, and adjacent to dark walls can create a dramatic effect. Seldom, however, is a dark ceiling advisable. In the search for space, a common need today, a light ceiling seemingly provides space by visually extending the room's height. A dark ceiling will decrease the feeling of space and may be oppressive.

Most people have difficulty visualizing a completed room. This capability develops through experience. Forming a mental picture of how colors will appear when juxtaposed is not easy, and students and clients may need visual help, which requires preliminary planning.

One way to envision a completed room is to make a chart using approximate proportions of various elements such as walls, floor, furniture, and accents. Some areas may then be painted similar to the desired colors, with fabric swatches applied where needed. This method will not show exactly how the completed project will appear, but it will be helpful. The ceiling should not be overlooked in planning.

Another method is to assemble a setup with actual samples of all items to be used. Students can use this procedure in the classroom, using materials that have

Figure 5.16. Walls in light chroma expand space in this living room, whose
color scheme was taken from the Kirman rug. (Photograph by Mark K. Allen.)

Figure 5.17. The same room as in Figure 5.16. Dark brown walls have unified the furnishings and have changed the mood from spacious formality to a warm, cloistered atmosphere. (Photograph by Mark K. Allen.)

been accumulated for such demonstrations. For clients, the method may be used in the home, but is more often accomplished in a department store or decorating studio, where a choice of materials is available. The setup, usually assembled with the help of an **A** frame, presents samples of all the materials to be used in approximate proportions. This method will most closely approximate the look of the completed room.

REFLECTING THE MOOD OF THE ROOM

More than any other element, color is capable of setting the general mood of a room. Rich, muted tones produce a mood of tranquility, and lively, contrasting colors produce an informal mood. General color moods seem appropriate for specific areas of the house.

The entrance hall is the room that introduces people to the home. The entrance way should emphasize the theme that has been chosen for the major rooms. Color in this area can be somewhat dramatic and daring.

Living areas used for more formal purposes should generally have neutralized color schemes to produce an atmosphere of tranquility. More informal living areas, such as family and recreation rooms, need more lively color shemes to produce a cheerful, informal atmosphere.

Dining rooms are at their best when the color schemes are unobtrusive, thus permitting a variety of table decoration as well as a serene dining atmosphere.

Kitchens and other work areas are usually more desirable when large areas of color are light, fresh, and clean looking, with bright accents of strong chroma.

Bedrooms and bathrooms are the private areas of the house, and personal preference should be the determining factor in the choice of colors. As a general rule, the master bedroom should be done in restful tones. Colors in children's rooms may be the choice of the individual occupant.

REFLECTING PERSONALITY

Color should reflect the personality of the individual for whom it is chosen. Color is the most valuable decorating tool and gives unlimited opportunity for individuality. The person may choose bold and modern colors, which need not be garish. Unusual combinations should be used if they are personally pleasing. If neutralized colors are preferred, they should be be used; they need not be drab. Neutralized color schemes are more difficult to achieve than bright contrasting ones, but when accomplished have a lasting quality. In the selection of colors, current trends should be taken into account; they should not, however, be the determining factor. Regardless of what colors are in fashion, individual preference should always be the main consideration.

COLOR IN WOOD

Since wood has color and each type of wood has a particular beauty, it should not be overlooked when planning a color sheme. Heavily grained woods call for heavier textures and stronger colors than do fine-grained woods. Mixing woods can add interest to a room, but woods used in the same room should have the same feeling. For example, rough-grained oak and formal mahogany are not good companions, but maple and walnut combine well.

Pine is a softwood, light in color but reddening with age. It is less expensive than hardwoods and may be stained to simulate other woods. **Knotty pine** is a favorite for paneling. *Birch* and *maple* are

Figure 5.18. Wood is a living material, and like all living things, its individuality is reflected in its myriad variations. Only in real wood are found the subtle intricacies of pattern formations, the endless variety of form within form, and the delicate nuances of color and shading. (Courtesy of U.S. Plywood Corporation, Champion Building Products.)

naturally light-colored woods, fine grained, and strong. *Oak* has a coarse grain and more texture than other woods. *Cherry* is the only true fruitwood now in general use, and it ranges from a tawny tone to a soft brown in its natural state. It is sometimes stained a rich reddish brown. *Walnut* is a versatile wood, and its natural color span stretches from a pale cocoa brown to a rich, dark color. It can be bleached or finished in any tone. *Mahogany* has a deep, rich, fine grain and is an aristocrat of woods. Although it is often associated with the deep red color used by early furniture designers, mahogany is now finished in many tones of brown and beige. *Pecan* ranges from reddish brown to creamy white. The large pores in this wood give it a distinctive pattern. *Elm* is a light brown wood that is hard and strong. *Teak* is extremely heavy, is richly grained, and ranges in color from honey tone to warm brown.

In addition to these woods, many rare and exotic woods are used in furniture making. Since they are too costly for general use, however, these unusual woods are often chosen for inlay to accent furniture. Some of these woods are golden-toned *satinwood*; golden brown, yellowish green, to purple *myrtle*; lustrous tan to purple *rosewood*; pale red *yew*; black and varied-striped *ebony*; black- or brown-striped *zebrawood*; pale blond *limba*; brown to red, black-marked *paldao*; and yellow-white or yellow-brown *primavera*.

Shibui in today's home

Shibui (or shibusa) expresses in one word the Japanese approach to beauty as well as the intrinsic nature of their culture. No single word in the English language precisely describes *shibui*, an elusive Japanese adjective (*shibumi* is the noun). The word *shibui*, however, suggests an appreciation of serenity and a protest against ostentation. Belief in the power of the understatement and the unobtrusive dominates the sophisticated philosophy of these Orientals who have an uncommon sensitivity to and awareness of beauty.

The color scheme essential in producing a shibui effect is one in which colors are brought together to enhance each other in a harmonious whole that will be quietly pleasing to live with for a long time. To be deeply satisfying for an extended time, livable schemes must have depth and complexity, or they will soon become tiresome. A shibui color scheme possesses such qualities.

Figure 5.19. In this assemblage of fabrics and carpets, textures and colors are drawn from nature to create the essence of shibui. (Courtesy of Rosecare Carpet Company.)

Figure 5.20. Shibui translated into to-day's interior design. The darkest color is on the floor, with the wall lighter and the ceiling lighter still. All the colors are blended and large areas are neutralized, with only small amounts of bright color. Subtle texture and patterns everywhere result in a sense of refinement and relaxation.

Understanding the shibui concept of color scheming requires looking to nature, on which the color scheme is based. Shibui uses colors and textures found in nature and combines them in the same ratios.

Colors found in the largest areas are quiet and undemanding (neutralized). Bright, vibrant colors are found in a small proportion. Nature has thousands of colors, but none of them match, and they are not uniform. In nature the darker, more solid colors occur under-foot. As one looks upward, colors become lighter and more delicate. Most of the natural landscape is a matte finish with little high shininess or glitter, such

as the sun sparkling on a ripple in a stream. Pattern and texture in nature are everywhere—in every stone, leaf, and tree trunk—but they have to be dis-covered through close examination. This subtleness accounts for the absence of uniformity and the dimension of nature's colors. Pattern in nature is not uniform. No two patterns are identical, yet unity prevails throughout. Nature's color scheme, which appears simple and natu-ral, on close scrutiny proves highly com-plex yet never tiring.

Translating the shibui concept into today's decorating means following the principles found in nature and applying them to the interior. In recent years, Americans have come to recognize the value of this Eastern influence, and inter-est in Japanese design has been gaining momentum. New expressions of old ori-

ental themes and soft, earthy colors mix pleasantly with today's contemporary fur-nishings, producing depths of beauty and an atmosphere of serenity essential to modern homes.

To achieve an atmosphere of long-lasting repose and tranquility, one will do well to emulate the Japanese, whose homes are most notable for the feeling of serenity and the absence of pretentious display and clutter.

Color forecasts for the 1980s

Most important to remember in the use of color is that no absolutes can be applied at any time. One should be aware of color fashions as they come and go, but every person should choose the colors with which he or she is most comfortable. The interior designer's responsibility is to help the client select colors that are right for him or her—regardless of trends. The greatest challenge—and possibly the greatest reward—to any designer is to achieve, through the knowledgeable choice and distribution of color, beautiful and livable schemes for every room throughout the house.

One organization that selects colors for American taste is the Color Association of the United States. During the early years of the eighties, colors for home fashion were soft and understated with a pearl-like quality. Designers drew on nature for dusky earth tones. Pastels in muted sand, oyster, and pearl were complemented with richer shades of desert hues. Colors borrowed from the American landscape, such as spice, pine, stone, and steel, were enlivened by orange and red accents.

The Color Association's forecast for environments of the mid-1980s suggests five major color directions: (1) gray tones from charcoal to pearl will be seen, as well as grayed hues of green, rose, and blue, (2) rose quartzes will emerge, (3) a new direction projected is soft tints and blackened, saturated colors, (4) neutrals and off-whites of green, pink, and yellow cast will replace previous earth tones, and (5) the essentially soothing palette will be punctuated by bright accents of violet, red-orange, and lemon yellow. The association's forecast may suggest that surrounding oneself with tranquil color schemes in the troubled mid-1980s may have a positive psychological effect. One thing is certain: When the mood of the country changes, fashions in colors will also change.

ASSIGNMENT

In the Student Work Packet are ten color plates. By applying the principles discussed in this chapter, complete the ten color plates according to the following directions, and submit them to the instructor for evaluation.

Note: In doing all color plates, paint neatly and creatively, and use paint *only*, except for Plate 8. In planning color schemes for the rooms in Plates 6 through 10, the dominant color desired should first be established, then a decision should be made on the subordinate colors and the ones for accent. Keep the law of chromatic distribution in mind, and plan each room with livability in mind.

PLATE 1 (Process for Mixing True Tints)

After carefully studying the lesson material on mixing tints, proceed as follows:

1 Paint the six circles in the left-hand column with white.

2 Paint the second vertical group with the hue that is indicated.

3 Starting at the top, from left to right, add a *small* amount of red hue to white and paint the circle that is labeled "Result." Notice that the result is a bluish pink. This is because white is an imperfect pigment and contains blue. To correct this, add a *small* amount of yellow (paint the fourth circle yellow). The final result on the far right (which will be made up of white and red plus a touch of yellow) should be a clear, light tint of the red in the second column.

4 Continue in this manner until all six tints are completed. To determine the proper hue to add for each correction, refer to the section on value.

5 *Caution:* Be sure that the tint results at the far right are *clear* and *light* and that all final tints are as near the same value as possible.

PLATE 2 (Process for Mixing Tones and Shades)

1 Begin with the top line and paint the first circle red.

2 Add a touch of black to the red to produce a *shade,* and fill in the middle circle.

3 Add a touch of white to the shade to produce a *tone,* and fill in the third circle.

4 Continue in this manner until a satisfactory shade and tone of each of the six hues in the left-hand column have been produced.

5 Each shade should contain the same amount of black, and each tone the same amount of white. Both shades and tones can be varied according to the amount of black and white added.

PLATE 3 (Value Distribution)

This is an exercise in the application of value distribution in creating two achromatic color schemes.

1 Fill in the circles on the left. Begin with black at the bottom, and raise the value of each succeeding circle. The top circle should be white.

2 Using black, white, and values in between, paint the two identical pictures to illustrate the dissimilar effect created when value is varied. Distribute the values differently, keeping in mind that the darkest value should be used in the least amount. Note the two sets of window drapery: sheers to the outside and drapery against the wall.

PLATE 4 (Color Neutralization Process)

This is an exercise in neutralizing colors.

1 Paint the circles in the left-hand column in the hues indicated.

2 Paint the circles in the middle column with the complementary hue of each.

3 In the third column, make three degrees of neutralization by adding a *slight* touch of the complement to the first section, a little more to the second section, and still a little more to the third section.

Caution: Be sure that all sections in the far right column remain neutralized shades of the original hue in the far left column and *not* muddy browns.

PLATES 5, 6, 7 (Monochromatic, Analogous or Complementary, and Shibui Color Schemes)

These are exercises in planning and executing color schemes.

1 Carefully examine Plates 5, 6, and 7. At the top of each one, the color scheme for the room to be painted is indicated: monochromatic, analogous or complementary, and shibui.

2 Plan each one carefully according to the scheme.

3 In planning the shibui color scheme, select an object from nature, such as a leaf, a piece of bark, or a stone, and use this as the basis for the color scheme. Carefully study the principles of shibui before completing Plate 7.

PLATE 8 (Color Scheme from Wallpaper)

This is an exercise in color scheming a room from wallpaper or fabric. Select a piece of patterned wallpaper or fabric and attach it to the entire wall area on Plate 8. Using this pattern as a basis, develop a color scheme for the room, using the following procedure:

1 If the wallpaper or fabric will be used on all four walls, cover the entire area indicated. If it will be used on only one wall, cover about two thirds of the area and paint the remaining area, using one of the most neutralized colors in the wallpaper or fabric. One of the lightest colors is usually the best choice.

2 Paint the ceiling a tint of the wall color.

3 Finish the wood trim in one of the following ways: paint it the same hue as the wall, using the same value and intensity; use the same hue as the wall but in a deeper value and intensity; use a contrasting color that is related to one of the room colors; or use a natural wood tone, in which case a picture of natural wood grain is acceptable.

4 Paint the floor a slightly darker shade of the wall hue for a blended effect, or use an appropriate color taken from the patterned wallpaper or fabric.

5 If the goal is to blend curtains and drapery with the plain wall or with the wallpaper or fabric background, follow the procedure given for wood trim. If a contrasting effect is desired, select an appropriate color from the wallpaper or fabric. (Note that the drapery is the one against the wall. The glass curtain is the one to the outside.)

6 For upholstery fabrics, pick up the colors from the patterned wallpaper or fabric, keeping the law of chromatic distribution in mind, in which the most intense colors are reserved for the smallest areas.

PLATE 9 (Color Scheme from a Picture)

This is an exercise in using the colors in a picture to plan a scheme for a room.

1 Find a small picture appropriate for a living room wall.

2 Mount it on Plate 9 over the area indicated. Follow the same procedure in color scheming the room as for Plate 8.

3 *Caution:* Examine the picture carefully and try to interpret the general feeling in the room.

PLATE 10 (Color Transition)

This is an exercise in planning a color scheme for three adjoining rooms to give a pleasant transition of color. The entrance, living room, and dining room should be artistically related in color.

CHAPTER SIX

Fabrics

Authorities in the field recognize that fabric, with the right color, texture, and design, and when skillfully used, is a sure means to a successful room. In every age, fabric has contributed immensely to the era's decorative beauty. For centuries fabric has been used to cover walls, drape windows and beds, and upholster chairs and sofas. The various components of a room—the walls, floor, and furniture—can be brought into harmonious relationship when fabric is used judiciously. Through knowledgeable use, fabric can add beauty and glamour and can establish a unity in design that is impossible to achieve through the use of any other design medium. Both natural and man-made miracle fibers are woven into fabric for every decorative purpose. As never before, today's interior designer can satisfy the desire for elegance and practicality at the same time.

The term *fabric* is freely applied to textiles or cloth manufactured by machine or by hand, which includes weaving, knitting, twisting, **felting,** and lacing, as well as the fabrication of plastics. The appearance and durability of a fabric are dependent on the type and qualities of materials used, the method of construction, the finish, and the surface embellishment.

Fibers

A fiber is a threadlike filament either derived from nature or man-made. A perfect fiber that will adequately serve every household purpose does not exist. Each fiber has its own desirable characteristics and its limitations. Manufacturers have found that by blending certain fibers together, the most desirable qualities of each can be incorporated into a fabric. With today's modern technology, new and improved methods are being employed to create new and better synthetic fibers and to improve old fibers.

Yarns are made by spinning various lengths of fibers into strands in preparation for fabric construction. Performance and appearance of the fabric are affected by the method and amount of twisting of the fibers. A high twist produces more strength and durability, but takes away some of the luster. Long filaments with little twist will maintain a high luster, but will lose much of their stability. *Ply* is the result of twisting two or more single yarns together before weaving, to give added strength or to create a novel surface effect.

NATURAL FIBERS

Fibers that come from nature fall into four classifications: *protein, cellulosic, metallic,* and *mineral.*

PROTEIN

The protein (or animal) fibers of most importance are wool and silk.

Wool, probably the most important natural fiber, was used as far back as the seventh or eighth centuries before Christ. In early Egypt, Greece, Asia, and the Middle East, it was used for clothing and for some household articles. Wool is resilient, resists abrasion, is a good insulator, is flame retarding, and can be

Figure 6.1. Fabric is the key to this room's distinctive charm. The color scheme, the mood, and the decorative beauty are due in large measure to the careful selection and use of fabrics. (Courtesy of Drexel Heritage Furnishings.)

woven fine or coarse, loose or tight. It can be dyed from palest to deepest colors, cleans well, resists dirt, and can absorb up to 20 percent of its weight without feeling damp. *Mohair* is a particular type of wool that comes from the Angora goat. It is extremely resilient, holds color remarkably well, and has a natural luster.

Silk is an ancient fiber that according to legend was discovered in China about 2640 B.C. The process of producing it from silkworms, known as *sericulture,* was kept secret for many years but gradually became known, through devious methods, in countries around the world. Silk is a beautiful fiber, soft and luxurious, and is surpassed in strength only by nylon. It takes and holds dye well, but the sun's rays break down the fiber, necessitating its protection from direct sunlight. Silk is scarce and hence costly.

Leather, although not a fiber, is an animal product that has long been used for household purposes for both utility and beauty. It is pliable, durable, and may be dyed or used in its natural color. Leather is expensive, but has been simulated to a remarkable degree.

CELLULOSIC

Cellulosic (or vegetable) fibers, which include stems, leaves, and seed hairs, are cotton, flax (linen), and some minor fibers.

Cotton is believed to have been grown in India during the fourth century B.C. and used in Rome before the time of Christ. Cotton is the most plentiful of the natural fibers. It takes and holds color well, washes easily, can be woven

any way, and is highly adaptable. Cost varies according to quality of fiber, weave, and finish.

Flax, the fiber from which linen is made, is the most ancient of all the fibers. It was used for weaving in Egypt as early as 4000 B.C. Linen is strong, pliable, washable, and takes and holds color. It is absorbent but wrinkles readily unless chemically treated, which then reduces its wear potential.

Other miscellaneous vegetable fibers that have been known and used since prehistoric times are ramie (China grass or grass linen, a fiber resembling linen), yucca, milkweed, **hemp,** jute, **henequen, sisal, kapok, maguey,** and palm leaves. These fibers make their appearance in household materials such as floor coverings, wall fabrics, upholstery, padding, and place mats.

METALLIC

Metallic fibers, which are strips of gold, silver, or copper, are used chiefly as accents in decorative fabrics. Metallic fibers glitter without tarnishing and are washable if used in washable fabrics.

MINERAL

Mineral fiber, which is found in asbestos, is difficult to spin without the addition of another fiber. Asbestos is best known for its fire retardant quality, but has been found to be unhealthy and unsafe.

MAN-MADE FIBERS

The increasing use of fabrics made from man-made fibers is due to new chemical research and modern technology, which has resulted in improvements in quality, durability, resistance to soil, mildew, and moths, and ease of care. Although costs vary, these fabrics tend to be less expensive than those made from natural fibers. Man-made fibers fall into two categories: *regenerated cellulosic* and **synthetic.**

REGENERATED CELLULOSIC

Regenerated cellulosic fibers are produced by changing the physical and chemical formation of natural ingredients. Some examples are rayon, acetate, and triacetate.

SYNTHETIC

Synthetic fibers are produced from chemicals and made from carbon compounds. Some examples are nylon, acrylic, modacrylic polyester, olefin, and glass. In the bewildering array of man-made fibers on the market today, the consumer is often at a loss in making a choice. To alleviate the problem, the Federal Trade Commission (FTC) established rules and regulations under the Textile Products Identification Act. Under these regulations, each manufactured fiber is defined in specific terms and is given a **generic** name, which along with the company's trade name must appear on the label attached to the fabric. The generic name is the term assigned to a chemical family, of which all members exhibit certain traits. For example, all members of the nylon family are characterized by unusual strength and resistance to abrasion, but they will not hold up well under direct sunlight. The polyester family is known for its drip-dry quality and its resistance to sun deterioration. The *trade* name identifies the manufacturer. Because manufacturers have a practical need to give specific names to their products, hundreds of trade names for man-made fibers exist, making it virtually impossible for the consumer to recognize them all. Familiarity with the general characteristics of each fiber family, however, and checking the label to make sure of the fabric content, will help one to choose the fabric that best serves his or her

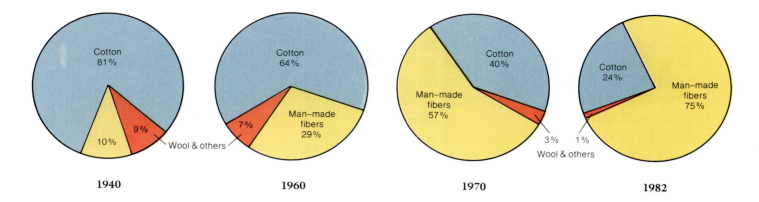

| 1940 | 1960 | 1970 | 1982 |

needs. The fiber alone, however, will not ensure good performance if the construction, dyes, and finishes are not properly handled.

During the last four decades, the production and consumption of man-made fibers has steadily increased. In 1940, man-made fibers accounted for only 10 percent of the fibers used. By 1960, the usage had increased to 29 percent. Man-made fibers now account for 75 percent of all fibers used by American textile mills, with polyester being the single most widely used fiber. The pie charts show the change in fiber consumption from 1940 to 1982.

Table 6.1 includes the most common man-made fibers, their generic names, an analysis of the qualities characterizing each, their most important decorative uses, and some trade names and their manufacturers.

Construction

The history of textile arts is almost as old as the history of humanity. The exact origin of the loom is not certain, but evidence leads to the belief that it was in use in Mesopotamia prior to 5000 B.C. A remarkable correlation exists between the history of the textile industry and the important economic, political, and social events that have transpired in many areas of the world since ancient times. Although modern mechanization has brought about great changes in textile production, weave structures are much the same as they were at the beginning of

the Renaissance, and the simple standard weaves are still basic to the industry. More intricate weaves that originated in the Orient, such as damasks and brocades, are now produced on *Jacquard* looms.

WEAVING

The following are the most common weaves, as well as some more intricate ones, that are used in producing today's decorative fabrics, with a brief description of the basic structure of each.

Plain weave Plain weave is made by the simple interweaving of warp (vertical) and weft (horizontal) threads, and may be single or double, regular or irregular.

In the plain *single* weave, one weft thread passes over each warp thread. When the weave is balanced in sequence of over and under so that the warp and weft have the same yarn count per square inch, it is called *regular*. A plain regular weave is also called a *tabby* weave. When the warp and weft differ because of different weights or textures of yarn, the weave is called *irregular* or *unbalanced*. Novelty yarns vary in appearance.

In the plain *double* (or *basket*) weave, two weft threads are interlaced into two warp threads. When the weave is regular, it is called *backed cloth*. This weave may also be irregular due to variations of weight or texture.

Twill weaves Twill weaves are those in which two or more threads pass over or under another set of threads, skipping at regular intervals to produce a diagonal effect. Twill weaves may be regular or irregular. In the regular twill, the long threads, or floats, pass over and under the same number of yarns. In the irregular twill, the floats pass over and under a different number of threads. Irregular twills account for many decorative fabrics, such as denim, gabardine, and herringbone.

Satin weave Satin weave has few interlacings and long floats. This combination produces a fabric with luster, softness, and drapability, such as satin and sateen.

Tapestry Tapestry weaving is a great art and has been known since ancient times. Some have said that the history of the world is woven into tapestry. This fabric was originally handwoven and was made with bobbins. Tapestry can be woven on practically every type of loom, but the Jacquard is most commonly used. The weave is essentially plain, but is made in a special way: across the warp in sections

COMMON TYPES OF WEAVES

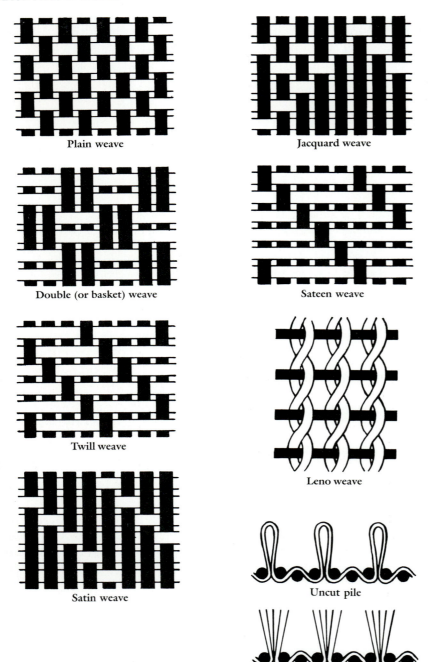

Plain weave

Jacquard weave

Double (or basket) weave

Sateen weave

Twill weave

Leno weave

Satin weave

Uncut pile

Cut pile

with the weft yarns interlocking around the same warp, into one another, or around adjacent warps, leaving a narrow slit. Tapestry has a rough feel. American Navajo and French Aubusson rugs, as well as a wide range of upholstery fabric, are made in this type of weave.

Pile weaves   Pile weaves are produced by loops or tufts of yarn that stand out from the surface of the fabric. These loops may be cut, uncut, or a combination of both. The piles may be formed from the warp or the weft threads.

A great many pile weaves are used in a wide variety of fabrics. The basic weave of the carpet industry is the raised-warp pile. Plush and velvet, originally woven by this method, are generally made today in a double cloth that is cut apart to produce the pile. Numerous household fabrics used for both utility and luxury are produced by one of the pile weaves: terry cloth towels, corduroy, frieze, velvet and shag, velvet, and tufted carpets.

Figure 6.2 (*facing page, top*). Handsome textures are created in these "fabric sculptures" in natural colors from off-white to brown. Woven of cotton, latex backed, and soil resistant, these fabrics are for use either as wall coverings or for upholstery. (Courtesy of Winfield Design Associates.)

Figure 6.3 (*facing page, bottom*). In this fusion of design concepts, fibers, textures, and colors, Jack Lenor Larsen creates a total environment with wool. For the window he uses a sheer leno weave, a twill weave on the wall, and a geometric Jacquard in deep jewel tones for furniture. All are placed against a giant floral carpet. (Courtesy of the Wool Bureau.)

Extra warp and weft pattern weaves
Extra warp and weft pattern weaves are those in which extra warp and weft yarns are added to the fabric during weaving. Inlay pattern weaving was a well-known art in ancient Egypt, China, the Near East, and Peru. Some of the most beautiful decorative fabrics are made by this type of weaving. For commercial distribution, the Jacquard loom is used. Inlay weaves fall into several classifications, but are all referred to as brocades.

Double-cloth weaves Double-cloth weaves, which are woven in two attached layers that often have a quilted appearance, account for many of the durable and beautiful fabrics used today, and were known to the ancient Peruvians. When these fabrics are woven for commercial use, the Jacquard loom is required. Among the many varieties of this type, warp-faced pile weave and matelasse are two of the most common.

Open, lacelike weaves Open, lacelike weaves can be obtained in a number of ways. One is the *leno,* a loose weave in which the warp threads are wound in half twists around each other, alternating in position on each row. The *gauze* weave is similar to leno, but differs in that the warp threads maintain the same position in relation to the weft. Gauze weaves range from simple to complex. Sheers, semisheers, and novelty casements employ these weaves.

Tension and texture-treated weaves
Tension and texture-treated weaves are those in which uneven tension in either weft or warp yarns produces an uneven surface effect. This may be accomplished in a variety of ways and with different effects. Yarns of different twists, warp yarns held at different tension, floated yarns combined with tightly woven yarns, combinations of yarns that react differently to heat, irregular battening, irregular reeds, and combinations of unusual fibers are all used to produce different surface effects. A commonly used decorative fabric of this type is brocatelle, in which floated and compactly woven yarns are combined to produce the raised effect.

Combination weaves Combination weaves occur in many fabrics used today; they are produced by combining two or more weaves. The weaves combined are often suggested in the name of the fabric, such as brocaded satin and voided velvet.

KNITTING

Knitting is a process of interlocking a series of yarn loops by means of blunt needles. Through a variation of stitches, patterns are formed. Knitted fabrics, either hand- or machine-made, range from loose, open construction to close, fine weave. Finely knit fabrics are used for many home furnishing needs because of their desirable qualities of wrinkle resistance, tight fit, and ease of care. The tendency of knitted fabrics to stretch is being overcome by new methods of production.

TWISTING

Twisting, interlocking, and knotting account for various types of mesh construction, such as nets, laces, and macrame, the intricacies of which are unlimited. With the current revival of handcrafts, macrame has become particularly popular for a number of household uses.

FELTING

Felting is a nonwoven process of subjecting a mass of fibers to moisture, heat, and pressure, which produces a compact sheet that does not fray, absorbs sound, and provides good insulation against heat and cold. Felt was formerly made from wool and hair fibers. Through modern technology, new fibers and fusing methods are employed to produce a variety of nonwoven materials.

BONDING

A bonded fabric results when two fabrics are adhered (or bonded or laminated) together. By bonding a layer of fabric to the underside, the face fabric can be stabilized. If care is not taken, however, cleaning may cause a separation of the layers.

Dyeing

Fibers and fabrics are dyed or colored through various processes. These processes include (1) direct physical action, in which the structural elements of the fiber absorb the color, (2) chemical action, in which certain dyes have the ability to unite chemically with certain fibers, and (3) intermediate action, in which a **mordant** is used to unite the dye and the fiber.

The various methods of dyeing yarns, fibers, and fabrics include (1) *solution* dyeing, in which the coloring agent is added to the viscous liquid of the synthetic before it is forced through the spinnerette to be formed into a fiber, (2) *stock* dyeing, in which the dye is applied to the fibers before they are processed into yarns, (3) *yarn* dyeing, in which the skeins or hanks of yarns are dyed before they are woven into fabrics, and (4) *piece* dying of the fabrics after they are woven.

Piece dyeing, which usually produces a solid color in fabrics, can be done in several ways. *Jig* dyeing passes the open fabric back and forth through a stationary dye bath. *Pad* dyeing runs the fabric through the dye bath and then between rollers that squeeze the dye deeper into the yarns of the fabric. *Winch, reel,* or *beck* dyeing immerses the fabric continuously without strain to the fabric. *Continuous machine* dyeing has compartments for wetting out, dyeing, after treatments, washing, and rinsing. High-temperature processes are sometimes used for greater dye penetration. These processes are used especially for synthetic fibers.

Finishing

The finish is a treatment that may be applied to the fiber or yarn before or after construction to change the appearance and performance. When the unfinished fabric comes from the loom, it is referred to as *greige* or *gray goods.* Before the cloth is ready for the market, it goes through a series of finishes: the preparation, the functional, and the decorative.

PREPARATION

Preparation of the gray goods consists of a variety of treatments that include *bleaching* (to whiten), *shrinking* (to prevent fiber contraction when exposed to moisture), *heat setting* (to add stability), *beetling* or pounding (to give luster), *gigging* or *napping* (to produce a flannel-like texture), and *singeing* (to remove surface fuzz or lint). Following the preparatory finishing, the cloth is ready for the functional and decorative finishes.

FUNCTIONAL FINISHES

Functional finishes, which are applied to improve performance, can make the fabric antistatic, soil resistant, crease resistant, fire and flame resistant, water-repellent, and insulated against heat, cold, and noise.

DECORATIVE FINISHES

Decorative finishes include printing and embroidery.

PRINTING

Printing may be done by hand or by machine.

Hand processes   With the exception of warp printing, fabrics are printed in the piece (after weaving). Fabrics done by the hand-printing processes of stencil block, **batik,** tie-dye, and spray painting are not readily available, since they are not produced on a commercial scale. Only the silk-screen process produces hand-printed textiles on a commercial scale. Some of these prints are so lovely in their design quality that they rival fine paintings. The process is essentially one in which a specially prepared fabric screen resists the color penetration except in desired areas. Dye in paste form is forced through the screen onto the fabric below. A separate screen is prepared for each color used in the artist's design.

Mechanical processes   Many prints are produced mechanically by the transfer of color from an engraved copper roller onto the fabric. This process is called *roller printing.* A separate copper roller must be engraved for each color of the design, but once prepared, the rollers can be used on a variety of color schemes for thousands of yards of fabric. Thus, the cost is greatly reduced. The roller can be adapted to do resist printing, discharge printing, **parchment** printing, etching, embossing, duplex, and warp printing. Warp printing is done on the warp yarns of a fabric before it is woven.

Printed fabrics come in designs of unlimited styles, from **documentaries**—designs copied from earlier patterns of a particular period, which can be used to establish an authentic style—to the most abstract contemporary.

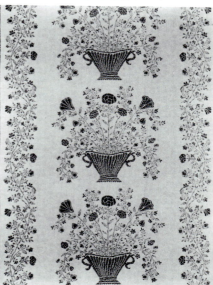

Figure 6.4 (*top*). A documentary print. This botanical coverlet screen-printed fabric was inspired by an appliquéd calico coverlet made in Connecticut in 1868. (Courtesy of Greef Fabrics, Shelburne Museum Collection of Decorative Fabrics and Wallpapers.)

Figure 6.5 (*bottom*). Flowering Centerpiece, a documentary print. (Courtesy of Greef Fabrics, Shelburne Museum Collection of Decorative Fabrics and Wallpapers.)

TABLE 6.I.   *Properties of man-made fibers*

GENERIC NAME	APPEARANCE	ABRASION	RESILIENCE	HEAT TOLERANCE	FLAMMABILITY
Acetate (regenerated cellulose)	Smooth; silky; drapes well; holds shape well	Fair	Poor	Poor	Slow
Triacetate a subdivision of the acetate group	Crisp; smooth; silky; drapes well; strong colors	Fair	Good; resists wrinkling; retains pleats	Less sensitive than acetate	Slowly combustible
Acrylic	Wool-like; soft; bulky; warm; may squeak; rich colors; pilling depends on quality	Good; needs treatment for static	Good; holds heat-set pleats	Sticks at 450 °F	Resists fire; burns with yellow flame
Modacrylic (modified acrylic)	Similar to acrylic; good color retention	Good	Fair to good	Does not melt	Self-extinguishing
Aramid	Stiff and smooth	High; exceptional strength	Excellent; low stretchability	Not affected	Low flammability
Glass	Soapy; lustrous; silky; color range fair; Beta Fiberglas has remarkable sheerness	Strongest of all fibers	Excellent	Fireproof	Nonflammable
Nylon (polyamide)	Squeaky; silky; cold; natural luster; good color range; drapes well	Excellent	Very good; resists wrinkling; can be heat set to hold shape	High resistance	Melts slowly
Olefin (propylene and ethylene)	Waxy; wool-like; color range fair	Good to excellent	Good; resists wrinkling	Poor; heat sensitive	Slow to burn
Polyester	Silky, cotton, or wool-like; drapes well; color range fair	Good to excellent	Excellent; resists wrinkles	Sticks at 400 °F	Burns slowly
Rayon (regenerated cellulose)	Soft; drapes well; excellent color range; bright	Fair to good	Low to medium; crease retention poor	Excellent; does not melt	Burns quickly
Saran	Soft; drapes well	Tough	Crease retentive	Shrinks in intense heat	Nonflammable
Vinyl (thermoplastic resins)	Smooth; variety of weights; expanded vinyl; closely resembles leather	Good	Low	Shrinks at 212–230 °F in dry heat, less in moist heat	Burns with difficulty

Notes: All man-made fibers are resistant to moths and mildew.

Insulation depends on construction and is primarily a function of thickness. Hollow polyester fibers provide particularly good insulation.

Costs are variable, depending on construction.

LIGHT TOLERANCE	DECORATIVE USES	CARE	SOME TRADE NAMES AND MANUFACTURERS
Long exposure weakens fiber; colors fade unless protected by special finish	Curtains, drapery, upholstery, rugs; for shower curtains in blends with other fibers; moderate cost	Soil resistance fair; wash in lukewarm water or dry-clean, depending on dyes, finishes, decorative designs; quick drying; iron at moderate heat	Ariloft (Eastman); Celanese Acetate (Celanese); Chromspun (Eastman); Estron (Eastman); Lanese (Celanese); Loftura (Eastman); Lanese (Celanese)
More resistant than acetate	Same as acetate	Same as acetate	Arnel (Celanese)
Good	Rugs, carpets, blankets, curtains, drapery, upholstery	Keeps bouyancy when washed with warm water; machine dry; does not shrink, sag, or stretch; steam pressing reduces loft	Acrilan (Monsanto); Creslan (American Cyanamid); Orlon (DuPont); Zefran, Zetkrome (Dow Chemical)
Excellent	Curtains, drapery, in carpet blends, furry rugs, blankets	Similar to acrylic; resists chemical stains; washable; use warm iron; shrinks unless stabilized; does not dry-clean well	Acrilan (Monsanto); Verel (Tennessee Eastman); Dynel (Union Carbide)
Weakens with long exposure	Carpets	Not affected by moisture	Kevlar (DuPont); Nomex (DuPont)
No loss	Curtains, drapery, bedspreads; Beta Fiberglas used for bedspreads	Impervious to moisture; hand wash; drip-dry; needs no ironing	Fiberglas (Owens-Corning); Pittsburgh PPG (Pittsburgh); Vitron (Libby-Owens-Ford); Unirove (Ferro Corporation)
Poor	Upholstery, bedspreads, carpets	Washable; quick drying; use warm iron; resists soil, easy spot removal; static electricity unless treated	Altron (Monsanto); Anso (carpet yarns) (Allied Chemical); Antron Nylon (DuPont); Cadon (Monsanto); Caprolan (Allied Chemical); Cumuloft (Chemstrand); Lusterloft (carpet staple) (American Enka)
Good	Rugs, blankets, upholstery, webbing, seat covers; low cost	Wash or dry-clean; iron at very low heat; good soil-resistance	Durel (Celanese); Herculon (Hercules Powder); Marvess (Alamo Industries); Patlon (Monarch Carpet Mills); Marquesa (Amoco Fabrics); Vectra (National Plastic Products); Polyloom (Chevron Chemical)
Loses strength in prolonged exposure	Curtains, drapery, upholstery, carpets and rugs, pillow floss blankets	Soils easily; machine wash in warm water; dries quickly; use warm iron; resists stretching and shrinking	Avlin (American Viscose Division, FMC); Dacron (DuPont); Encron (Enka Manufacturing); Fortrel (Celanese); Kodel (Eastman Chemical Products); Trevira (Hystron Fibers)
Fades when not solution dyed	Curtains, upholstery, drapery, table linen, rugs; relatively inexpensive; probably most versatile fiber	Same as acetate; fair soil resistance	Avril (Avtel Fibers); Coloray (solution-dyed staple) (Courtaulds North America); Enkaire (flat filament staple) (American Enka); Enkrome (American Enka); Fibro (Courtaulds North America); Zantrel (American Enka)
Excellent	Outdoor furniture, upholstery and screening, curtains, drapery, wall coverings	Excellent ease of care; resists wrinkling and stains; water-repellent	Saran (Dow Chemical); National (National Plastics); Rovana (Dow Chemical); Velon (Firestone Plastic)
Weakens with long exposure	Shower curtains, wall coverings, upholstery when backed with fabric	Stain resistant; waterproof; wash and wipe clean	Beautafilm (Hartford); Boltaflex (General Tire and Rubber); Duran (Masland); Fabrilite (DuPont); Ford (Ford Motor); Koroseal (B.F. Goodrich); Lumite (Chicopee Mills); Naugahyde (U.S. Rubber); Rucaire (Hooker Chemical)

Figure 6.6. Freesia, a contemporary stylized design by Jason Pollen and Jack Lenor Larsen, printed in three degrees of value contrast via a new printing process blending halftone colors. (Courtesy of Jack Lenor Larsen.)

NEEDLEWORK

Needlework, embellishing fabrics with colorful and intricate stitchery, is an ancient art. With the present renaissance occurring in all handcrafts, stitchery of all kinds, both hand- and machine-made, is being enthusiastically revived. A wide variety of handwork, such as embroidery, needlepoint, candlewicking, appliqué, and quilting, are again embellishing wall hangings, pillow covers, seat covers, and bedspreads in homes across the country.

Principal uses of decorative fabrics for the interior

Today's interior designer has at his or her disposal a wider choice of fabrics than ever before. The market abounds with fabrics suitable for every taste, style, decorative purpose, and in every price range, with new fabrics appearing almost daily. Adding to the appeal of new and improved fibers is the seemingly unending variety of designs ranging from folk patterns from around the world to traditional and contemporary. Selecting from this abundance the right fabric for the purpose at hand may sometimes seem overwhelming. With some study and careful planning, however, fabrics can be selected to create rooms that are pleasant and comfortable and that will satisfy personal taste and fulfill individual needs.

The following are the principal decorative uses of fabrics in the home, the purposes each can serve, the qualities necessary for each use, and some fabric examples.

SHEERS OR GLASS CURTAINS

Sheers or glass curtains may hang permanently over the glass to filter the light, thereby giving softness to the room and providing daytime privacy.

Fabric should be sheer enough to permit light and frequently a view, should be sunproof as to colorfastness and splitting, and should wash or clean well without shrinkage. Any sheer fabric that has the necessary qualities can be used for sheers or glass curtains. Batiste and ninon are two of the most common, and chiffon is becoming popular.

CASEMENTS OR SEMISHEERS

Casements or semisheers serve as side drapery during the day and are drawn at night for privacy.

Fabric should be heavy enough for nighttime privacy, but should permit some light. It should be drapable, sun resistant, nonsplitting, and should wash or clean well without shrinkage. Leno weave will control sagging. Fabric choice is unlimited. The style of decor will determine the type of weave.

DRAPERY

Drapery serves as stationary side drapery or is drawn for nighttime privacy. It can add beauty, height, and dignity to a room. When the correct design, texture, color, and method of hanging are employed, drapery can provide a feeling of authenticity of a style, and can set the mood of the room (i.e., formal or informal).

Fabric should drape gracefully, clean without shrinkage, and meet the particular needs of the room in which it is used. Any drapable fabric that is appropriate for the style of furnishings and type of window treatment can be used.

UPHOLSTERY

Upholstery covers furniture permanently, adds beauty and comfort, conceals or emphasizes furniture, and adds to or sets the theme or mood of the room.

Fabric used for upholstery should have a tight weave, should be durable, and should clean well. Any fabric that has the necessary qualities can be used, such as matelasse, tapestry, velveteen, damask, tweed, cut velvet, brocatelle, bouclé, frieze, or vinyl.

SLIPCOVERS

Slipcovers cover worn, upholstered furniture, protect more expensive fabrics, and brighten or change a room's atmosphere.

Fabric for slipcovers should have a tight weave that will not snag or stretch, unless it is a stretch variety. Fabric should be easily cleaned or washed, should be pliable to make fitting and sewing easy, and should be durable. Indian Head, sailcloth, ticking, chintz, whipcord, and corduroy are all good choices for slipcovers.

WALLS

Fabric is usually used on walls to add beauty, but it may also solve many decorative problems. (See Chapter 7 for uses of flexible wall coverings.) The fabric should have a tight weave with firm body.

Felt, canvas, burlap, ticking, heavy cotton or linen, velveteen, and damask are practical for wall coverings.

Framed fabric can add interest and glamour.

LAMP SHADES

Lamp shades are used most often to diffuse light.

Fabric for lamp shades should usually be in a neutral color, with a texture that is appropriate for the lamp base and the room. Shantung, taffeta, and loose homespun weaves can be used for lamp shades.

Figure 6.7. Walls with draped fabric provide a contrast for wicker furniture and an atmosphere of relaxation. (Courtesy of Van Luit and Company.)

Use of pattern, texture, and color when combining fabrics

Perhaps the most common question that clients ask professional interior designers is, "What fabric goes with what?" This question has no pat answer. Combining fabrics is a matter of training and skill. Some people seem to have an aptitude for acquiring this skill; others require much patient study and practice. Although an unexpected combination of materials may create a feeling of great interest and charm, some general principles may be helpful to the inexperienced designer when combining colors, textures, and patterns. For example, bold informal patterns call for heavy textures and strong color combinations; refined formal patterns call for smooth textures and softer colors.

PATTERN

Pattern indicates that the design has motifs sufficiently large in scale, or with enough contrast in color or tone, to permit the eye to clearly distinguish them. When the parts of the pattern are so subtle or are blended in such a way that they are indistinguishable, the design becomes more one of texture than of pattern.

Many people are afraid of patterned fabrics and avoid them entirely. Others may use them ineffectively. Although they are not a necessity, well-chosen patterned fabrics can enhance most rooms. In skillful hands, the adroit use of pattern can camouflage defects, create beauty and glamour, and perform decorating miracles.

As with color, no absolute dos or don'ts govern the use of pattern. A few general guidelines, however, may be helpful:

Patterns used within the same room should have a pleasing relationship to each other. Common elements should tie them together to create a workable relationship. One or more of the elements, such as color, texture, or motif, running throughout will give an easy flow of unity to the entire scheme.

The principal pattern need not be repeated in the room so long as one or more of the colors in that pattern are carried over into another area. The same pattern, however, may with pleasing results be repeated on several pieces of furniture, used at the windows and on the furniture, or used on the walls, windows, and furniture, depending on the overall effect desired. Odd pieces of furniture are unified when covered in the same fabric, and the repetition of the fabric will bring unity into an entire room. The pattern should be chosen with discrimination, since the final product should not be too busy, too stimulating, or overpowering.

A room should have no more than one bold pattern of the same type of design, such as a floral, except in rare cases. Once the dominant motif is established, it may be supplemented by a small pattern, a stripe, a check, or plaid, and appropriate plain textures if a common denominator is present throughout.

Bold patterns should be used with discretion. Too much pattern becomes overpowering.

When combining patterned fabrics, scale should be considered. For example, if a bold floral print is combined with a plaid or a stripe or both, these must also be in bold scale. If an unobtrusive floral pattern is used, then the accompanying fabrics should blend in well and should not overpower the basic pattern.

Unusual juxtaposition of fabric may create a dramatic effect, but this kind of carefree sophistication usually develops from knowledge and practice that have produced confidence to do the unexpected. The novice is wise to follow some basic guidelines.

A knowledge of what makes a fabric formal or informal is essential in successfully combining textures and patterns.

FORMAL FABRICS

Formal fabrics are those with smooth texture, usually stylized patterns, and traditional stripes. Colors will likely be neutralized. Some examples of formal fabrics are velvet, damask, brocade, brocatelle, satin, shantung, and taffeta.

INFORMAL FABRICS

Informal fabrics are those with a rougher texture, such as burlap, canvas, hopsacking, muslin, tweed, and bouclé. Patterns may be bold, naturalistic, abstract, or geometric. Color will usually be strong and contrastive. Fabrics that look handcrafted come in this category.

Many fabrics can be used in either category. For example, glazed chintz may have a stylized pattern and rich colors that fit into a formal setting, or it may have a lively pattern and colors that are at home in an informal room. Tapestry may also go anywhere, depending on the color and pattern.

Experience in training the eye while trying out innumerable fabric combinations, along with general guidelines, will develop a sense of what goes together and what does not.

Solving design problems with fabrics

Problems that can be solved through the skillful use of fabrics are unlimited. The following are some of the ways in which fabric may serve many purposes and come to the rescue of the interior designer if he or she is knowledgeable about its use. The correct fabric can:

□ Lighten or darken a room.

□ Emphasize or conceal windows, walls, or furniture.

□ Set the mood of a room: give it a feeling of formality by the use of stylistic design, smooth weave, and rich colors—or of informality by the use of naturalistic or abstract designs, textured weaves, and bold color (see "Fabrics for Specific Areas").

□ Bring harmony and unity to a room, in which furnishings previously seemed unrelated, by repeated use of the same fabric.

□ Bring balance to a room. For example, a bold-patterned fabric hung at a window or used to upholster a small piece of furniture will balance a larger piece of plain furniture at the other side of the room. A spot of bright color will balance a larger area of muted color.

□ Change the apparent size and proportion of a piece of furniture or of an entire room. For example, a sofa covered in a large pattern or bold-colored fabric will appear larger than if it is covered in a light, plain color or a small, allover pattern. A chair or love seat covered in a vertical stripe will look higher than the same piece covered in plain fabric.

□ Relieve an otherwise monotonous room by adding sparkle, interest, beauty, and glamour.

□ Change the look of a room for different seasons. For example, a couch and chairs in deep, warm colors may be slipcovered in light-colored ticking for summer. Heavy winter drapery may be changed for light, sheer glass curtains to create a cool atmosphere for summer.

□ Establish the room's color scheme. A successful method of color scheming a room is choosing a favorite patterned fabric as a starting point, which was discussed in Chapter 5.

□ Establish the authentic style of a room. If the room is based on a certain period, the fabric, more than any other item of furnishing, can set the desired feeling.

□ Add beauty and comfort in greater measure than any other decorative element.

FABRIC CAN CHANGE THE PERSONALITY OF A CHAIR

The floral pattern gives a traditional appearance.

A plaid fabric accentuates the square silhouette and gives the chair a modern appearance.

Fabric can solve design problems. Radiator wall can be covered with fabric-sheered shutters; and the same fabric can be repeated on and above the bed.

Fabric can conceal an unsightly heating vent, making a feature out of a fault.

In the absence of a headboard, fabric can be attached to the wall for height and glamour.

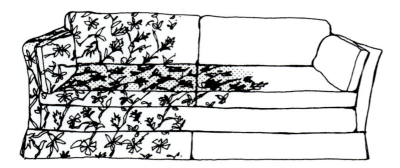

Large or conspicuous pattern tends to make furniture appear larger.

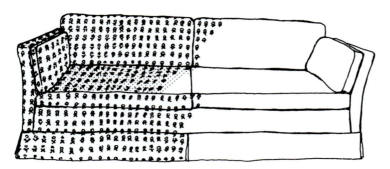

Small pattern diminishes size.

Figure 6.8 (*facing page*). The stylized traditional pattern of this fabric sets the room's formal eighteenth-century mood. (Courtesy of Henredon Furniture Industries.)

Figure 6.9 (*above*). An atmosphere of informality is set by the vibrant plaid fabric on the furniture. (Courtesy of Armstrong World Industries.)

Figure 6.10. Through the repetition of one beautiful fabric, a room can be given unity and a special atmosphere. This formal room was made more informal through the use of a lively chintz on furniture and at the window. (Courtesy of Ethan Allen.)

Fabrics for specific areas

Because fabric more than any other element can set the mood and atmosphere of a room, each fabric should carefully be selected, with color, texture, and pattern keyed to the specific area or room in which the fabric will be used. In general, a specific mood is appropriate for each room, although this necessarily varies according to individual preference.

Fabrics for period and contemporary rooms

Design in textiles was used in ancient times as a symbolic media for religious purposes. With the passage of time, fabric became a significant media for aesthetic expression of people throughout the world. A discernible *affinity* is present in the primitive designs in fabrics of all countries. For example, the design motifs used in the early rugs of East Turkistan are much the same as the designs used in the early rugs of the Inca and Navajo Indians, halfway around the world. This similarity is easily explainable. Primitive people everywhere represented the phenomena of nature in their early art forms. The sun and stars have always been represented in identifiable form by people throughout the world. The difference in early textile weaves is minimized because all were done on simple looms, and primitive people all over used natural fibers and dyes. Although each country developed characteristics peculiar to its origin, a common quality in their early crafts blends them harmoniously together.

A close relationship also exists among the designs of Western countries, which ties these periods together, making the interchange not only acceptable but also oftentimes desirable. A brief look at history reveals the explanation for this relationship. The conqueror of a country imported artisans of all kinds to his homeland, where they continued to carry on their trades. In time, they were influenced by the designs of their new environment, and the eventual blending

Figure 6.11. The lavish use of well-coordinated fabrics created this attractive bedroom. (Courtesy of Mitchell Designs.)

Figure 6.12. This stunning room was created primarily through the knowledgeable use of fabric. One pearl gray fabric unifies the diverse furniture. Contrasting purple accents contribute to the sophistication of this formal contemporary setting. (Courtesy of Mark Epstein.)

of different methods and motifs produced art forms with distinct individuality. These individualities differentiate the designs of one country or period from another, and make it possible today to give a room a distinctive character through the use of correct art forms, particularly in fabrics.

With the increased sophistication in today's interior design, many people are drawing on historic designs to establish the authentic feeling of a specific period or to bestow a dramatic contrast in their

homes (see Figure 6.8). To accomplish this, documentary fabrics, bearing designs from a wide range of historic periods, are being produced by the finest manufacturers.

Since interest in decorative styles of the past is growing, incumbent on the interior designer is a familiarity with historic fabrics. Seldom does a domestic client wish to have an authentic period room; this is usually reserved for projects of restoration. In creating a decorative scheme based on a specific period, however, the choice of authentic fabrics will set the theme of a room more surely than any other decorative element.

To serve those clients who prefer the modern look, a knowledge of contemporary fabrics is a must for today's interior designer. Decorative fabrics with colors, textures, and designs to meet the needs of every modern room are in abundance, and new ones are reaching the market with regularity. Improved production methods and new designers are making possible a wealth of decorative fabrics with remarkable qualities to serve the diverse desires of almost anyone.

The following information should assist the interior designer—both professional and nonprofessional—in getting the maximum service from decorative fabrics.

Types of decorative fabrics and terms

The following are the most commonly used household fabrics, with the decorative name and most common uses of each:

Batiste A fine, soft, sheer fabric of plain weave made of various fibers. Curtains.

Bouclé A French word meaning "curly." It indicates that yarns are curled or looped in a flat fabric or a pile fabric. Upholstery.

Bouclé marquisette Sheer material of leno weave with a bouclé yarn. Glass curtains.

Brocade A pattern is embroidered and stands out in relief against a satin or ribbed background. Drapery and upholstery. Jacquard weave.

Brocatelle A Jacquard fabric with an extra set of wefts for backing unequally twisted, which produces a high relief *repoussé* appearance on the surface. Drapery and upholstery.

Buckram Stiffened material sized with glue and used to reinforce draperies and valances.

Burlap Coarse cloth woven from jute. Wall coverings, drapery, lamp shades.

Canvas A heavy, closely woven cloth. Has many decorative uses. Upholstery, drapery, walls.

Casement A broad term that covers many drapery fabrics, usually light, neutral colors in plain or novelty weave.

Chenille A fabric woven with chenille yarns that have a pile effect similar to velvet. When woven in a fabric, can create a pile similar to velvet; if woven on a Jacquard loom, can look similar to cut velvet. Upholstery.

Chiffon A sheer fabric used for glass curtains. Tight weave, lightweight.

Chintz A plain, tightly woven cotton fabric with fine yarns, sometimes processed with a glazed finish, used as a plain-dyed fabric or a printed fabric. Drapery, slipcovers, bedspreads.

Color flag The series of clippings attached to a purchase sample to show the colorline.

Colorline Refers to the complete color range of a given series.

Colorway Refers to an individual fabric in its color.

Corduroy Cotton pile fabric, ribbed or corded lengthwise. Drapery, slipcovers, upholstery, bedspreads, and many other uses.

Crewel Embroidery made with a fine, loosely twisted, two-ply worsted yarn on a plain weave cotton, linen, or wool fabric. Worked by hand, for the most part, in the Kashmir province of India. Drapery and upholstery.

Crocking Rubbing off color from dyed or printed fabrics.

Damask A Jacquard-woven fabric with patterns created with different weave effects. Can be woven self-tone, one color warp, different color filling, or multicolor in design. Distinguished from brocades because face of fabric is flatter. The color is reversed on the wrong side. Drapery and upholstery.

Denim Heavy cotton twill made of coarse yarns. Drapery, upholstery, bedspreads, walls, and numerous other uses.

Dotted swiss Sheer fabric woven with extra yarns that form dots when clipped. The effect may also be produced by flocking. Curtains.

Faille A flat-ribbed fabric woven with fine yarns in the warp and heavier yarns in the filling, using a plain weave. The ribbed effect is flatter than grosgrain and smaller than rep. The fabric can be the base cloth used for moiré. Drapery.

Felt   Wools or mixed fibers pressed into a compact sheet. Walls, table covers, and other areas needing a heavy cover.

Fiberglass   Fibers and yarns produced from glass and woven into flexible fabrics. Noted for its fireproof qualities. Beta Fiberglas is a trademarked glass fiber. Curtains.

Frieze   A strong fabric with a fine, low-loop surface woven on a wire loom to maintain an even size to the loops. Upholstery.

Gimp   Ornamental braid used to cover upholstery tacks.

Gingham   Medium-weight cotton or cottonlike fabric for informal use. Made of colored yarns forming checks, plaids, or stripes.

Grass cloth. Coarse grasses glued to rice paper, used for wall coverings.

Gros point   Needlepoint embroidery. Upholstery.

Homespun   Loosely woven fabric made to resemble handwoven material. Curtains or drapery, depending on the weight.

Hopsacking   A rough-surfaced fabric loosely woven of various fibers in a plain basket weave. Mainly for drapery and slipcovers.

Jacquard   Damasks, brocades, tapestries, and all fabrics requiring the Jacquard loom.

Lampas   Fabric having a rep ground, with satinlike figures formed of warp threads and contrasting figures formed of weft thread. Drapery and upholstery.

Matelasse   A double-woven fabric that gives a quilted appearance to the fabric. It comes from the French word *matelasser,* meaning "to cushion" or "to pad." Used for upholstery, especially in rooms of Spanish and Mediterranean styles.

Moiré   A wavy effect pressed into a ribbed surface such as taffeta or faille. Drapery, upholstery, bedspreads.

Muslin   Unbleached—plain, lighweight cotton weave. Has many uses in decorating, especially in Early American and modern rooms. Walls, drapery, slipcovers.

Ninon   A plain, tight weave used for glass curtains. It has a smooth, crisp, lightweight, gossamer appearance.

Oxford cloth   A plain-weave fabric. Large filling yarn goes over two warp yarns. An informal fabric with many uses.

Pilling   Formation of fiber fuzz balls on fabric surface by wear or friction, encountered in spun nylon, polyester, acrylic, cashmere, or soft woolen yarns.

Plissé   A lightweight fabric with a crinkled or puckered effect, created by chemical treatment. Curtains.

Plush   A pile fabric with greater depth than velvet. Usually has a high sheen. Upholstery.

Polished cotton   A plain- or satin-weave cotton cloth characterized by a sheen ranging from dull to bright. Polish can be achieved either through the weave or by the addition of a resin finish.

Quilted fabrics   A pattern stitched through a printed or plain fabric and through a layer of batting. Outline quilting traces around the pattern of a printed fabric. Loom quilting is a small repetitive design made by the quilting alone. Ultrasonic quilting produces thermally bonded welds in place of stitching threads.

Rep   Plain-weave fabric with narrow ribs running the width of the fabric. Usually a fine warp and heavier filling yarns. Drapery, upholstery, slipcovers, bedspreads, and other informal uses.

Sateen   A highly lustrous fabric usually made of mercerized cotton with a satin weave. Drapery lining.

Satin   *Plain:* Fine yarns woven in such a manner as to give a more lustrous surface. May be lightweight or heavy enough for upholstery. It has many decorative uses when a formal style of decor is desired. *Antique:* A smooth satin face highlighted by slub (or twisted) yarn in a random pattern. Today it is an important fabric for drapery.

Seersucker   A special weaving process that produces a permanently wrinkled or puckered effect.

Suede   Leather with a napped surface. Polyester suede washes and wears well. Used for upholstery.

Taffeta   *Plain:* Tight, smooth weave with slight horizontal ribbed effect. When woven of silk, it is a luxury fabric for drapery, bedspreads, and lamp shades. *Antique* or *shantung:* A smooth, soft weave with random slub yarn, creating a textured effect. A luxury fabric with many decorative uses, especially drapery and lamp shades.

Tapestry   A figured, multicolored fabric woven on a Jacquard loom. The design is formed by varying weave effects brought to the surface in combination with colored yarns. The surface is rough to the hand. Upholstery. (Made up of two sets of warp and weft.)

Terry cloth   Pile fabric. May be cut or uncut. Loops may be on one side or both.

Ticking   Heavy, strong cotton fabric, usually striped. Used for pillows and mattresses, walls, drapery, slipcovers, and numerous budget projects.

Toile de Jouy   A floral or scenic design usually printed on cotton or linen. Originally printed in Jouy, France.

Trapunto   Quilting that raises an area design of the surface of upholstery fabric.

Tweed   Plain-weave upholstery fabric with heavy texture because of flake (or knotted yarn). Upholstery.

Velour   A French term loosely applied to all types of fabrics with a nap or cut pile on one side. Specifically, it is a cut-pile fabric similar to regular velvet but with a higher pile. Upholstery.

Velvet   A fabric having a short, thick warp pile. May be of any fiber. *Crushed:* Most often the fabric is pulled through a narrow cylinder to create the crushed effect. *Cut:* Jacquard design, usually cut and uncut pile on a plain ground. *Antique:* Velvet that has an old look. Upholstery.

Velveteen   A weft-pile fabric with short pile, usually of cotton. Drapery, upholstery, bedspreads, and innumerable uses.

Vinyl   A nonwoven plastic fabric capable of being printed or embossed to produce any desired finish, such as leather, wood, floral, or textured design. Cloth backing prevents tearing. Walls and upholstery.

Voile   A fine, soft, sheer fabric used for sheers. Has a rough, sandpapery feel.

Caring for upholstery and decorative fabrics

PROTECTING FABRICS

Fabrics should be protected from the sun. Draperies should be lined, and even interlined, when fragile fabrics are used. Blinds should be drawn during the day, and awnings should be used whenever practicable. The winter sun and reflection from the snow are even more harmful than the summer sun. Window glass magnifies the destructive elements in the rays of the sun. Trees or shrubbery can protect windows. Some colors are more fugitive than others. Colors can fade by oxidation (gas fading) if unaired in storage for a period of time. Impurities in the air may cause as much fading as the direct rays of the sun.

CLEANING FABRICS

A reputable dry cleaner who specializes in home furnishings should be used. Fabrics should be vacuumed often to remove dust; this also saves on cleaning. Dust has impurities that affect fabrics. Spots should be removed immediately. Few fabrics are washable.

FLUCTUATIONS IN FABRICS

Small fluctuations in lengths of draperies may occur. No fabric is completely stable. A completely stable fabric would have no textural interest.

Fabrics breathe and absorb moisture, resulting in stretching or shrinking. A reasonable expectation is a 3 percent change in a 108 in. (3-yd) length, which would amount to 3 in., depending on the fabric involved.

WEAR IN FABRICS

Fabrics wear—they are not indestructible. Wear will vary with use given. A favorite chair will not last as long as a seldom-used showpiece in the living room. Some weaves are stronger than others.

FINISHES

Finishes may help fabrics *resist* spotting, but they are not necessarily the be-all and the end-all to every problem. Light colors are likely to benefit most. Dining room chairs will soil no matter what fabric is used. A finish does not eliminate the necessity of properly caring for fabrics. Spots should be removed immediately.

MAN-MADE FIBERS

Man-made fibers have made an invaluable contribution to weaving technology, but they cannot perform miracles. Performance will vary with the construction of the fabric.

In the final analysis, as it is in every industry, the integrity and experience of your supplier is your best assurance as to the intrinsic value of your purchase, but it must be combined with knowledge and understanding on the part of the consumer.

(Courtesy of Upholstery and Decorative Fabrics Association of America.)

ASSIGNMENT

After class demonstrations and supervised practice in coordinating compatible materials for floors, walls, windows, and upholstery, complete the following project.

FORMAT 1

1 On two sheets of white mounting paper, approximately 9 in. by 12 in., draw a rectangle approximately 6½ in. by 8½ in. Indicate a ½-in. ceiling and ⅜-in. wood trim.

2 Following the format used in Figure 6.13, make two layouts for rooms of your own choosing.

3 Each completed layout should contain:
Ceiling. Usually painted white or an off-white to blend with the room.
Floor. Sample of flooring or floor covering.
Walls. Cover the entire wall with paint, paper, fabric, or paneling. (When paneling is used, contact paper or a clear picture of wood is advisable.)
Wood trim. Paint or indicate natural wood grain.
Windows. When sheers or side draperies or both are desired, use actual materials. When shutters or louvers are used, submit a picture.
Upholstery. Include an appropriate number of upholstery fabrics for the particular rooms you have chosen. The size of each sample will indicate the approximate area it will cover in relation to the other pieces.

4 Using professional lettering, indicate the type of room (e.g., informal family, formal living room).

Note: Each fabric should be chosen appropriately with discriminating taste and should be neatly presented.

Figure 6.13. This is an example of a completed fabric layout using Format 1. Compatible colors, textures, and patterns are coordinated to produce a formal contemporary grouping. The size of the various upholstery fabrics indicates roughly the proportion in which each would be used in the room.

FORMAT 2: AN ALTERNATIVE

Although the juxtaposition of fabrics in the preceding layout shows more clearly the relationship of fabrics and colors, some students of interior design may prefer to use the format employed by most professional designers.

1 Select two *neutral* (not white) colored mat boards, approximately 9 in. by 12 in.

2 Carefully coordinate background colors, materials, and fabrics for each room.

3 Mount fabrics and carpet samples on small scraps of mat board. If the fabric is heavy, it may be cropped to fit the board. If it is lightweight, it may be better to wrap the board.

4 Vary the size of the samples according to the amount of fabric that will be used (e.g., a sofa will require a larger sample than a small chair).

5 Submit paint chips for walls, ceiling, and wood trim, and a sample of tile, hardwood, or whatever flooring you have chosen. Arrange these neatly and professionally on the 9-by-12-in. boards to create two complete room layouts (see Figure 6.14).

Figure 6.14. A fabric layout employing Format 2. Samples of materials affixed to small boards in relative scale are appropriately arranged and attached to the board.

*Floors, Walls,
and Ceilings*

T*he general scheme of any room* is
established by the architectural background: walls, floors, ceilings, plus such
items as windows, mantels, paneling, and
moldings. The decorative treatments that
are added to these as well as to the
movable objects in the room should be in
keeping with the overall feeling if the
room is to have an atmosphere of harmony and unity. Since backgrounds are
for people, generally a wise choice is to
make large areas—walls, floors, and ceilings—unobtrusive.

**Figure 7.1. The natural stone wall is the
focal point of this pleasant solarium. The
practical, no-wax, quarry-tile-like floor,
sound-deadening ceiling, large-scaled
furniture, and cheerful fabrics create an
atmosphere of informal relaxation.
(Courtesy of Armstrong World Industries.)**

Floors and floor coverings

Hard-surface flooring

The decade of the sixties witnessed a
renaissance in hard-surface floor coverings, with the market abounding in both
old and new materials. Perhaps the most
notable characteristic of today's materials
is the merging of beauty and practicality.
Time-tested materials such as concrete,
terrazzo, quarry, and ceramic tiles have
taken on a glamorous quality due to new
and improved methods of production,
modern developments in the techniques
of surface enrichment, and better methods of installation. Larger-sized ceramic
tiles are in increasing demand. New
setting methods for all types of tile allow
installations over most surfaces. Quarry
tile and marble, as well as natural stone in
aggregate form, continue to supply demand for beauty, durability, and natural
colorations. Hard floor materials are no
longer confined to limited areas of the
house, but may go anywhere. Many are
so durable that they may flow from the
inside entrance hall or the family room

out onto the porch or patio, thus expanding space, creating unity, and
providing a practical surface that requires
little upkeep and adds beauty to any type
of home. A new emphasis is on wood,
and this versatile and timeless flooring is
once again in the fashion foreground.

In every area of hard floor covering,
great strides have been made in the
improvement of both practical and aesthetic aspects. Tables 7.1 and 7.2 list the
most commonly used floor coverings—
both nonresilient and resilient—their
characteristics and uses, and some suggestions for the treatment and care of
each.

NONRESILIENT AND RESILIENT FLOORING

Resilient flooring refers to the material's
ability to spring back when depressed.
Nonresilient flooring is devoid of flexibility. The initial cost of hard-surface
nonresilient flooring is generally high. In
long-range planning, however, this is
more than compensated for by its extreme durability, versatility, ease of maintenance, and timeless usage.

Figure 7.2 (*top left*). Flagstone flooring provides a versatile and durable floor with easy upkeep. (Photograph by Mark K. Allen, residence of Mr. and Mrs. Karl E. Young.)

Figure 7.3 (*above, left*). Highly worked bricks provide an adaptable transition in a foyer. (Photograph by Stanley F. Mac-Bean.)

Figure 7.4 (*top right*). Mexican tile in warm earth tones is the perfect flooring for this hacienda bathroom. (Courtesy of American Standard.)

Figure 7.5 (*right*). This handsome contemporary room is well planned, comfortable, and uncluttered. The deep pile shag against the unglazed quarry tile floor and the undraped windows offset by well-placed plants are a fitting background for classic contemporary furniture. (Courtesy of American Olean Tile Company.)

TABLE 7.1. *Hard-surface flooring: nonresilient*

MATERIAL	CHARACTERISTICS	USES	TREATMENT AND CARE
Flagstone	Any flat stone that varies in size, thickness, quality, and color Versatile, durable, handsome Easy upkeep Colors range from soft grays through beiges and reddish browns May be cut or laid in natural shapes Surface slightly uneven Absorbs solar energy	Walks, patios, foyers, greenhouses, any heavy traffic area May be dressed up or down, making it appropriate for wide range of uses	Careful waxing will soften rugged effect and produce soft patina Coating of vinyl will protect bricks from grease penetration Dust with dry mop, wash occasionally For stubborn stains, use trisodium phosphate
Slate (special kind of stone)	More formal than flagstone Qualities similar to flagstone, except for color, which runs from gray to black Absorbs solar energy	May be used in traffic areas in formal rooms Appropriate for some period rooms—particularly sun rooms and dining rooms—and for greenhouses	May be polished or unpolished, but more often waxed and highly polished
Mexican tile or terra-cotta	Crude base made of clay as it comes from earth Hand shaped and sun dried with smooth surface in limited range of colors Durable, informal, inexpensive Absorbs solar energy	Wherever a hard, cementlike surface is desired or wherever energy storage is desired	Care same as for terrazzo Surface seldom waxed
Concrete tile	May be solid or in squares, smooth or textured, polished or unpolished Color may be added before pouring or after Tile liner may be grouted to give a tile effect Absorbs and stores solar energy	Particularly desirable for some hard-wear areas and for support of heavy equipment Tile patterns appropriate for foyers, penthouses, and any area where energy storage is required	Heavy waxed surface necessary for maintenance Do not use lacquer, varnish, or shellac Special finishes available Wet before cleaning and use detergent Easy to maintain
Brick	Durable, little upkeep Comes in many textures, sizes, and colors Transmits moisture and cold readily and absorbs grease unless treated Absorbs and stores solar energy	Walks, patios, foyers, greenhouses, any room where a country look is desired	Treatment and care same as for flagstone
Exposed aggregate	Surface in which stones are laid in concrete and polished to smoothness, but surface remains uneven Absorbs and stores solar energy	Especially appropriate for walks and fireplace hearths	Dust, wash occasionally
Quarry tile	Type of ceramic tile formed and fixed as it comes from earth One of hardest and most durable May be glazed or unglazed Heat and frost resistant, easy upkeep, and durable Both ceramic and quarry tile practically impervious to grease and chemicals Absorbs and stores solar energy	Suitable for many period rooms, especially Italian, early English, and rooms with Mediterranean feeling Can be used wherever hard surface is appropriate, such as in greenhouses Coolness makes it desirable in hot climates	Unglazed: may be waxed to give soft sheen Glazed: dust with dry mop, wash when needed with soap and warm water

TABLE 7.1, CONTINUED

MATERIAL	CHARACTERISTICS	USES	TREATMENT AND CARE
Ceramic tile	Has unique aesthetic quality One of hardest and most durable floor and wall coverings Common type using small squares is called mosaic. May be glazed or unglazed, comes in many colors, patterns, and textures Glossy surface squares usually 4½ in. New developments producing handsome tiles 12-in. square with variety of designs, textures, and colors Pregrouted tile sheets up to 2 by 14 sq ft now available Absorbs and stores solar energy	Especially attractive for foyers, sun rooms, bathrooms, but may be suitable for any room, depending on color, texture, and period of room	Care same as quarry tile
Marble	Hardest of nonresilient flooring materials Now available in many varieties Marble gives feeling of elegance More expensive than most other flooring materials, but is permanent New stone-cutting techniques have made marble lighter and less expensive Tiles are reinforced by epoxy-fiberglass coating	Wherever elegant durability is needed Especially appropriate with classic styles of furnishing	Wash with soap and warm water
Travertine	Porous limestone characterized by irregular cavities that should be filled with either clear or opaque epoxy resin Clear resin has three-dimensional appearance	In formal settings where durability is required	Wash with soap or detergent and warm water
Terrazzo	Consists of cement mortar (matrix) to which marble chips (aggregate) are mixed Custom or precast; comes in large or small mable chips Larger chips give more formal appearance Available in limited range of colors Sanitary, durable, and easy to clean	Patios, foyers, halls, recreation rooms, bathrooms, or wherever traffic is heavy	Dust with dry mop, wash occasionally with detergent Some varieties need occasional waxing
Glass tile	Modules 1⅝ in. by ³⁄₁₆ in. of impervious and homogenous glass Stable, inert, and nonporous with nonslip surface Unaffected by fire, heat, or frost Available in white and some earth tones May be custom colored Easy maintenance	Suitable for dark areas Adaptable for walls or floors	Clean with detergent and warm water
Glass block or vista-brick	Solid glass blocks 8 in. by 8 in. by 3 in. offer excellent light transmission, good visibility, and provide high-impact strength	Used as pavers, covers for light fixtures recessed in floor	Clean with detergent and warm water
Poured seamless vinyl	Plastic from a can Has glossy surface Nonslippery Easy to maintain	Kitchens, bathrooms, family rooms	Does not require waxing Clean with soap and warm water Avoid heavy detergents

Figure 7.6. Extremely durable, ceramic tile is no longer confined to kitchen and bathrooms but is at home in any room of the house. (Courtesy of Villeroy and Boch.)

Figure 7.7. Elegant Moorish-inspired design ceramics flow from the interior of the house to the spacious courtyard. The subtle tile colors in ebony, sapphire, and gray incorporate the house into the surrounding countryside. (Courtesy of American Olean Tile Company.)

Figure 7.8. This handsome ceramic tile kitchen offers durability and easy maintenance. Textured counter tops provide a working surface that resists scorching and blistering from hot pans. Textured hearth tile floor complements wall and cabinet tile, and is easily cleaned. (Courtesy of American Olean Tile Company.)

Figure 7.9. Ornamental tile adds interest to the plain ceramic tile walls in this uncluttered bathroom. (Courtesy of American Olean Tile Company.)

Figure 7.10 (*above*). The soft shadings, tonal qualities, and precise definition of this inlaid vinyl flooring results in versatility, beauty, and practicality. (Design by La Mesa, courtesy of Congoleum Ultraflor Imperial sheet vinyl flooring.)

Figure 7.11 (*right*). Inlaid sheet vinyl simulating crafted brick supplies warmth, durability, and easy maintenance. (Courtesy of Armstrong World Industries.)

TABLE 7.2. *Hard-surface flooring: resilient*

MATERIAL	CHARACTERISTICS	USES	TREATMENT AND CARE
Asphalt tile	Low in cost, durable Due to advanced technology, is being phased out	Wherever hard-surface, low-cost flooring is required	Coat of water-emulsion wax will improve surface Use mild soap for cleaning
Linoleum	After more than 100 yr of production, no longer produced Vinyl floors dominate market		
Cork tile	Provides maximum quiet and cushiony comfort underfoot Cork with vinyl or urethane surface highly resistant to wet and stains, but natural cork not suited for abuse of kitchen traffic, water damage, etc. Colors light to dark brown Dented by furniture	Especially appropriate for studies and other rooms with little traffic	Maintenance not easy Dirt hard to dislodge from porous surface Wash with soap and water, coat with wax Vinyl coating will protect surface

TABLE 7.2, CONTINUED

MATERIAL	CHARACTERISTICS	USES	TREATMENT AND CARE
Leather tile	Resilient, quiet, but expensive Natural or dyed colors	Studies and other limited areas with little traffic	Warm water and mild soap
Vinyl asbestos Vinyl composition or **Reinforced vinyl**	Excellent all-around low-cost flooring Available in tile or sheets Resists stains and wears well Hard and noisy Tiles may have self-adhesive backing Popularity has declined	May be used in any room	Exceptionally easy to maintain
Vinyl cork	Has appearance of cork, but resists stain and easy to maintain Colors richer than natural cork	Wherever effect of real cork is desired	Wash with soap and water; wax
Vinyl tile	Tough, nonporous, resistant to stains, durable Comes in clear colors or special effects, including translucent and three-dimensional effects The more vinyl content, the higher the price Comes in great variety of patterns and colors	Extremely versatile, may be used in any room	Easy care Some varieties have built-in luster and require no waxing
Cushion-backed vinyl	Vinyl chips embedded in translucent vinyl base Has pebbly surface Shows no seams Goes on any floor Has cushion backing, making it resilient	Wherever desired	Easy care, same as for other vinyl
Sheet vinyl	Lies flat with adhesive only on sides Excellent do-it-yourself product	Wherever vinyl flooring is desired	Same as for other vinyl
Rubber tile	Tiles available 9 in. by 12 in., thickness ½ in. and ³⁄₁₆ in. Usually marble or travertine pattern laid at right angles to each other Sound absorbing, durable, nonskidding	Kitchens, bathrooms, utility rooms	Wash with soap and water Avoid varnish or shellac
Sheet rubber	Available in 36-by-¾-in. untrimmed widths Plain or marbleized Durable, nonskidding	Hard traffic areas Safe covering for stair treads	Same as for rubber tile
Vinylized fabric	Has appearance of vinyl Fabric bonded between layers of vinyl	Wherever specific pattern is desired	Same as for vinyl
Stainless steel or brass	Comes in sheets High-gloss or satin finish	Wherever effect is desired Usually custom contrasts	Soap and water

The development of vinyl for floor use is in large measure responsible for the new interest in hard floor coverings. The effects that can and are being produced in vinyl are limitless. Vinyl can be clear or vividly colored, translucent or opaque, textured or satin smooth. It comes in tiles, 6- and 12-ft sheets, or in a can. Vinyl can be informal or formal. Resilient hard-surface floors were once used only for kitchens, utility rooms, and bathrooms, but their present-day elegance has admitted them into any room of the house. Small patterns mask tracking and spillage, pebble vinyls achieve a natural stone effect, and embossed patterns are reminiscent of Old World designs such as moorish tile. Vinyls may simulate, among other patterns, handsome grained wood, cork, delft tile, travertine, and marble. An all-purpose vinyl in sheet or tile requires no adhesive. A conductive tile is made especially for hospitals and chemical and electronic laboratories as a safety against the hazard of static electricity. A foam cushion backing makes it possible to have a practical vinyl surface with the luxurious feel of carpet.

WOOD FLOORING

Wood is the most versatile and widely used of all flooring materials. It combines beauty, warmth, resilience, resistance to indentation, durability, availability, and ease of installation. The quiet harmony and beauty of wood floors provide a background for any style of furnishings, and wood floors are always in good taste. A standard flooring for centuries, wood waned in popularity during recent decades, but today symbolizes high fashion and is the choice of many interior designers and home owners. New methods of treatment have made wood a practical flooring for any and all areas of the house.

METHODS OF LAYING WOOD FLOORS

The three basic methods of laying wood floors are: *strips, planks,* and **parquetry.** In the first method, strips of wood, usually about 2½ in. wide with **tongue and groove,** are nailed in place. This method is the most common, and in contemporary homes the wood is usually finished on the site. For many traditional homes, the wood is stained and finished at the factory. In the plank method, the planks may be uniform or **random,** varying in width from 3 in. to 7 in. Some have square edges; others are tongue and groove. The parquetry method makes use of short lengths of boards, arranging them in various designs such as checkerboard, herringbone, and others. For ease of installation and economy, 9- to 12-in. squares are assembled at the factory.

WOOD VENEER

Sometimes a thin layer of hardwood is veneered to a less expensive wood, such as prefabricated parquet squares that are veneered and finished at the factory. These veneers are less expensive than solid wood, but will not hold up as well under heavy wear. Sometimes thin layers of wood are laminated to backing that makes it durable and more resilient. Hardwood veneer is placed under a surface of vinyl sheeting that protects it from moisture, wear, and household chemicals. The veneer is backed with aluminum, vinyl, and asbestos to assure a permanent, moisture-free bond to almost any subfloor. This veneer is available in almost any wood. It should be maintained the same as vinyl.

PATTERNS OF HARD FLOORS

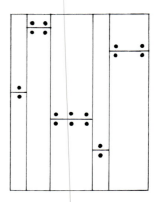

Random plank

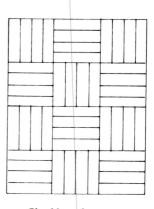

Checkboard parquet

Herringbone parquet

Figure 7.12. Random plank floor provides a warm atmosphere. Plugs give a feeling of authenticity. (Courtesy of Bruce Floor Company.)

Figure 7.13. A parquet wood floor adds distinction to this room. (Courtesy of Bruce Floor Company.)

PLASTIC (ACRYLIC) IMPREGNATED WOOD FLOORS

Acrylic-wood flooring is a relatively new development in which real wood is impregnated with a liquid plastic that is hardened throughout the pore structure by irradiation. The result is a floor with the warmth of wood and remarkable durability, tough enough to withstand the heaviest foot traffic. It is available in 12-in. square prefinished parquet tiles, 5/16-in.-thick, and comes in a variety of tones. Installation cost is comparable to other high-quality materials like terrazzo. Acrylic-wood flooring is an answer to the increasing demand for flooring with a natural, mellow look that is durable and requires little maintenance. Because of its physical characteristics, acrylic-wood flooring is finding increased acceptance among interior designers as an alternative to natural, untreated wood and other hard-surface flooring materials, particularly in high-traffic areas.

PARTICLE BOARD

Particle board is flooring made of pressed sawdust and small wood chips, and is usually used for subflooring, since it has little strength. When finished with **polyurethane,** however, particle board can serve as a temporary or an informal floor.

STAINED WOOD FLOORS

Wood is exhibiting a bright, new look in some of today's floors. Flooring need not be only in familiar tones of natural wood, but it may also be as varied in color as fabric. Colored stain may be applied in basically the same way as natural finish, and the natural grain of the wood is not impaired. Some color tones emphasize the pattern in the wood and may even produce a three-dimensional effect. This effect can be achieved by a *stain-and-sealer* method, in which only the surface is stained, then sealed with polyurethane, or the *stain-wax* method, in which the stain penetrates into the wood, leaving a wax residue on the surface. When the latter process is repeated and the wood thoroughly rubbed, the surface has a soft, protective **patina.** Preparation, application, and maintenance of wood with color stain is the same as for natural stain.

STENCILED WOOD FLOORS

Used by our early forebears as a substitute for expensive carpets, stenciled floors are available today. They come in designs from borders to allover patterns, and are protected by a sturdy layer of polyurethane.

Soft floor coverings

MACHINE-MADE CARPETS

With the great emphasis being placed on carpeting today, one could assume that until recent years, floors had been neglected. History, however, reveals that this is not so. As early as 3000 B.C., carpets were used in Egypt, as evidenced by the pictorial paintings in the great tombs. Writers of the Bible and the poets of early Greece and Rome mention carpets, although walking on such floor coverings was the prerogative of royalty. Colorful oriental rugs have been produced in Persia, China, Turkey, and other Asiatic countries for centuries, where they were the principal item of home furnishing. Early in the eleventh century, when the Crusaders came into contact

with the elegance and luxury of Constantinople, Antioch, and other Eastern cities, they carried back many of these fine rugs, creating a great demand in the West, on which the Eastern trading companies capitalized from the fifteenth to the nineteenth centuries. These fine floor coverings soon became a symbol of status in Europe and America.

Since the thirteenth century when the first rug looms were established in Aubusson, France, weaving of fine floor coverings has been an industry that has grown continuously and has now reached boom proportions, with still greater volume predicted for the future. New manufacturing techniques and improvements in fiber chemistry have produced a new generation of carpets that look better, are more durable, are easier to maintain, and cost less than ever before.

A number of factors have been responsible for this unprecedented boom: (1) the magnitude of the interest and research that the carpet industry attracted during the 1960s, (2) new and improved fibers, which have given people carpeting with the properties they have demanded at reasonable cost, (3) the numerous uses found for carpets in modern living that were not dreamed of a decade ago (such uses as application on walls and ceilings for color, texture, and insulation against noise, covering for furniture in place of traditional upholstery, and even lining for swimming pools), (4) modern Americans view carpeting as no longer a luxury but a necessity (it has been made standard equipment in most buildings and is often written into the contract), and (5) carpeting is one of the few products that offers more value per dollar now than it did 20 years ago.

With the wide variety of floor fashions at their disposal, little wonder that consumers often become confused in making a selection. Since floor covering is often the biggest single investment in a room, it should provide satisfaction for many years; and because it takes more rough wear than all other furnishings in the home, it ought to be chosen wisely.

DECORATIVE AND FUNCTIONAL VALUES

A carpet can be the basis for the room's entire decor. It can bring furnishings into harmony, create personality and a feeling of luxury, and alter the apparent size and proportion of a room. The same carpet carried throughout the living areas of the house will serve as a transition from room to room and will give a feeling of unity. An art rug may serve as the room's focal point.

A carpet insulates the floor against drafts, muffles noise, gives a feeling of comfort, and provides safety. The National Safety Council warns against accidents caused by slippery floors, and a well-anchored carpet gives sure footing and helps prevent home accidents. Carpets are easy to maintain with a good vacuum.

Before selecting a carpet, the consumer should become knowledgeable about what constitutes quality in carpeting, what he or she can expect from various fibers, and what carpet construction has to do with floor covering.

QUALITY

Quality in carpeting is dependent on four ingredients: (1) the type and grade of fiber, (2) the depth of pile, (3) the density of pile, and (4) the construction.

Fibers Over the years, virtually every fiber has been used in carpets. Today, however, 90 percent of all carpeting sold in the United States is composed of synthetic fibers. By the early 1970s, the field was narrowed down to five principal fibers: nylon, acrylic, polyester, olefin, and wool. Each of these fibers has an outstanding quality that accounts for its success, but all have other supporting qualities. Fibers are often blended to bring out the best characteristics of each. To affect quality, at least 20 percent of one fiber must be present. The label will give the percentage by weight of the fibers.

Nylon is the single most important fiber regarding quantity, accounting for about 80 percent of the carpet sold today. Nylon has excellent abrasion resistance, resists crushing and matting, and reduces static electricity, **pilling,** and fuzzing. It repels soil and cleans well, particularly in spot cleaning for stains. It is non-allergenic and is mold-, mildew-, and mothproof. Improvements in methods of construction, and adaptations to fashion trends, have contributed to its use in prestigious areas. In some styles, it leads the field. When combined with polyester, the two complementary fibers' specific strengths offset their respective weaknesses. Antron Plus and Anso IV are new fourth-generation nylon fibers that have excellent performance features and exceptional soil and stain resistance.

Acrylic is much like wool in appearance. Its outstanding characteristic is solution dyeability. Resistance to abrasion and soiling is good. It cleans exceptionally well and has good crush resistance, but is susceptible to some pilling.

Polyester is an exceptionally soft fiber that offers good abrasion resistance. It combines the look and feel of wool with a durability approaching that of nylon. Stain and soil resistance are good, and it is easily cleaned. Although polyester has great bulk and bounce, some criticize its crushing and pilling. Growth in polyester use since its beginning in 1966 has been phenomenal. It is now in a number two position.

Olefin is another fiber of the 1960s. Polypropylene is a specific type of olefin and is the best known. It is predominant in needle-punch carpets, which are especially popular for kitchen and indoor-outdoor carpets. Ease of care and its nonabsorbent nature are outstanding characteristics. Most stains lie on the surface, making it the easiest fiber to

clean. Wearing qualities are comparable to nylon, and it is completely colorfast. At present, color and design potentials are limited. Colors sometimes have a dusty look. Resilience can be controlled by construction. Polyethylene is also a specific olefin.

Wool is the luxury fiber and has long been regarded as the top carpet fiber, possessing all of the most desirable characteristics. Other fibers express their aesthetic qualities in relation to how nearly they resemble wool. Great resilience accounts for the vital quality of wool in retaining its appearance. Wool has warmth, a dull matte look, durability, and soil resistance. It takes colors beautifully, cleans well, and when cared for, keeps its new look for years. Although having all but priced itself out of the market, wool unquestionably continues its prestigious position in the carpet field. Since the mid-1970s, the use of wool has increased, and some estimates indicate that by the mid-1980s, wool will have 13 percent of the market.

Source is not considered one of the big five fibers, but is the newest of the man-made fibers used for carpets. A combination of polyester and polyamide in a one-fiber filament, Source is a product with the strength of nylon and the aesthetic qualities of polyester, and promises to assume greater importance in the decades ahead.

Cotton is being woven into carpet that is latex backed and soil resistant.

Each company that produces these fibers has developed variants that add to the fibers' practical and aesthetic qualities, such as better soil resistance, less static, more dyeing possibilities, more bulk, and more luster. Since each manufacturer has a need to use a special name to designate its product in the carpet industry, more trade names are on the market than the consumer can remember. The generic name will therefore be the key to fiber content.

Depth of pile   Pile depth will affect carpet wear. Because deeper pile requires more yarn, it will be more durable.

Density of pile   The more dense the surface, the better the carpet will wear. Density—the number of threads per square inch—can be examined by bending back a piece of carpet. If wide spaces are between the threads, or if wide gaps are between rows and large amounts of backing show, the carpet, in all probability, will not wear well.

Construction   Because of the many new technical developments, the old and well-known weaves no longer account for the bulk of present-day carpets. Most carpets on the market today are tufted, with woven, needle-punched, knitted, and flocked accounting for the remainder.

▫ *Tufting* accounts for approximately 90 percent of all carpet construction today. The principle is based on the sewing machine, in which thousands of threaded needles are inserted into a backing material. Heavy latex coating is applied to the backing to anchor the tufts permanently. Some have a double backing for greater strength.

Although tufted carpets are generally made in solid colors, new advances in dyeing technology make it possible to produce multicolor effects. Pattern attachments produce textural effects.

▫ As recently as 1951, *woven carpets* accounted for 90 percent of all broadloom produced. This amount was cut to less than 10 percent during the early seventies. The three types of woven carpets are Axminster, Wilton, and velvet.

The *Wilton* carpet takes its name from the town in England where it was first made in 1740. It is woven on a loom with a special Jacquard attachment by which the yarns are carried along the

THREE LEADING CARPETS

Axminster carpet. The top diagram shows different colored yarns. The bottom diagram shows use of curled-down yarns for multilevel effect in face of carpet. (Courtesy of James Lees and Sons Company.)

Wilton carpet (loop pile). Pile is woven over strips of metal, which are removed during weaving process.

Velvet carpet (cut pile). Backing of jute and cotton holds pile yarn in place.

background of the carpet until they are drawn to the surface to form loops. This process adds strength, body, and great resilience, and produces a carpet with great design flexibility and a rich, soft texture with multilevel loop piles that may be cut or uncut. After more than 200 years, the Wilton carpet is still regarded as a standard of high quality.

The *Axminster* carpet also derives its name from the town in England where it was first manufactured in 1755. Originally a hand-knotted carpet, it is now made on a specialized American loom in which yarns are set in a crosswise row permitting each tuft to be controlled individually. This process makes possible an almost unlimited combination of colors and patterns. Quality is determined by the closeness of the weave and depth of the pile. The Axminster carpet can be identified by the stiff crosswise backing yarns.

Velvet, the simplest form of carpet weaving, is traditionally a smooth-surface pile, cut or uncut, in a solid color. It is available today in a wide range of textural effects. The pile loops of velvet carpet are woven over long wires that extend the full length of the carpet.

☐ Until recently, needle-punch construction has been used almost entirely for indoor-outdoor carpet. In this process, an assembly of corded fiber webs is compacted and held together by felting needles that mechanically interlock the fibers. The back is coated with latex or other weather-resistant materials. A wide variety of textures is possible by this method, and the carpet sells at a low cost.

☐ The *knitted* method is much like hand knitting, in which single-pile yarn is interlooped with backing yarn using three sets of needles. The backing is then coated with a weather-resistant material. These carpets are usually solid colors or tweed. Only a small percentage of today's carpets are produced by this method.

☐ *Flocked* carpets have a cut pile with the appearance of velour. They may be produced by three basic methods: by beater bars, by spraying, and by an electrostatic method—the latter method accounting for most of the flocked carpets. In the electrostatic process, chopped fibers, introduced into an electrostatic field, become charged and are then projected toward a backing fabric coated with adhesive, where they become vertically embedded. This type of carpet has future possibilities for walls.

The performance of a carpet is also dependent on the degree of twist and the heat setting of the fiber. A tight twist helps the fiber spring back under crushing foot traffic, and proper heat setting prevents unraveling.

The unseen part of a carpet—the backing—is important. A good foundation prevents stretching, buckling, and shrinking. The backing yarns should be firmly woven. Jute, the most widely used fiber, is strong but may mildew and is therefore not suitable for use where floors may be damp, such as in some basements or outdoors. Polypropylene resists mildew, is also strong, and may give better service where dampness is a problem. Tufted carpets should have a secondary backing applied for extra strength. It may be jute, polypropylene, rubber, or vinyl. All but jute and high-density rubber are placed on carpet for outdoor use.

STYLE CHARACTERISTICS

Before selecting a carpet, the surface texture should be considered. Definite style characteristics may be chosen. The area to be carpeted should first be studied. Then, from the numerous styles available, the one that is most appropriate for individual needs should be chosen. The following are the surface characteristics produced in most fibers:

Level loop pile has looped tufts that are all the same height. This carpet is generally made from nylon or olefin fibers. It often has a rubber backing and is usually moderate to low in cost.

CARPET CHARACTERISTICS

Level loop   Cut or plush

Level tip shear   Multilevel loop

Random shear   Sculptured

Cut or plush pile has upright loops that are cut to form an even surface. When lightly twisted yarns have great density, the carpet is a luxurious one. The plush elegance is enhanced by highlights and shadings that give an extra dimension. These carpets are appropriate for more formal rooms.

Level tip shear has both cut and uncut pile. The even surface does not hide footprints as well as loop pile does.

Multilevel loop surfaces have loops at several different heights. This carpet is practical, hides footprints, and masks spots and soiling. Tweeds, the easy-to-live-with carpets, are of this type. Tweed carpets are looped with a decided texture, often a high-low pile of multicolored yarns. They are most appropriate for informal rooms.

Random shear is similar to multilevel loop, except the highest loops are sheared, providing a more formal appearance.

Embossed carpets are woven with high and low pile. The pile may be all loop, all cut, or a combination of both. This carpet is one of the most popular. It comes in all fibers and colors, is extremely versatile, and has a wide price range.

Sculptured carpet is one in which part of the surface has been cut away to form a pattern, or the pattern itself has been cut away from the background. This carpet is often custom-made, tends to be formal, and is expensive.

Twist or *frieze* texture has a twisted yarn that gives a rough, nubby appearance. Twists are available in light and hard twists. Hard twists lie flat, will keep a fresh appearance, and are less likely to show signs of wear.

Splush is a term used to describe carpets with the characteristics of both shag and plush.

Shags, which were popular for more than two decades, are now all but obsolete. They have pile yarns that vary from one to four inches in length and may be looped or cut.

Saxony is a combination of plush and short shag, twisted and heat set under high temperature and pressure, which produces a deep, rich surface.

Flat-woven fiber rugs are machine-made of coarse flax fiber, paper pulp or "kraft" fiber, sisal, hemp, and various other grasses and rushes. They come in 1-ft squares to be sewn together, or in full-sized rugs. Fiber rugs are usually in natural colors, but they are sometimes dyed. Popular in warm climates, they also provide inexpensive year-round floor covering and are appropriate in many contemporary settings.

Patterned carpets of all kinds are on the market today and are gaining in popularity. A printing process that is basically a screen-printing technique has contributed to the interest in patterned floors. Printed designs, at first simple geometrics, are now numerous and highly refined for any type of decor. Patterned carpets are also being produced by standard methods—particularly Axminster—and are becoming a fashion item in residential as well as in commercial interiors.

CARPETS FOR SPECIFIC NEEDS

Fortified with information about quality and style characteristics of carpets, the consumer should make an evaluation of his or her special needs. What is the size of the room to be carpeted? How will the room be used? What style of furnishings does it have? How much natural light enters the room and from which direction? What are the consumer's color preferences?

The following are some suggestions that may be helpful in answering the preceding questions.

☐ Room size is important. Where space is limited, wall-to-wall carpets in solid colors or overall texture will give a feeling of spaciousness. Pattern tends to fill up space and is usually better reserved for larger areas.

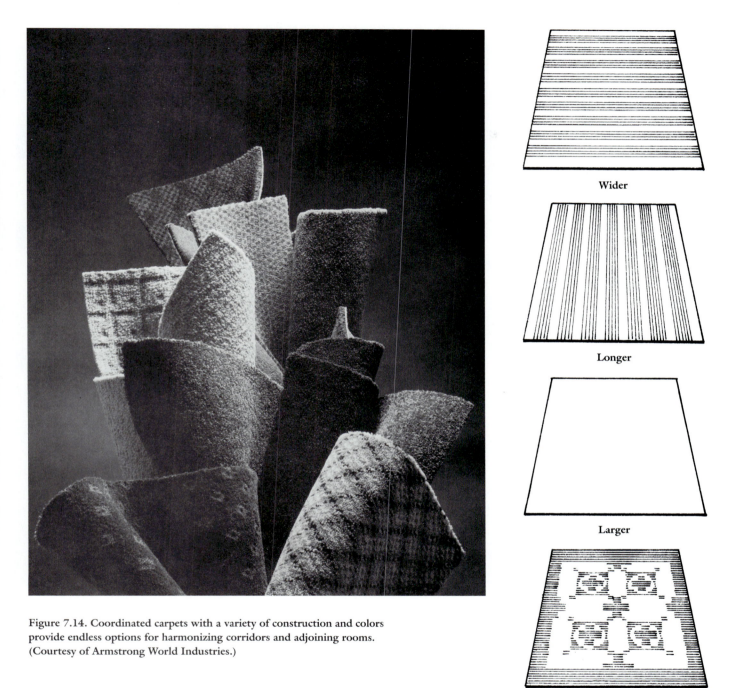

Figure 7.14. Coordinated carpets with a variety of construction and colors provide endless options for harmonizing corridors and adjoining rooms. (Courtesy of Armstrong World Industries.)

Wider

Longer

Larger

Smaller

Carpet can change the apparent size and proportion of a room.

□ For heavy traffic areas such as family rooms, stairways, and passageways, the choice should be a good-quality carpet that wears well, is crush resistant, and resists soil. Tweeds in tight loop pile are an excellent choice.

□ Furniture style matters. The carpet should express the character of the furniture, whether it is traditional or modern, formal or casual. If it is carefully chosen, carpet can coordinate all furnishings of the room.

□ The lighting situation should be considered. A sunny room may call for a carpet in a cool color or a deep shade. For a northern exposure or a dark room, one of the warm colors in a lighter tone may be a better choice.

□ Color is of vital importance, since the floor is the largest usable area of the room, is the least-often changed, and is the background for all other furnishings. Personal choice should be the determining factor, but much thought and experimenting with samples will make the decision a wiser one. A neutral-colored carpet will show footprints and dirt less than a dark color will.

A neutral-colored carpet will show footprints and dirt less than a dark color will.

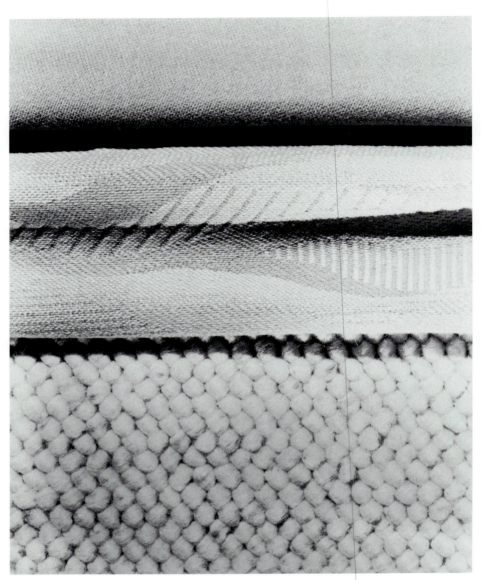

Figure 7.15. The felted and uniquely textured carpet in natural shades flecked with color and blended with stretch wool, and the wool upholstery in fluid gem tones and classic designs, are equally appropriate for home or office. (Courtesy of the Wool Bureau.)

□ If the carpet chosen has a definite pattern, then walls, drapery, and upholstery should be in plain colors or with unobtrusive designs. Carpets with a plain overall effect will permit a wider choice of furnishings.

RUG AND CARPET SIZES

Size is another consideration in selecting a carpet or rug. For convenience, the terms *rug* and *carpet* are often used interchangeably, although technically they are not the same. A carpet is a floor covering made in strips, intended to cover an entire floor, and often attached to the floor. Carpet is woven in widths from 27 in. to 18 ft., wide widths being known as broadloom. Strips can be seamed or taped together, and can thus cover great areas. A piece of carpet can be used as a rug. A rug is a floor covering made in one piece, often with its own delineating border, and usually not intended to cover the entire floor.

Wall-to-wall carpeting has some distinct advantages: it creates continuity within a room or from room to room, makes rooms look larger, adds warmth and a feeling of luxury, requires only one cleaning process, and provides maximum safety from accidents. This carpeting also has some disadvantages: it must be cleaned on the floor, it cannot be turned for even wear, and only part can be salvaged if moved.

A *room-sized rug* is one that comes within a few inches or even a foot or so of the walls, leaving a marginal strip of floor exposed. Standard-sized rugs will fit most rooms, the 9-by-12-ft. rug probably being the most common. The room-sized rug has most of the advantages that wall-to-wall carpeting has, plus some extra benefits. It can be turned for even distribution of wear and removed for cleaning. Two processes, however, are necessary for complete cleaning—one for the rug and the other for the exposed wood around it.

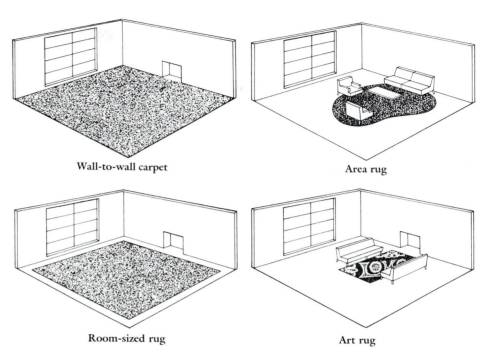

Wall-to-wall carpet

Area rug

Room-sized rug

Art rug

An *area rug* does not cover the entire floor but is used to define an area of a room according to its function. The rug should, however, be large enough to accommodate all of the furniture used in the area grouping. The size is comparative, depending on that of the room in which it is used. In a large room, a 9-by-12-ft. rug might be considered an area rug. This type of rug is versatile and may easily be changed for different grouping arrangements or moved to a different room of the house.

An *art rug*, which is usually smaller than an area rug, is generally handcrafted and used as an accent, or treated as a focal point. This rug is often placed so that furniture does not encroach on it, enabling it to be admired like a picture on the floor. Usually patterned, it may be modern or traditional, such as a fine oriental, an eighteenth-century needlepoint, or one of the new dhurrie rugs so popular in contemporary interiors.

Carpet squares are available in 12- or 18-in. squares that may be laid loose and are totally interchangeable. This type of carpeting has great potential for young Americans.

CARPET UNDERLAY

Every carpet deserves a good underlay; it gives tremendous value for the money spent. Furthermore, cushioning improves and helps to maintain the appearance of the carpet, enhances the resiliency, which assists in preventing pile matting, and prolongs the life of the carpet by as much

Carpet is available in 12-in squares.

Figure 7.16 (*facing page*). Rich wall-to-wall Saxony plush carpet covers the bed frame, creating a look of high fashion in this attic room. (Courtesy of Burlington Industries.)

Figure 7.17 (*left*). Carpet squares, a do-it-yourself item for hard-use areas. (Courtesy of Armstrong World Industries.)

as 75 percent. It absorbs noise and creates a feeling of luxury. Even low- or moderately priced carpet, when laid over a good pad, will take on the feeling of cushioned elegance.

On the market today are five basic types of carpet underlays:

□ Solid foam underlays are made of prime urethane. They are firm, resilient, and durable, and are not affected by heat or moisture. Their cost is higher than bonded foam.

□ Bonded foam underlays are made of reconstituted urethane and are usually 9/16-in. thick. They are not affected by heat or cold, go on almost any surface, hold up well, and are moderately priced. This type of padding accounts for the highest percentage of underlay sold today.

□ Waffle sponge is made of a natural or synthetic rubber with a variety of fabric backing. This type of pad may deteriorate in the presence of heat or moisture.

□ Flat sponge rubber is made of natural or synthetic rubber with a variety of finishes and fabric backing. This type is used less than foam.

□ Fiber cushion underlays are made of jute, animal hair, rubber-coated jute, or combinations of plain or rubber-coated jute with animal hair. This type of pad is firm and extremely durable, but the high cost limits its volume of sale.

□ Carpet with attached cushioning accounts for about 20 percent of all carpet sold today. This type of carpet is increasing in popularity and promises to be the answer for many Americans on the move, since it can easily be picked up and relaid.

From this array of carpet cushioning, the choice should be based on individual needs that take into consideration the condition of the floor, the amount of traffic, the functions of the area to be covered, and the carpet being used.

When all the necessary information is at hand, and the consumer is ready to make a carpet purchase, he or she should follow these recommendations:

Package deals with costs of carpet, installation, and padding lumped together should be avoided. The price per square yard, as well as the charges for installation and padding, should be determined. Door-to-door or telephone salespeople should not be relied on.

The carpet dealer should be reputable. The buyer should always take a sample of the carpet home, observe it in the light at different times of the day and under artificial light, walk on it, and be sure it is what he or she wants.

Figure 7.18. Sculptured Saxony carpet of Antron III nylon has exceptional luxury, durability, and easy care. (Courtesy of Armstrong World Industries.)

The brand should be dependable. A label on the carpet should give the name of an established manufacturer, which is an assurance of obtaining good value in the price range selected. A label bearing the generic name is an assurance of the fiber content.

The best quality the budget will allow should be chosen. The owner can always be proud of good-quality carpet, and it will add beauty, luxury, and a world of comfort to the home.

CARPET CARE

Soil-hiding fibers and special protective treatments help, but proper care is the surest way of keeping a carpet bright and

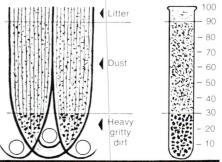

The test tube shows proportion of dirt by weight in an average carpet. (Courtesy of Hoover Company.)

beautiful. Regular vacuuming is essential. Heavy traffic areas need light vacuuming each day to maintain brightness and texture and to remove surface soil and dirt. Thorough vacuuming once a week is desirable for most areas. Spills should be removed immediately to prevent permanent damage. Carpet retailers can provide consumer brochures containing detailed information on carpet care.

HANDMADE RUGS

ORIENTAL RUGS

The making of oriental rugs is a great art. Appreciated by discriminating people the world over, oriental rugs have been coveted possessions for hundreds of years, and proud owners have found that the joy of living with them increases with the years. During the eighteenth and nineteenth centuries, rugs from China and the Near East were in great demand by well-to-do Americans to adorn their great Georgian and Federal period mansions. Not until late in the nineteenth century, however, were they imported in great numbers.

With the advent of wall-to-wall carpeting, oriental rugs went out of fashion in America. After having languished in warehouses and attics for a number of decades, they have been rediscovered and once again have taken their place as high-fashion floor coverings. With the return to elegance, many selective home owners are finding these handsome and versatile carpets desirable for contemporary homes, regardless of style. To meet the current demand, American manufacturers are duplicating authentic oriental designs in loom-woven rugs that retail at a fraction of the handmade ones. These rugs are called "oriental design rugs" to distinguish them from the hand-loomed rugs that are made in the Orient and are called "oriental rugs."

The great majority of oriental rugs imported into America have come from

Persia (Iran) and Turkey. Rugs brought from the Orient to America prior to 1905 were made for local consumption, not for export trade. They were of varying proportions and sizes, and some extremely large ones were made for the floors of palaces and homes of the wealthy. In the homes of the peasants, who made up the majority of the population, rugs comprised the principal item of furnishing. They were used for bed coverings, wall hangings, room dividers, and storage bags. When used on floors, they did not have hard use, since people removed their shoes before entering their dwellings.

These rugs are made by hand-tying a knot in each weft thread as it crosses the warp. The knot is either the Ghiordes or Turkish, or the Sehna or Persian type, depending on the area in which it is made. Rugs are frequently made by members of a family, who use the same pattern generation after generation. The name of the particular rug is usually that of the family or is taken from the name of the village or the area in which it was made.

The beauty of an oriental rug depends on the quality of the wool fiber (a few are made of silk), the fineness of the weave, the intricacy of the design, and the mellowness of the color. Traditional design motifs range from simple geometrics, made by nomadic tribes, to the most intricate of patterns, which combine flowers, trees, birds, and animals, and which sometimes have become so stylized through the years that the original source is uncertain. The mellow patina and soft coloring of the early imports, so highly prized by Americans, was a result of years of constant use, often exposure to light, sun, and sometimes sand and rain.

By the early part of the twentieth century, the supply of valuable old rugs was becoming scarce. New ones were being produced, but since Americans preferred the soft colors of the old ones to the vivid tones of fresh vegetable dyes, a way had to be found to produce the "old" look. To accomplish this, plants

PRINCIPAL KNOTS USED IN MAKING ORIENTAL RUGS

Ghiordes or Turkish knot, used in Turkey and throughout Asia Minor

Sehna or Persian knot, used in many parts of Iran

were set up around New York City for chemically bleaching new rugs after they arrived in this country. Rugs were bleached, were retouched by a special painting process, and finally were run through bat rollers that gave them a high glossy finish. This process necessarily damaged the rug and lessened the wearing quality. Fortunately, the high cost of the procedure soon made it prohibitive. Since about 1955, most oriental rugs are given only a light lime wash, either before they leave the country in which they are made or after they arrive in this country. This wash produces a mellow look and does little harm to the rug.

Oriental rugs are classified according to *antique,* semiantique, and modern. A rug 50 years old is usually considered an antique, and rugs made before 1830 are admitted into America duty free. Semiantiques are rugs slightly newer but with a natural patina acquired through gentle use. Modern orientals, which may employ traditional or new designs, are those made in the Orient during the past decade. Age alone, however, does not make a rug valuable. Certain rugs were coarse and poorly made, and were not valuable at any time, but good ones will always be valuable.

An oriental rug is probably the most versatile of all floor coverings. It is at home in a seventeenth-century saltbox, a modern twentieth-century house, and anything in between. One of the satisfactions of using an oriental rug in a design scheme is knowing that the choice is a worldwide symbol of good taste. These rugs are unique among home furnishings in that they may disappear from favor for a time, but they keep coming back. Their rich patterns and lustrous colors have a look of luxury that few other furnishings possess. Their beauty is enhanced through use and time, and their value is increased with the years.

Oriental rugs from the Near East   The three types of Near East oriental rugs particularly pleasing to American taste are the Kirman, the Sarouk, and the Tekke, commonly called Bokhara. Many other rugs of fine quality, however, are made in the Near East and are exported to Western countries. But with the invasion of modern technology, and the economic, political, and religious unrest throughout the Middle Eastern countries, the production of handmade rugs is seriously threatened.

A top-grade *Kirman* is among the most costly of oriental rugs. The most familiar type is one with a central medallion surrounded by a plain ground with a wide border of intricate design. Sometimes the entire ground is filled with delicate blooms. This rug is one of the few orientals with an ivory ground.

The predominant colors in the *Sarouk* are exotic jewel tones of red, rose, and deep blue, with black and ivory as accent colors. Although the pattern is predominantly floral, it does feature some geometric devices. The Sarouk may also have a vibrant medallion outlined in dark colors. The pile is usually heavy.

The *Bokhara* (Tekke) rug, originally from Turkistan, is made in many Middle Eastern countries. The background of the Bokhara may be red, cream, or blue, but the predominant color is always red. The easily recognizable design is made up of octagons or polygons called "guls" (roses), which are repeated uniformly about the field. When the guls are quartered by narrow lines running the length and width of the field, the design is popularly called "Royal Bokhara."

The following are some other well-known rugs from Iran:

The *Siraz* usually has a geometric pattern on red and blue. Both warp and weft are wool. An unusual feature is the varicolored fringe. In the *Saraband,* the

Figure 7.19 (*top*). The most familiar of the Kirman designs: an open ground, a wide, uneven border, and a medallion center. (Courtesy of Karastan Rug Mills.)

Figure 7.20 (*bottom*). This Sarouk rug is made in Iran. The allover floral with rose or red ground is typical. (Courtesy of Chas. W. Jacobsen.)

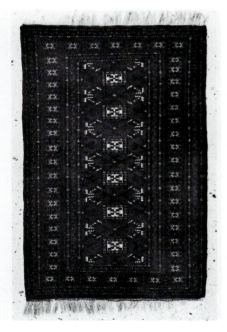

field is usually red, covered with a palm leaf design. The *Isfahan* is one of the rarest and oldest of all antique rugs. This carpet features a fine weave, a short nap, and colorful floral patterns around a central medallion.

The *Hamadan* comes in many sizes, qualities, and designs. Hamadan is the largest rug-producing section of Iran. Although made of some of Iran's best wool, this rug is less expensive than many. Colors are reds, chestnuts, and blues. A stylized floral with a corner motif is typical.

The *Kashan* has intricate floral patterns, inspiring its name, "heavenly rug." A deep rose field is typical, but a few are blue. A tight weave is characteristic. The *Herez* has a bold geometric design on a red field, with a medallion design and ivory corners.

The *Gorevan* is characterized by a bold geometric pattern; this rug and the Herez are among the largest sellers. On the *Ingelas,* the intricate allover design of flowers with a small geometric turtle design on the border is typical. The *Nain,* which is probably the finest carpet woven in Iran today, contains exceptionally intricate designs. The *Qum* is one of the finest oriental rugs being woven today. Designs may vary, with the paisley motif being the most common. The field is frequently ivory.

Although Persia has been the primary source of these rugs, oriental rugs have been made for centuries throughout the Middle East from Turkey and the Caucasus to India, China, and Japan.

Oriental rugs from China The art of rug making has been practiced in China for over 12 centuries. The oldest-known rugs were from the T'ang dynasty (A.D. 618–906). The oldest existing rug dates from the Ming dynasty (A.D. 1368–1644). Early designs were taken from ancient Chinese silk weaving and are symbolic of ancestor worship. Ancient symbols, of which there are over 100, fall into a number of categories. Among the oldest are geometrical designs used primarily as border ornamentation. The Chinese T or key designs are the most familiar. The circle with a square in the center, and two curved cells within a circle, symbolizing male and female, are common motifs. Some religious symbols are the dragon, which symbolizes God and emperor, and waves and closed bands, which symbolize eternity. Among the mythological symbols, the lion symbolizes authority, the horse symbolizes strength, the fish symbolizes abundance, and the stag and crane symbolize longevity. Symbols of good fortune include the bat, which symbolizes happiness, the scepter, which symbolizes success, and the swastika, which symbolizes good luck. Three of the most common flowers used are the lotus, which symbolizes purity, the peony, which symbolizes prosperity, and the chrysanthemum, which symbolizes fidelity.

Chinese rugs are made from complete paper models, and the design is outlined on a cotton warp. The pile is higher than rugs made in the Near East, and the designs are sculptured by clipping the yarns along the contour of the pattern. The field of Chinese rugs is typically blue, yellow, cream, or white. Flowers are depicted in their natural colors.

Figure 7.21 (*top*). This Tekke-Turkoman (Bokhara) is made in central Asia. The straight line of geometric forms is typical. The ground is usually red. (Courtesy of Chas. W. Jacobsen.)

Figure 7.22 (*bottom*). The craftsmanship of the Turkish people is represented by this rug from eastern Turkey. Patterns vary from coarse to fine and from geometric designs to intricate florals. (Photograph by Mark K. Allen.)

Figure 7.23 (*above*). A Chinese design rug in the Bengali design. (Courtesy of Stark Carpet Corporation.)

Figure 7.24 (*above, right*). This Numdah rug is made of rough felt with wool embroidery in the tree of life design. (Photograph by Mark K. Allen.)

Figure 7.25 (*facing page, left*). The French Savonnerie is a velvety pile carpet, typically with intricate French designs on a dark ground. (Courtesy of Stark Carpet Corporation.)

Figure 7.26 (*facing page, right*). Aubusson rugs are made of tapestry weave, usually with French designs in pastel colors. (Courtesy of Stark Carpet Corporation.)

Rugs made in eastern China usually have allover patterns reflecting the Near East influence. The two most familiar Chinese rugs are the *Mandarin,* which has no border, an open ground, and a different asymmetrical floral spray in each corner, and the *Peking,* which has a wide border, similar corner motifs, and a round central medallion. Peking design rugs made in India are called *Bengali.*

Few rugs were made in China after the Second Sino-Japanese War (1937–1945), but after World War II, production increased and some Chinese rugs were exported indirectly from the mainland. With the opening of trade with China, rugs are again exported directly, but most Chinese-style rugs found today come from Japan and India.

Oriental rugs from India   Today many rugs of excellent quality are handmade in India for export to Europe and America. Rugs employing old and authentic designs from China, Iran, Turkey, and France are made from top-quality wool, mostly from New Zealand, and sell at moderate prices. Rugs imported into America from India come under several trade names: *Benares* rugs have a 100 percent wool nap, usually in natural colors with an ivory or cream ground. *Indo-Shahs* are some of the most common of the India-made rugs. The field is usually beige or pastel, with designs in deep royal blue, aquamarine, green, or gold. Indo-Shahs are made in French Aubusson or Savonnerie designs, or in old Chinese patterns. *Chinda* are among the finest of the India rugs woven today. Designs are mostly French. *Bengali* is a Chinese design. A center medallion is typical, and blue usually predominates. *Pakistani* rugs are made in West Pakistan and are of fine quality. The designs are traditional Turkoman, and they come in a wide color range. The best known of these is the *Mori-Bukaro* (Bokhara).

In addition to the heavy, deep-pile rugs just listed, many finely woven Indian

rugs are made in traditional Persian and Turkoman designs. In Kashmir they make the flat-stitched tapestry Aubusson, employing authentic French designs. The *Numdah* rug, used in India for centuries, has been imported into the United States for many years, and recently has had a revival in popularity. This rug is an informal type made of felt, with the wool surface traditionally enriched with bird and floral motifs worked with a long, open stitch. The tree of life design is one of the most familiar being used; others have been modernized. Colors are in rich combinations of greens, blues, reds, and yellows on a natural ground. Numdahs are used for wall hangings or accent rugs and are effective in almost any informal room. *Dhurries* are flat-weave rugs hand-woven in India (see Figure 8.14). They are tightly woven in wool or cotton, and incorporate both stylized and geometric designs in a contemporary mix of color. These versatile rugs bring a new excitement into today's homes and are much in vogue at the present time.

With the expanding market for India-made rugs of various types, some predict that in both output and export, India will soon surpass Iran, where modern technology is threatening the ancient art of hand weaving.

FRENCH RUGS

Two French-style carpets that have been produced with little interruption since the seventeenth century are the *Savonnerie* and the *Aubusson*.

Savonnerie is a pile carpet made by hand, with knotted stitches in the manner of the Eastern orientals but with French patterns. The Savonnerie factory, established in France in 1663 by Louis XIV, was an outgrowth of a workshop founded earlier in the Louvre. Although it was the first factory to produce tapestrylike carpets, it is best known for its velvety pile carpets, usually made in strong colors on a dark ground with elaborate designs that were sometimes taken from the formal French gardens. Early Savonneries were made primarily for the royal families of France and often bore the emblem of the king or prince for whom they were made. During the reigns of Louis XIV, XV, and XVI, these rugs added warmth and splendor to the

magnificent rooms of Versailles, Fontainebleau, and other great palaces and châteaus. Rugs of this type are still being produced to fill the present demand.

The exact date and circumstance of the establishment of the *Aubusson* factory are uncertain. During the late seventeenth century, however, when the upper classes of France became interested in beautifying their homes, long established, privately owned workshops at Aubusson strove to imitate the weaving being done at Savonnerie and Gobelins to meet the new demand. Some of the oldest Aubusson rugs have an oriental flavor, but later ones follow the French textile designs. These carpets are made in the tapestry weave, but are somewhat less refined than the tapestries that inspired them. Colors are usually muted pastels, which give a faded effect. Although these rugs are no longer produced at Aubusson, the name persists to designate the type of carpet rather than the name of the factory.

Figure 7.27 (*right*). North Africa is the source of this Moroccan rug commonly called Berber. (Courtesy of Ernest Tregavowan.)

Figure 7.28 (*below*). A textured Berber rug in natural earth tones is an attractive and popular floor covering in this contemporary setting. (Courtesy of Stark Carpet Corporation.)

Figure 7.29 (*extreme right*). Wilton Berber carpets with acrylic pile and treated for static control. (Courtesy of Philadelphia Carpet Company.)

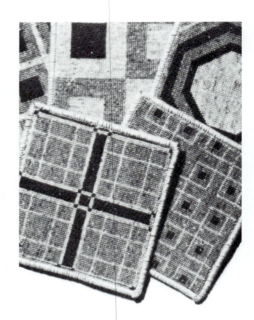

MOROCCAN RUGS

The Moroccan is a type of oriental rug made primarily in northwest Africa. The character of the rug has changed little in 1000 years. Its distinctive informality has made it a great favorite in contemporary decor. Moroccan rugs are of two basic types: the Berber and the Rabat.

Berber rugs are the traditional types made primarily by Berber tribes in the Atlas mountains. The designs are abstract and geometric. Some are primitive, often of natural wool color with simple black or brown design, and others are vividly colored. Top-quality carpets referred to as Berbers are being made today by leading American companies. They are usually in natural colors and may be plain or have geometric designs. Berbers are particularly in demand for contemporary homes in which high fashion is desired.

Rabat rugs are made mostly in factories in the larger population centers. The designs show an oriental influence, which was introduced into Morocco in the eighteenth century.

In 1938, a law was passed in Morocco prohibiting machine-made rugs. The law's intent was to safeguard employment for some 100,000 artisans and their

families and to preserve the character of the handmade product. To ensure continuity in rug making, the government set up schools for girls between the ages of 9 and 15, in which the art of carpet weaving was taught. These *centres d'apprentissage* are located in half a dozen towns throughout Morocco. The students live on the premises and take a two-year course, after which they work either at home or in cooperatives. One school is located in the sultan's palace in Tangiers, which is part of the picturesque Casbah.

THE SPANISH MATRIMONIA

The Spanish Matrimonia, the traditional bridal gift in Spain, is the fringed, bold-figured Manta rug. Woven on the Jacquard loom, these rugs have subtle shadings, a handcrafted-like texture, and a three-dimensional quality. The Spaniards' legendary love of color is typified in the bright color combinations. Patterns are inspired by medieval motifs, classic Aubussons, Far East orientals with mythical figures, the tree of life, and ornate *arabesques.* Adaptations of these rugs are being made today and are particularly appropriate for homes built in the Spanish tradition and for those with the Southwest look.

THE NAVAJO RUG

The Navajo rug is a handwoven rug or blanket made by the Navajo Indians. Those of finest quality are made of wool and colored with vegetable dyes. Designs are usually geometric with frequent zigzag, *chevron,* and diamond motifs, combined with stripes. Quaint representations of birds and human figures are sometimes used. A remarkable similarity exists between the geometric designs of these rugs and the designs of many made in the Caucasus and in Peru. Navajo rugs do not have a pile and are usually only large enough for accent rugs. They are especially appropriate in houses with a Southwest look. The adobe houses such as are found in Santa Fe, New Mexico, and in parts of Arizona are particularly enhanced by Navajo rugs.

Figure 7.30. This Navajo rug is characteristic of much of the art of the North American Indian and is similar to Peruvian rugs. (Photograph by Mark K. Allen.)

Figure 7.31. A similarity is often present in folk rugs from remote areas. The Inca Indian influence that is evident in this rug from Peru bears a striking resemblance to the rug from eastern Turkey (see Figure 7.22). (Courtesy of Ernest Tregavowan.)

Figure 7.32. The Yeibechai (Yei) is a ceremonial rug made by the Navajo Indians of North America. Representations of animals and humans are found in folk art the world over. (Photograph by Mark K. Allen.)

Figure 7.33. A contemporary Danish rya rug. (Photograph by August Anselon.)

THE RYA RUG

Rya is a name derived from an old Norse word meaning "rough." This rug is a traditional import from Scandinavia, where such rugs have been used for centuries. The rya is a high-pile shag rug, combining coarse texture with bright colors. These area rugs are superb for today's interior design and are ideally suited for either Early American or contemporary interiors. American manufacturers are now producing a similar type of rug to meet the current demand.

RAG RUGS

Rag rugs were the first floor coverings made by the American colonists. Scraps of cotton, linen, or wool were cut in narrow strips, which were sewn together to form long strands that were woven in a plain weave on a cotton or linen warp. Through ingenious methods, rags were turned into colorful rugs, a craft that is still practiced.

BRAIDED RUGS

Braided rugs were originally made in homes from scraps of clothing and blankets. They are still a favorite for rooms with a provincial atmosphere. Strips of rags are stitched together on the bias, then braided into long ropes, which are either sewn or woven together in round or oval shapes. Varying bands of color can create colorful effects that add a warm informality to any room. Rugs of this type are produced commercially at reasonable cost.

HOOKED RUGS

Hooked rugs have been familiar to Americans since the late seventeenth century, and during the nineteenth century, rug hooking became a highly developed art. Although generally thought of as native to America, hooked rugs were previously made in England. These rugs are made by hooking colored rags or yarns through a tightly stretched burlap or canvas to form a pile that may be cut or left in loops. The foundation fabric and the type of material used for filling determine the degree of durability.

NEEDLEPOINT RUGS

Needlepoint rugs were originally made by embroidering with wool yarn on a heavy net canvas. Designs range from simple to highly complex floral motifs in a wide array of colors. A popular floor covering during the nineteenth century, needlepoint rugs (now machine-made) are finding favor with many Americans today.

A striking similarity in appearance exists among folk rugs from most countries of the world. Accounting for this similarity may be the fact that all primitive people use simple geometric designs adapted from nature, and quaint representations of human and animal forms. Colors are invariably natural wools, or vegetable dyes, and construction is done by hand on the simplest looms. Whether these rugs are made by Berber tribes of North Africa, peasants in the highlands of Greece, or Navajo Indians on the Western reservations of North America, they have a feeling of kinship and may be used together to add charm to rooms with an informal country atmosphere.

Walls and wall treatments

The background elements of every room are important factors in setting and maintaining the decorative scheme. Walls, floors, ceilings, windows, and doors are all part of the room's enclosure and are rarely hidden except in small areas. Although these background elements provide a setting for furniture and fabrics, their most important function is to provide a background for people. Areas in which people spend little time, such as foyers, may be successful with backgrounds in bold and dramatic patterns. Rooms for relaxing are better if the backgrounds are unobtrusive.

Walls occupy the largest area of a room, define its size and shape, and serve purposes of both function and beauty. Functionally, walls provide protection and privacy from the exterior surroundings and create interior areas of various shapes and sizes for particular activities. Walls provide space for plumbing pipes and electrical and telephone wires, as well as insulation against heat and cold. Aesthetically they contribute significantly to the success of a room and to the general atmosphere and personality. Some walls emphasize openness and informality. Others stress protection and formality.

Traditionally, walls were stationary, supporting ceilings, and rooms were usually square or oblong. In many of today's homes, walls are not part of the basic structure. They may stop short of the ceiling, providing privacy but permitting the flow of air and light from one area to another. Walls may be of glass or plastic and may slide into sockets or fold like accordians. In many modern houses, the materials used on exterior walls are carried into the interior and are left exposed to form the room's architectural background. This arrangement accentuates the flow of space from the outside to the inside.

The materials available for wall treatments today are varied and plentiful. Each type has advantages and disadvantages with regard to appearance, cost,

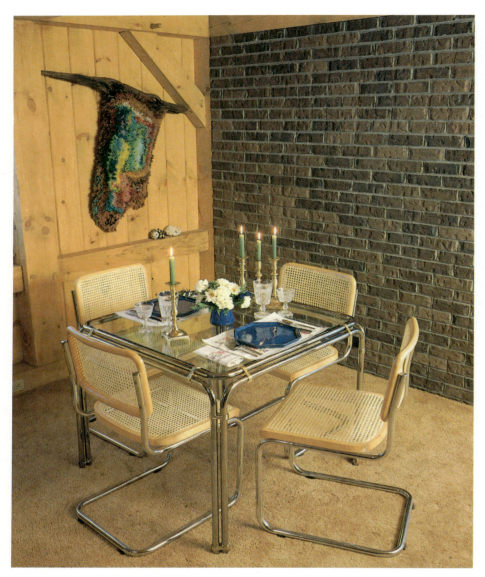

Figure 7.34. The brick-faced wall carried from the exterior not only provides a warm and appealing texture in this dining area but also stores solar heat during the day and radiates it through the house at night. (Courtesy of Timberpeg.)

upkeep, noise insulation, and longevity. Important in making a choice is that the wall materials are appropriate for the particular house. Some wall treatments are extremely versatile, and others belong to certain moods and period styles. Heavy masonry is most appropriately used in large contemporary rooms and calls for large-scaled furniture, heavily textured fabrics, and strong colors. A current vogue is for natural textures, and brick and stone are used abundantly both inside and out (See Figure 7.1). Brick, which has been used since the time of the ancient Babylonians and the pharaohs, has a timeless quality of warmth and adaptability. Its natural look is equally at home in Old English, Mexican, or modern. Stone is less warm than brick, but its durability and strength make it particularly desirable for contemporary rooms. Stone is, however, at home in many rooms with a traditional but rustic atmosphere.

Plaster is the simplest and the most versatile of all wall treatments (see Figure 7.53). Plaster is a thick mixture of gypsum and water combined with lime and sand. This mixture must be applied to a metal lattice, a special hardboard, or any rough masonry surface. Plaster has been used for centuries, but today the cost makes is prohibitive for most housing. Hardboard (gypsum plasterboard), which is used almost exclusively, provides insulation against heat, cold, and noise, and when painted produces the effect of plaster. Different techniques can produce a variety of effects from rough to smooth (see Figure 7.54). Rough plasterlike walls are appropriate for informal rooms and some period rooms such as Spanish. If it is painted in the right color, smooth plaster can be used in any style room and with any style of furniture. Because of this, the plain wall is the safest background to use in rooms in which furnishings may likely be changed from time to time.

The plain-walled shoe-box look, which held sway from about the 1920s to the 1950s, has long been out of fashion. The decorative background has been re-established. Architectural interest and

Figure 7.35. Brick walls shape space with a fluid quality that echoes the pattern in the brick floor. (Photograph by Stanley F. MacBean.)

Figure 7.36. The warmth of brick is evidenced in this fireplace wall. The texture is emphasized by the accent lighting. (Courtesy of General Electric Company.)

Figure 7.37. Ceramic tile comes in factory-prepared sheets of attached tiles, making its application a highly successful do-it-yourself project. (Courtesy of American Olean Tile Company.)

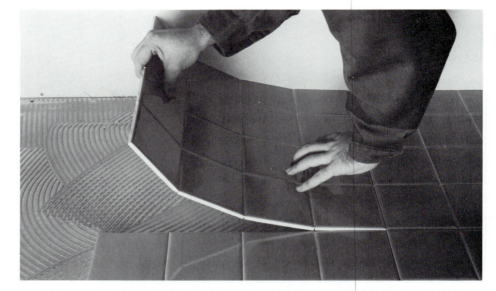

Figure 7.38. The timeless beauty and warmth of natural wood create an atmosphere of homeyness and relaxation in this living room. (Courtesy of Ethan Allen.)

pattern are the vogue. Paint, paper, and wood paneling—the time-tested stand-bys—have been much improved and are in great demand, and the market abounds with new materials. New techniques in preparing and installing all types of masonry have increased its use. A resurgence in ceramic tiles has produced patterns, textures, and shapes for every room and purpose. New metal tiles of steel, copper, and aluminum are also available for many areas.

A new emphasis is on wood paneling. Carefully selected and prefinished hard-wood plywood sheets can add warmth and beauty, and can go to any height and around curves, adapting easily to any application. Solid wood planking is costly and requires custom labor, but many satisfactory substitutes are available. Beautifully grained, factory finished, and at reasonable prices, they are ready for easy installation. Hardboard and plastic *laminate* panels, simulating real wood but impervious to dents, are available at unbelievably low cost.

To satisfy the current demand for architectural interest, manufacturers have made available many items to be applied to walls. Available are stock moldings that when applied, give the impression of a dado or complete period paneling. A three-dimensional composition material is so lightweight that it can be glued into place. It is made to resemble carved cornices, moldings, and *boiseries,* or it may cover a wider area to simulate brick or stone. This decoration stands out in sharp relief and is amazingly realistic. When skillfully used, it adds interest, dimension, and period effects to otherwise plain walls. To provide an authentic look of Old English or French manor, or to create a rustic atmosphere, lightweight beams of polyurethane are on the market. When glued against plaster ceilings, they have the uncanny appearance of old hand-hewn wood.

The use of mirrors is growing, and their ability to make rooms appear larger has a great appeal in today's diminished living spaces. Available are mirrors in large sheets and precut panels ready to

ARCHITECTURAL INTEREST IS ADDED WITH STOCK MOLDINGS.

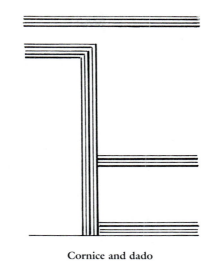

Cornice and dado

Dado, decorative cornice, and wall panelling.

Figure 7.39. This traditional sunburst design can add formality to a front door. It is sturdy, lightweight, and easily installed. (Courtesy of Focal Point.)

Figure 7.40. This exquisite *fretwork* cornice, made of amazingly tough, lightweight modern material, is molded directly from notable wood or plaster originals. Through a precise process, architectural enrichment is produced in authentic detail for any style. (Courtesy of Focal Point.)

Figure 7.41 (*above*). A mirror panel opens up the corner of a small area and adds spaciousness. Unique features are the side grooves through which pole lamps can easily be adjusted. (Courtesy of Virginia Burdick Associates.)

Figure 7.42 (*above, right*). A mirrored wall doubles the size of the room and adds glamour. (Design by Loughheed Interiors, courtesy of the National Association of Mirror Manufacturers.)

install which can open up tight places, be spaced on a vertical surface, or cover an entire wall or ceiling to create unexpected vistas.

Wallpapers, which have never before been so plentiful for every purpose, nor in such a wide price range, are discussed in the section on resilient wall coverings.

Fabric, which has been used on walls for centuries to provide warmth and elegance, has again returned to fashion. Many fabrics with paper backing come prepared for easy application. Commonplace materials such as burlap, ticking, felt, and many others can add charm to both traditional and modern rooms. Damasks and other fabrics with documentary designs can set the feeling of authenticity to period rooms. Fabric not only adds character and beauty but also insulates against sound.

Remarkable developments in vinyl for all decorative purposes have revolutionized wall coverings. Natural textures such as stone, cork, bamboo, grass cloth, and wood veneers, architectural interest such as ornate plastic work, moldings, paneling, and pilasters, formal and informal fabrics such as damask, moiré, velvet, burlap, and ticking—all have been simulated in vinyl to a remarkable likeness.

Nonresilient (or rigid) wall coverings

Table 7.3 lists the most frequently used nonresilient wall coverings, their general characteristics, comparative costs, finishes, fire ratings, insulation properties, uses, and care.

TABLE 7.3.   *Nonresilient wall coverings*

MATERIAL	GENERAL CHARACTERISTICS AND COST	FINISHES	FIRE RATING	INSULATION PROPERTIES	USES AND CARE
Brick (fired clay)	Solid and durable Variety of sizes, shapes, and colors Old, natural brick has feeling of warmth May be laid in regular or varied patterns Pleasant texture High Cost	No finish necessary May be painted or waxed	Fireproof	Reflects noise Conducts heat and cold	Interior and exterior walls Appropriate for large- or small-scaled rooms in a wide range of styles, and for fireplace facings and hearths Little or no upkeep
Concrete blocks (lightweight aggregate)	Substantial, cold, regular shape, large scale, textured Moderate cost	No finish necessary May be painted Waterproofing necessary for exterior	Fireproof	Fair insulator	Interior or exterior walls; fireplace facings Best when used in large-scaled rooms Lacks domestic warmth Little or no maintenance
Ceramic tile (clay)	Comes in variety of shapes, sizes, colors, and patterns, and in pregrouted sheets Desirable aesthetic quality Durable, resists water and stains, but may crack or break Moderately high cost	No finish necessary	Fireproof	Reflects noise Poor insulator	Bathrooms, kitchens, utility rooms Particularly appropriate for dados in Spanish and Mexican rooms Becoming more widely used Minimum upkeep
Fiberglass (panels)	Translucent panels of reinforced fiberglass Most often ribbed or corrugated Also available in flat sheets and in several thicknesses Comes translucent, white, or colored; may simulate brick, stone, or wood Moderate cost	No finish necessary	Fireproof	Good insulator	Room dividers, folding screens, tub enclosures, translucent lighting panels for ceilings, built-ins, and sliding doors Easy upkeep
Glass (architectural)	Can be clear, rubbed, corrugated, pebbled, frosted, colored, and curved Metal mesh core will prevent breakage and will add to attractiveness May be tempered Moderately high cost	No finish necessary	Fireproof	Poor insulator	Sliding doors, screens, room dividers, clinical purposes, numerous other uses Mirror can usually expand space and add dramatic element to room One-way glass has many functional uses
Glass (block)	Excellent light transmission High-impact strength	No finish necessary	Fireproof	Solid glass blocks conduct heat Blocks with hollow air centers good insulators	Suitable to lighten most dark areas Easy upkeep

TABLE 7.3, CONTINUED

MATERIAL	GENERAL CHARACTERISTICS AND COST	FINISHES	FIRE RATING	INSULATION PROPERTIES	USES AND CARE
Metal (panels and tiles)	Stainless steel, plain, or grained—not reflective finish Serviceable, sturdy, not affected by acid, steam, or alkalies Solid copper: eye appeal May be plain, hammered, or antiqued Sealed to prevent tarnish or corrosion Aluminum glazes: solid aluminum coated with permanent vitreous glaze of porcelain, enamel, or epoxy enamel Sturdy, easy to maintain Lightweight and strong, but subject to dents that are difficult to repair Tends to have commercial effect Moderate cost	Factory finished with grain, or enameled in variety of colors	Fire resistant	Reflects heat	Kitchens, bathrooms, utility rooms, and wherever sturdy wall is desired Numerous functional and decorative uses Easy maintenance
Plaster and stucco	Smooth or textured, no seams or joints Easy to change Tends to chip and crack Moderately low cost	Paint, paper, or fabric	Fireproof	Special types have good insulation against noise	Most versatile of all wall treatments Appropriate for any room and any style Washable
Plastic (tiles)	Durable, rigid, thin, lightweight, variety of colors Simulates ceramic tile Decreasing in use Low cost	None	Poor	Poor insulator	Kitchens, bathrooms, utility rooms Excellent do-it-yourself item Easy upkeep
Plastic (sheets)	Durable, resilient Comes in variety of colors, patterns, and textures Moderately high cost	No finish necessary	Poor Some do not burn but emit noxious gas	Poor insulator	Wherever durable, resilient walls are needed Resists stains and cuts Easy maintenance
Stone	Great beauty If covering too large an area, may appear cold, depending on color Natural colors and textures Feeling of strength and durability Improves with age High cost	Waterproofing sometimes required	Fireproof	Poor insulator Reflects sound	Fireplace surround or entire wall No upkeep

TABLE 7.3, CONTINUED

MATERIAL	GENERAL CHARACTERISTICS AND COST	FINISHES	FIRE RATING	INSULATION PROPERTIES	USES AND CARE
Wallboard (gypsum)	Surface may be finished in attractive colors and patterns, or imprinted with wood-grain appearance Lowest cost	Same as plaster: paint, paper, or fabric	Fire resistant	Excellent insulator	In any room in which low cost is primary consideration Care depends on finish
Wallboard (plastic laminate)	Extremely durable Surface of laminate similar to plastic counter top Photo process can produce textured appearance, wood grains, colors, or patterns Matte or shiny surface High cost	Finished at factory Needs no additional finish	Smokes and melts	Reflects noise Fairly good insulator, depending on density and thickness	Hard-use areas of house (e.g., family rooms, children's rooms, basements) Resists stains and moisture Scratches are irreparable Wash with damp cloth
Wallboard hardboard (pressed wood)	Extremely durable, dent resistant, low cost, many wood grains and colors Wood grain applied via high-fidelity photo process Factory coated, virtually indestructible, easily installed Also available in embossed and textured surfaces simulating fabrics Moderate cost	May be stained, painted, or waxed	Surface melts Pressed wood burns	Reflects noise Insulation depends on thickness of pressed wood	In any area in which wood paneling of low cost and durability is required Wash with damp cloth
Wood (solid)	Natural grain throughout Comes in variety of natural grains from rough barn wood to rich grains for formal rooms Can be installed tongue and groove, plain edged, flush joint, or grooved Natural colors vary, but may be stained any color Subject to denting, but can be refinished indefinitely High cost	Needs protective finish to seal against stains and water	Susceptible to burning	Good insulator and noise reducer	Depending on type of wood and method of installation, will go in any room—period or modern Beauty improves with age and care Dust only
Wood (plywood)	Thin surface of wood veneer bonded to rugged and inexpensive panel backing Appears much like solid wood, but less expensive Comes in sheets 4 ft by 8 ft for easy installation May or may not have vertical grooves Moderately high cost	Same as solid wood	Susceptible to burning	Good insulator and noise reducer	Same as solid wood

Paints and finishes

To change the character of a room quickly and with a minimum of expense, nothing works like paint. Of all the wall treatments, paint is the easiest to apply. It is made to adhere to any surface and is appropriate for any room or for any style of decor. New improvements in manufacturing have produced paints that are easy to apply, have little or no odor, dry quickly, and can be washed. Some paints resist rust, sun, and fire. Water-based paints are easy to handle, and cleanup with water is no problem. Paints come in numerous colors that can produce unlimited shades, tones, and tints. A painted wall surface can be smooth or can be given a variety of textures by the use of a stiff brush, a sponge, or a special roller. A bonus with the textured surface is a muffling of sound. Paint used on the exterior needs to be weather resistant and heavier than interior paint.

TYPES OF PAINTS AND FINISHES

Alkyd paint   Alkyd paint, which has virtually replaced oil paints, is resin enamel that is fast drying, leaves no brush or roller marks, resists yellowing, and cleans better than latex. One coat, depending on the color, is generally sufficient. It is produced in high-gloss, semigloss, and matte finishes. Alkyd enamels are solvent mixed and must be thinned with turpentine or solvent. They are recommended for plaster or plasterboard, woodwork and wood siding, and are probably the best for metal.

Acrylic paint   Acrylic paint is a water-based synthetic resin paint. The more acrylic the paint contains, the better it is. Acrylic is extremely durable, odorless, easily applied, quick drying, and washable. Some acrylic paints resemble baked-on enamel and are almost impervious.

Latex   Latex is a type of acrylic; it is a water-mixed paint, so cleanup jobs are easy. Rollers, brushes, and drippings can be washed with water. Latex leaves no overlap marks, is quick drying, and the characteristic odor fades quickly. Latex enamel, however, shows brush marks more readily than alkyd does. A difference between indoor and outdoor latex is that outdoor latex "breathes," thus allowing moisture to escape, which eliminates blistering. Enamel latex is a recent development. Latex paints are recommended for plaster or plasterboard, masonry, wood siding, *acoustical tile,* and metal. Since latex includes several varieties, one should depend on familiar and reputable brand names.

Enamel   Enamel is a special type of paint similar to an oil paint and is made with varnish or lacquer. Its finish is exceptionally hard and durable, and is available in high gloss, semigloss, and matte.

Epoxy paint   Epoxy paint is prepared in two ways. The first is ready mixed in a single can. The second type is a two-stage finish, or catalyzed epoxy, which when used as directed puts a tilelike coating on almost any surface. Once it hardens, this coating can be scratched, struck, or marked with crayon or pencil, and can still be washed back to a high gloss. Epoxies may be used on such surfaces as worn laundry tubs, basement walls, shower stalls, and swimming pools.

Varnish   Varnish is a word sometimes used as a generic name for all clear, resinous finishes. A resin is a natural or synthetic substance, that when dissolved in a suitable solvent leaves a hard, glossy film. Natural resins are the saps of certain trees or the deposits of insects that feed on the sap. Synthetic resins are man-made. Varnish is made from natural resins with alcohol or a drying oil and with volatile thinners and dryers. It is usually a transparent coating commonly used on wood to protect the surface and to allow the natural grain to show through. Some varnishes have a colorant added to darken the wood, but the result is usually less satisfactory than when the staining is done before the clear varnish is applied. Varnish comes in high-gloss or matte finishes.

Shellac   Shellac is a protective coating similar to varnish. It is made of a resinous substance called "lac," which is deposited on trees in India and the Far East. Its solvent is alcohol. Shellac dries more quickly than varnish, but is less durable and is subject to water spots. Clear shellac does not discolor when applied to a light-colored surface.

Lacquer   Lacquer is a superior, quick-drying varnishlike finish made from resin from an Asiatic sumac (Chinese or Japanese lacquer) or from a synthetic nitrocellulose resin. The finish ranges from high gloss to matte and comes in white, black, brown, or beige.

Polyurethane   Polyurethane is a varnishlike finish that provides an exceptionally tough plastic surface coating. It comes in high- or medium-gloss or matte finish. It is an excellent protective surface for hardwood floors in heavy traffic areas, and is also used to protect furniture surfaces and wood paneling.

Stain   Stain penetrates wood pores and contains various colorants that can enhance the natural color or give the wood a different color. Care, however, must be taken to make sample tests before staining begins, since woods react differently to the same stain.

Sealers and fillers   Sealers and fillers are special substances that are used as preparatory bases for new surfaces to ensure a more professional finish.

Resilient (or flexible) wall coverings

PAPER WALL COVERINGS

Decorative paper, as a wall covering, has played an important role in enhancing interiors since the late sixteenth century in Europe and since early colonial times in America. Although wallpapers have been more fashionable during some periods than others, they have always been esteemed by discriminating individuals as a valuable tool in transforming the visual aspect of interior space. No other element of interior design offers more artistic or dramatic possibilities.

A brief review of the fascinating history of wallpaper may be of interest. Hand-painted wallpapers are known to have been made in China as early as 200 B.C., where they were used for decorating tombs. The earliest-known example used on walls was found in England, where a fragment of crude brown paper adhered to a beam in the master's lodge, Christ College, Cambridge. One side of the paper was hand blocked with an English coat of arms, Tudor rose, and large-scaled flowers. On the reverse side, dated 1509, was printed a proclamation announcing the accession of Henry VIII.

The first manufacture of wallpaper on an organized basis was in France toward the close of the sixteenth century. The first papers were painted in marbleized effect—a design copied from imported Persian papers—and were made for facing book covers and lining boxes. These were called "domino papers," and the group of artisans who produced them called themselves "dominotiers." Soon other groups were organized to fill the growing demand, and when Henry IV granted a charter in 1599 to the Guild of Paperhangers, the wallpaper industry had arrived.

The introduction of flocked papers during the early seventeenth century made it possible for people to simulate the elegant damasks used in homes of the wealthy. Two events occurring during the latter half of the century added momentum to the wallpaper industry: the establishment of trade with East India, bringing the oriental influence into western Europe, and a new printing method developed by Jean Papillon. For the first time, wallpaper was produced that could be matched to make the pattern continuous around the room. Thus, Papillon became the father of wallpaper—as we know it today. His skillful use of **chinoiserie** design, together with this new method of application, produced a style much in demand for the decoration of great houses all over Europe.

Through the work of Baptiste Reveillon in France and John Baptiste Jackson in England, pictorial murals became popular in these two countries during the latter half of the eighteenth century. During the second quarter of the nineteenth century, the use of copper rollers, turned by a rotary machine, was first accomplished in northern England.

During the eighteenth century in America, hand-painted papers from China were much in vogue for the great Georgian mansions being built along the Atlantic seacoast. Carrington House in Providence, Rhode Island, is probably the most notable example. The high cost of imported papers, however—not only from China but also from France and England—prohibited their common use. In an attempt to make these highly prized wall coverings available to everyone, Plunket Fleeson established in Philadelphia in 1739 a plant for printing wallpapers. Because of the difficulties encountered in competing with the high quality of the imported products, the local endeavor met with only moderate success.

Although wallpaper was frequently used during the early nineteenth century, it was not until the industrial revolution, when quantity replaced quality, that the wallpaper industry flourished in America. With the advent of the modern style of architecture and home furnishings early in the twentieth century, however, wallpaper went out of fashion, and plain walls were the vogue. Late in the 1930s, wallpaper again became fashionable, and when the industry developed a new method of silk-screen printing that produced papers of high quality at prices most people could afford, the demand multiplied. Since that time, the wallpaper industry has grown at an unprecedented rate.

VINYL-COATED WALL COVERINGS

For today's practical interior designer, numerous flexible wall coverings are available that have been treated with varying thicknesses of vinyl and are made to simulate any type of wall covering, nonresilient or resilient. They may be washable or scrubbable, are waterproof, highly durable, and stain resistant, and can be used on nearly any type of wall. Vinyl wall coverings are applied like wallpaper; unlike wallpaper, however, they can sometimes be stripped off walls and even reused.

Figure 7.43. Vinyl simulates any wall surface: travertine, plain foil flocked, tortoise shell, cork chips laminated to vinyl, patterned foil, velvet, and wood grain. (Photograph by Stanley F. MacBean.)

The following are the most common vinyl wall coverings:

Vinyl-protected wall covering is ordinary wallpaper with a coating of vinyl plastic to make it washable. *Vinyl latex* wall covering is a paper impregnated with vinyl, laminated to lightweight fabric or paper, then vinyl coated. The thickness of the vinyl may vary. This process produces a durable wall covering that is scrubbable. *Coated fabric* is a wall covering with a woven cotton backing that is treated with an oil or plastic coating before the design is applied. This durable, tough, scrubbable material is ideal for kitchens and bathrooms. *Plastic foam* is a soft, flexible material available in rolls, squares, or rectangles. Its special virtues are that it absorbs sound and insulates, and is soil and stain resistant. It is easy to clean with soap and water. Although it is more expensive than some wall coverings, plastic foam is ideal for apartments with thin walls or for television rooms. Foam coverings come in solid colors, embossed patterns, or large scenic designs.

Today's flexible wall coverings have much variety, beauty, and practicality. Patterns, styles, and surface effects are unlimited. Photo murals can be used for one wall, or more restrained murals can be used continuously on four walls, thus deepening the perspective of a room. Three-dimensional wall coverings can look like straw matting, bamboo, wood, brick, stone, marble, tortoise shell, and so on. Wall coverings can add architectural dimension to a room. Design motifs are taken from oriental stone rubbings, famous tapestries, and chinoiserie prints. Wall coverings with everything from authentic period designs to supergraphics are at the disposal of the interior designer—both professional and

nonprofessional. In spite of their beauty and elegance, these new wall coverings have a practicality never dreamed of a few years ago.

Because wall coverings play such an important role in interior design, and because many people at one time or another will purchase and hang wall coverings, familiarity with the more common methods of production, the types produced, and some common terms is helpful.

METHODS OF PRODUCING WALL COVERINGS

The three most common methods of producing wall coverings today are roller printing, hand blocking, and silk-screen printing. Embossed and flocked wall coverings are also in great demand to meet the present desire for elegant walls.

Roller printing is the most common process in use today and is the least expensive. This method is a cylinder process in which each color is applied in rapid succession. *Hand blocking* is a process in which each color is applied separately after the preceding one is dry. This method is slower and more costly than the roller method. *Silk-screen printing* is a more complicated process in which a wooden or metal frame tightly stretches a silk, nylon, or metal screen made for each color of the pattern. The frame is the full-sized pattern repeat. The portions of the pattern not to be printed are heavily varnished or bleached out. Each repeat is made by applying pigment, which seeps through the screen as it is pushed across by a squeegee implement edged with rubber. Each color is allowed to dry before the next frame is printed. This method produces a high-quality wall covering at reasonable cost.

Embossed paper is made by a machine process that produces high and low surface effects. This method is used where texture and three-dimensional effects are desirable. Wall coverings of this type may simulate brick or stone with surprising realism. *Flocked paper* is produced by a method in which the

design motif is outlined and covered with a glue or an adhesive material. A fine wool-like fuzz is then blown onto it, producing a surface resembling cut-velvet. Flocked coverings are now produced in vinyl. *Plaster-in-a-Roll* is a newcomer to the market. It is a decorative wall covering that becomes a permanent part of the wall. Combining woven jute with partially set up gypsum, sealed with a soil-resistant, clear acrylic coating, it is flexible and unrolls to apply like wallpaper. Special antigraffiti coating can add extra protection. This wall covering can be applied directly to clean, rough surfaces—even concrete block.

COMMON WALL COVERING TERMS

The following are the most commonly used wall covering terms.

Washable Usually refers to a wall covering that may be washed with lukewarm, mild suds, but not scrubbed excessively.

Scrubbable Refers to a wall covering more resistant to rubbing than the washable types. Stains such as crayon marks can generally be removed from scrubbable materials with cleaning agents recommended by the manufacturer, or with soap and water.

Pretrimmed Refers to rolls of wallpaper from which the selvage has been trimmed.

Semitrimmed   Means that the selvage has been trimmed from one edge only.

Prepasted   Paper has had paste applied during the manufacturing process. Detailed instructions for hanging are usually included. In general, prepasted paper should be soaked in water and applied to the wall while wet.

Single roll   Wallpaper is always priced by the single roll, but is usually sold by the double or triple roll. Regardless of width, a single roll contains 36 sq. ft.

Double and triple rolls   Regardless of width, a double roll contains approximately 72 sq. ft., and a triple roll contains 108 sq. ft. Generally, 18-in. and 20-in. wallpapers come in double rolls, and 28-in. wallpapers come in triple rolls. Double or triple rolls are used to minimize waste when cutting into strips.

FABRIC

Fabric for walls is by no means a new idea. Fabric gave warmth to stone-walled rooms during the Gothic period. During the fifteenth and sixteenth centuries, the walls in European houses of the wealthy were covered with tapestries and leather. In the seventeenth century, velvets, brocades, and damasks were used, and in many well-preserved palaces and châteaus, the fabric on the walls still remains beautiful. Fabric-covered walls have a depth of texture and richness that no other wall treatment can produce.

Today, fabrics of many varieties are being used on walls. The best choice, except when using the shirred method of application, is a medium-weight, closely woven fabric such as sailcloth, burlap, ticking, felt, Indian head, or glazed chintz. Some fabrics that come prepared for pasting on walls are laminated to a paper backing. Allover, nondirectional patterns are the easiest to use, since they require no matching. When a repeat pattern is used, allowance for matching must be made the same as for wallpaper.

METHODS OF APPLYING FABRIC TO WALLS

The *shirring method* is the simplest way to cover a wall with fabric. The effect is pleasant, and the fabric is easy to take down and clean. Cut-to-fit rods are fastened just above the baseboard and near the ceiling. Single lengths of fabric are cut with a 3-in. allowance, top and bottom for headings. The fabric is gathered the same as for sash curtains. The *double-faced masking tape* method is not permanent, since masking tape will dry out in time. Fabric is prepared by sewing together and pressing seams. The tape is placed around the edges of the wall, then the outer coat is peeled off. The fabric is applied first at the top and bottom, then at the sides. The straight grain of the fabric should be kept vertical. The *Velcro method* is similar to the masking tape method, except that one side of the Velcro tape is stitched along the edges of the fabric, then attached to

Figure 7.44. Miscellaneous wall fabrics from natural fibers. (Courtesy of Wall Fabrics.)

Figure 7.45. Few wall coverings are as highly functional and as versatile as grass cloth. Textures vary from fine to coarse to gnarled. (Photograph by Stanley F. MacBean.)

the other side of the tape, which has been placed around the edges of the wall.

In the *staple method*, the fabric is prepared as in the masking tape method. The top is stapled first, then the bottom, and the sides last. Exposed staples may be concealed with braid or molding. The *paste method* is the most professional looking and the most permanent method, but also requires special care and a set of wallpaper tools. The wall is prepared by a coat of liquid sealing or sizing to fill the pores in the wall surface. When the lengths of fabric are ready to be applied, a second coat of sealing is painted on the first section and the first strip of fabric is positioned like wallpaper. The same procedure is then followed for the remaining strips. When the job is completed, the fabric dries over-

night and is then sprayed with a protective material.

Whichever method is used for application, the room will be enhanced if the fabric is carefully chosen.

OTHER RESILIENT WALL COVERINGS

Japanese grass cloth or *hemp* is made from grass grown in Japan. Women gather the grasses with crude implements and carry them to the village, where they are boiled and allowed to ferment in the hot sun. The grasses are then washed in sparkling streams; the outer cover is removed and dried in warm breezes, then inspected. Next follows the meticulous arranging, cutting, and knotting of fibers to appropriate lengths for skeining in preparation for hand looms. Stray strands and knots are snipped, then are woven and pasted to the grass cloth. Finally, the grass cloth

is hand stained in beautiful colors, packed, and shipped. Beautiful, long lasting, and easy to care for, grass cloth provides a background for a great variety of decorating. Colored grass cloth, however, does not hold color well. Other woven reeds, such as sisal, can provide handsome and practical wall coverings.

Wood veneer with fabric backing, another method of "papering" walls, produces a beautiful, true wood surface. One great advantage over wood paneling is that this material can fit around corners or curves. It is available in sheets up to 24 in. wide and 12 ft. long. The cost is high.

Real leather tile, made of top-grain cowhide, provides a soft, warm, rich surface. It comes in a variety of fast colors to blend with traditional and contemporary decor. The leather is permanently bonded to an aluminum tile base with preapplied adhesive for easy installation. It is highly resistant to scuffing, and the only maintenance required is an occasional washing with mild soap and water. Leather is ideal for use around fireplaces, for dadoes on walls in family rooms, for dens, or wherever a handsome, durable wall covering is appropriate to the room's decor. Leather tile in suede is also available on a custom-ordered basis. The depth of the brushed nap provides desirable texture, but the high cost limits its extensive use.

Cork is a handsome, textural, moderately high-priced material. It produces a warm atmosphere in natural colors of brown. It is particularly adaptable for studies and for rooms in which sound insulation is important. Unless plastic impregnated, cork is not suitable for bathrooms and kitchens.

Carpet is now going up the walls and even appears on ceilings. Carpet material made especially for walls is slightly thinner than typical carpeting and comes both in squares and by yardage. The kinds of adhesives and proper installation methods are still being developed; however, considering the aesthetic and acoustical values that wall carpeting offers, it promises to become an important new development in the last quarter of the twentieth century. *Hemp-woven carpet* for walls adds texture or pattern. Carpet also spot cleans and muffles sound.

DECORATIVE VALUES OF RESILIENT WALL COVERINGS

Using wallpaper or wall fabric is perhaps the surest way of completely changing the atmosphere of a room. Through appropriate selection, a wall covering can

□ Bring beauty and charm into an otherwise uninteresting room.

□ Add architectural detail. Many wall coverings simulate architectural features such as pilasters, cornices, dadoes, and latticework.

□ Establish the period or theme for the room's decor.

Figure 7.46. Wallpaper is used to supply architectural interest. The lower part simulates a dado; near the ceiling, wallpaper assumes the appearance of a cornice. (Courtesy of C. W. Stockwell.)

Figure 7.47. A documentary wallpaper establishes an authentic feeling of the period and changes the visual aspect of the room. (From the Winterthur Museum Collection, courtesy of Van Luit and Company.)

Figure 7.48. Coordinated wallpaper and fabrics fashion a room of serene beauty. (Courtesy of the Warner Company.)

□ Set the mood of the room: formal and restrained or informal and lively.

□ Make a room appear sturdy or delicate.

□ Supply an effective background for display with a blended or contrasting effect.

□ Supplement the lack of adequate furnishings.

□ Supply dramatic focus by the use of a striking mural or a framed panel of a beautiful fabric or wall covering.

□ Change the visual aspect of a room by the skillful use of *trompe l'oeil.*

□ Conceal architectural defects. (A small allover pattern is the best choice for this effect.)

□ Bring harmony into a room by the use of a wall covering that will unify the different components of the room.

□ Add interest and sparkle to a room by the use of a casual wall covering.

□ Change the apparent size and proportion of a room (i.e., make it appear larger, smaller, higher, or lower). A pattern with a three-dimensional effect can achieve spaciousness, and a bold pattern in advancing colors can make the room appear smaller. Using a vertical stripe, or running the wall covering onto the ceiling about 12 to 18 in., especially if the ceiling is coved, can make a room look higher. The use of horizontal lines or dropping the ceiling covering down onto the wall, can make a room look lower.

Despite the area they occupy, walls can be changed with less effort and for less expense than furniture, floor covering, or any other decorative element in the home. The wonders that can be brought about through a well-chosen wall treatment can be challenging to every interior designer—whether professional or nonprofessional.

Plain light walls give a feeling of spaciousness but may lack interest.

Horizontal lines make a high room seem lower.

Vertical lines make a room appear higher.

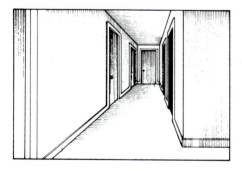

A scenic paper with a third dimension can add perspective and can create the illusion of space.

Figure 7.49. This bronze Chinese Peony wall covering creates a luxurious background for the straight-lined furniture and the carefully chosen accessories. (Courtesy of Jack Denst Designs.)

Ceilings

The ceiling—the largest unused area of a room—has been given special attention for hundreds of years. In palatial interiors, ceilings were magnificently *coffered,* inlaid, *frescoed,* and adorned with decorative plaster. Since the early decades of the twentieth century, however, the decorating potential of the ceiling has generally been neglected. Today, however, the ceiling is once again being brought into focus. Older, ornate ceilings are being restored, and new ones are often designed in dramatic ways.

As today's living space becomes smaller due to rising costs, a need exists for creating the illusion of more room. The plain, horizontal ceiling, although still the most common, is no longer considered the norm. By employing previously unused vertical space, architects are creating the illusion that small areas are larger than they are. Soaring vertical lines that draw the eye upward are producing dramatic effects in otherwise plain rooms. One caution, however, is that high ceilings make heating more expensive, and with the importance of energy conservation, this disadvantage should be considered.

The ceiling is an important element in establishing the character and atmosphere of a room. One that is much above or below the average main-floor height of 8 ft. will tend to alter the general feeling of the room. A high ceiling will emphasize space and will tend to create a feeling of dignity and formality. A low ceiling, which decreases space, will produce a warm, informal atmosphere.

Figure 7.50. The use of vertical space is dramatized in this architect's drawing of the interior of a solar house. Space is maximized by exposing all levels to the high gable ceilings and to the informal garden room. (Courtesy of Timberpeg.)

Figure 7.51. In this condominium of limited floor space, open vertical space adds to the room's dimension and increases the general feeling of size. (Photograph by Mark K. Allen.)

Making ceilings appear higher or lower

Ceilings may be made to appear higher or lower by a number of methods. Ceilings can be made to appear higher by running the wall color or covering a short distance onto the ceiling, especially when the corners are *coved* (where walls and ceiling are joined by a curve instead of by a right angle). This treatment causes the eye to move upward, and the illusion of height is created. A predominance of vertical lines in the architecture of the room and in the decorative elements will also contribute to the feeling of height. Gabled ceilings can be made to appear even higher when diagonal beams, which draw the eye upward, are used.

Ceilings can be made to appear lower by painting them with a dark color or by the use of a patterned wall covering. The color or covering can also be extended down onto the wall a short distance (dropped ceiling), where a border or a small molding may be used. As one's attention moves upward, it stops at the molding, and the impression is that the ceiling begins at that point. In this way, the ceiling can be psychologically lowered as much as 3 ft. Wood ceilings and horizontal beams also tend to make a ceiling appear lower, particularly when in natural wood or when painted in a bold or dark color. A predominance of horizontal lines in the room's architecture and in the decorative elements of the room will also seem to diminish the height.

In recent years, a number of ceiling designs have been developed to meet the needs of changing architectural styles, many of which add important dimensions to interiors.

Types of ceilings

The *flat-beamed* ceiling is one in which the structural beams are exposed or lightweight beams have been applied. The *shed* ceiling rises diagonally to one side in a single slope. A room with this ceiling requires particular care in the arrangement of furnishings to achieve a comfortable balance. The *gabled, or double-pitched*, ceiling expands vertical space

Wallpaper extended beyond the walls and into coved ceilings gives the appearance of greater height.

Angled beams draw the eye upward and expand space.

Figure 7.52. Flat beams make the ceiling appear lower. Combined with wide plank floors and vertical pine-paneled walls, the room reflects a reverence for traditional architecture while using contemporary furnishings. (Courtesy of Timberpeg.)

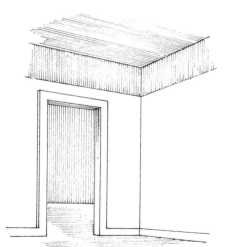

A dark paint on the ceiling or a wall covering coming down on the wall makes a ceiling appear lower.

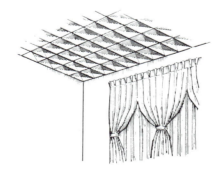

A patterned ceiling appears to advance and seems lower.

Figure 7.53. Large, dark beams contrasting with white plaster walls dominate the room and seem to lower the ceiling. (Courtesy of Ethan Allen.)

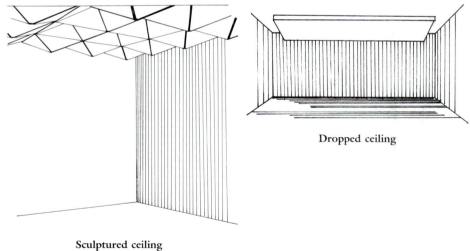

Sculptured ceiling

Dropped ceiling

and is popular in both traditional and contemporary styles of architecture.

The *sculptured* ceiling is not designed as an unobtrusive background, but calls attention to itself as the room's focal point. Sometimes designed in highly dramatic ways, sculptured ceilings follow no set pattern and usually require ample space. The *coved* ceiling is one in which the ceiling and wall flow into each other by means of a curved surface in place of right angles. The *dropped* ceiling is one in which a portion or the entire area of a ceiling is lowered below the main structure. This type of ceiling can define an area of a room (such as a dining area in a dual-purpose room), provide indirect lighting, and add an element of interest to living space.

Figure 7.54. The gabled ceiling expands space, and the natural wood enhances the rough plaster walls, ceramic tile floor, and leaded glass casements. (Courtesy of Bernhardt Industries.)

Figure 7.55. In this double-pitched ceiling, dark beams against white draw attention upward and expand vertical space. (Courtesy of Timberpeg.)

Figure 7.56. Prefinished oak-grained ceiling panels descending about 1 in. below a black grid give a three-dimensional pattern. (Courtesy of Armstrong World Industries.)

Types of ceiling materials

To satisfy the demands of contemporary architecture, new ceiling materials are being developed, and old ones are being revived. *Plaster and wallboard* (which simulates plaster when finished) are the most common materials used for ceilings today. They are appropriate for any type of room, are inexpensive and easily applied, and create a unified background with the walls. The finished surface may be plain or textured. Flat paint is usually preferable, with high gloss reserved for special purposes. *Tiles for ceilings* come in a wide variety of materials and patterns and are made to simulate surfaces such as wood, cork, marble, and fabric. Many have acoustical properties for absorbing noise. Others have a foil backing that cuts down on air-conditioning and heating costs. A new easy method of installation for do-it-yourselfers employs metal tracks and clips that replace the unwieldy furring wood strips previously used. Tiles can also be suspended from a supporting gridwork to create a three-dimensional effect. *Glass or plastic panels* are sometimes

Figure 7.57. Corklike ceiling tiles are easily installed on metal tracks by the use of clips that snap onto the track and slide over the tile lip. (Courtesy of Armstrong World Industries.)

employed in ceilings to provide overhead light—either natural daylight or recessed artificial light. Overall illumination may be provided, and striking lighting effects from high-up windows can be achieved. Skylight views can also add a new dimension.

Stamped metal ceilings, which were popular during the nineteenth century, are being made today. These ceilings are used primarily in the restoration and construction of Victorian buildings. *Natural wood beams*, which tend to lower the ceiling, create an atmosphere of warmth and informality desirable in many types of decor. Where natural beams are not feasible, ceiling beams of polyurethane (which simulate hand-carved wood to a remarkable degree) can be glued to a regular ceiling. *Flat wood strips* or plywood, either painted or left in a natural finish, can add warmth. Wood tends to lower the ceiling and may create a feeling of heaviness unless the ceiling is of above-average height. Although *fabric* is frequently used on walls, it is not commonly used on the ceiling. Exotic effects can be achieved by draping ceilings.

Insulating against noise and heat loss

A major challenge facing architects and builders today is combating noise. With the steady increase of disturbing sounds in metropolitan areas, caused by such things as traffic, construction, street repairs, helicopters, and jets, as well as the increase of interior noise from televisions, appliances, new electronic equipment, and other sources, a pressing need in both commercial and residential construction is to insulate against noise.

New materials and building techniques are being used to remedy the problem. Sound is being muffled by an increase in the mass and density of sound-deadening materials. In masonry construction, the space between units is filled with insulation. Where formerly 2-by-4-in. studs were standard, 2-by-6-in. studs are now used to allow for more insulation. Where double studding is employed, an air space in between the partitions is used in addition to insulating batts. Interior walls are often made by a series of slats, with spaces between filled with sound-absorbing materials. A finished wall material made of woven reeds, such as sisal, can be adhered to rigid insulation, thus providing a durable and attractive surface while adding to noise absorption.

In double ceilings, where one ceiling is above another, the lower one is suspended by means of clips so that the plasterboard is not attached directly to the joints, thus leaving a space for insulation material. Floors are often given a deadening coat of plaster or a coat of lightweight concrete.

With energy conservation a major concern in today's housing, the use of solar energy is increasing substantially. In addition, architects and builders are employing a variety of means to control heat loss. Windows are given **double** and triple **glazing,** extra-thick insulating batts are used, and extra foam is blown between partitions and ceilings. Although used to deaden sounds, insulation also helps immeasurably in avoiding heat loss. Thermobreak weather stripping is used around doors and windows, which separates the metal by nonconductive nylon or neoprene and prevents heat from escaping. Orienting a building to take the best advantage of the climate can save energy. Windows on the sunny side can absorb heat that can be stored for later use. Well-insulated walls on the cold side preserve heat.

CHAPTER EIGHT

Windows and Doors

Windows

CONSIDERATIONS IN THE APPROACH TO WINDOW TREATMENT

TYPES OF WINDOWS

WINDOW TERMINOLOGY

TYPES OF WINDOW TREATMENTS

WINDOWS AND WINDOW TREATMENTS THAT CONSERVE ENERGY

Doors

TYPES OF DOORS

PLACEMENT OF DOORS

TREATMENT OF DOORS

Although glass walls were known to the ancient Egyptians and Romans, historically windows have been merely small "cut outs" or "wind eyes" in the walls of a house to permit smoke to escape, let in fresh air, and allow protective glimpses of the outside. Over the years, many types of windows have been planned as an integral part of the structural design. While window treatments change with style trends, they should be attuned to the architectural spirit of the structure, both exterior and interior.

Doors originally were purely functional, used only for necessary passage. In modern times, they have assumed different forms with varying degrees of design importance and traffic control.

Windows

The window is an important architectural and decorative element in a room, and its enhancement has been the consideration of people everywhere for centuries. Traditionally, windows were often symmetrically placed in the facade of the house, with small panes as the norm. With modern architecture, however, great changes were made, and many new types of window openings have been introduced that are planned as integral parts of the basic design. Placement is usually asymmetrical, and frequently openings of unusual shapes are employed. Many types of windows unknown only a few decades ago are now common. Such windows as the glass wall with or without sliding doors, the straight or slanting clerestory, the peaked two-story window of the A-frame house, the *jalousie,* and the corner window are now as familiar as the double-hung or casement types that have been standard for so many years.

The window is a conspicuous element in both the exterior and the interior design of a house. As a source of interior light, the window is the first point to which the eye is drawn during the daytime, and at night a lighted window is the first thing seen from the outside.

Unfortunately, window openings are not always planned with indoor function in mind. Good planning can be ensured if an alert home owner or interior designer works closely with the architect. For example, a window originally pushed into a corner—a placement that creates a problem for decorating—can easily be relocated on the plans of the house.

The principal function of windows is to admit light and air. Even though light and air can now be controlled, and windows are not absolutely necessary, planning a house without windows seems inconceivable. As efficient as modern technology is, no substitutes exist for fresh air, natural light, and an outdoor view to create a psychological association with the outdoors, which gives people a sense of well-being.

Figure 8.1. In this glass-walled seashore home, miniblinds control the light without obstructing the view. Skylights are left bare. (Photograph by Leland Lee, courtesy of Levalor Lorentzen Company.)

CONSIDERATIONS IN THE APPROACH TO WINDOW TREATMENT

The approach to the treatment of any window should be made with a number of primary considerations:

□ What is the architectural background of the room against which the window is seen?

□ What type of window is it?

□ What is the placement in the wall in relation to the other architectural features of the room? Should it be emphasized, blended into the background, or camouflaged?

□ What is outside the window? Does the view need to be brought into focus or blocked out? For example, is the view that of a public thoroughfare, the neighbor's barbecue, or a private garden or distant vista?

□ Does privacy need to be created? Even if it does not, consider the cold, black appearance at night if a large expanse of glass is present.

□ What about light? Is it excessive or insufficient? What is the exposure? North light will be cool, and too much south or west light can fade and damage furnishings.

□ Is wind a problem? If so, how can protection against wind be arranged?

□ Does noise need to be controlled? Is traffic noise a problem? Many window treatments can help muffle sounds.

□ What about energy control? Window treatments can be an important factor in conserving energy and cutting utility bills.

TYPES OF WINDOWS

The three general classifications of windows are movable, stationary, and a combination of movable and stationary. All three types are available in standardized sizes. Glass panes may be supported by wood, metal, or plastic, each of which has advantages and disadvantages. Wood shrinks, swells, requires a protective finish, and is the most expensive. It discourages moisture condensation, however, and emits less heat than metal. Metal is strong and does not shrink or swell perceptibly. Except for aluminum and stainless steel, however, it requires protective paint and causes moisture condensation in cold weather. Newer metal windows have plastic thermal breaks built in to eliminate excessive heat loss and condensation. Plastic is stable and resists heat and cold.

MOVABLE WINDOWS

Movable windows are made to open to permit ventilation. The following are some of the most common:

□ Double-hung windows are made up of two *sashes* that may be raised or lowered to provide 50 percent ventilation. They are simple and inexpensive.

□ Casements may swing inward or outward, and permit up to 100 percent ventilation. Those that swing outward present no draping problem, but can create a potential hazard outside. In-swinging casements must have special treatment. Valances should be hung high enough to clear the window. Side draperies should be out on the walls or hung on swinging arm rods. Sheers should be on sash rods attached to top and bottom.

□ Ranch or strip windows are wide and shallow. They are set far enough above the floor to allow furniture to be set against the wall, but are not ceiling high.

□ Horizontal sliding windows may be made up of two sliding panes, or a large stationary central pane with a sliding pane on either side.

□ Awning (or louvered) and jalousie windows consist of strips of glass, hinged at the top or bottom, that open outward or inward. Strips in jalousies are narrower than the awning type. Both allow for draft-free ventilation control.

□ Single pivoting sash windows are raised for ventilation by means of side mechanisms. These windows are most often used as skylights or in light wells.

□ French doors are paired doors of glass. Since they are basically enlarged casement windows to walk through, they should be treated the same. Draperies and cornices should clear the operating portion of the door. *Louvers* are a popular alternative. Whatever the treatment, it should conform to the other windows in the room.

STATIONARY WINDOWS

Stationary windows are built as an integral part of the wall construction and require no special framing. They may be plain glass or nonglare. Where large areas of glass are used, thermopane or triple glaze and nonshatter glass is advised. Some common stationary windows are picture windows, window walls, bow bays, and clerestory.

□ The stationary window wall is a common feature of today's contemporary homes, and may extend from floor to ceiling or begin a short distance above the floor. The window wall is expensive, requiring double or triple glaze for energy conservation. Some disadvantages of the window wall are: (1) it may not allow enough privacy, (2) it may let in excessive light that creates glare and fades furnishings, (3) the expanse of a cold, black area at night is uninviting, (4) the window wall requires large quantities of drapery or shades, and (5) the arrangement of furniture is made difficult. All of these

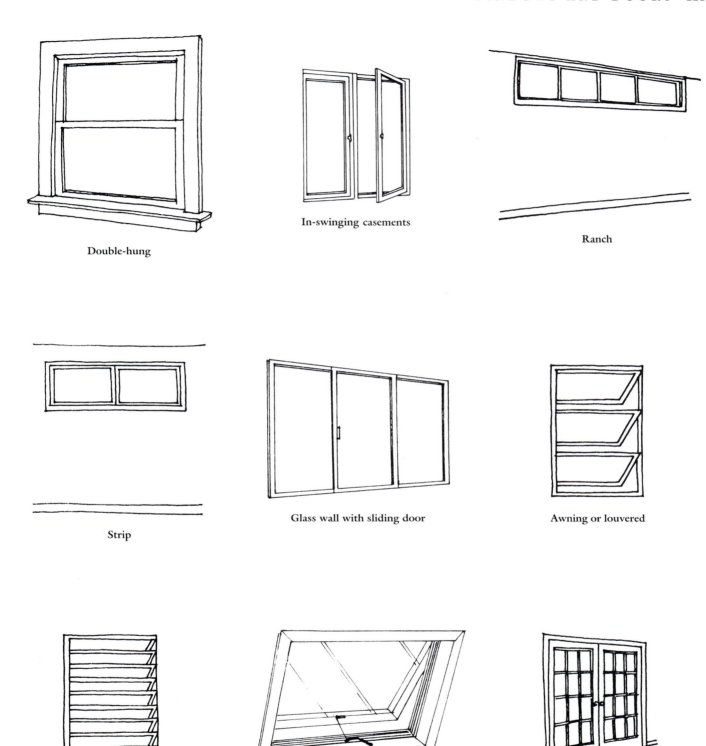

Double-hung

In-swinging casements

Ranch

Strip

Glass wall with sliding door

Awning or louvered

Jalousie

Single pivoting pane

French doors

Figure 8.2 (*above, left*). A nonmovable arched window near the ceiling opens this bathroom to the trees and sky, and adds a new dimension to the interior. (Photograph by Mark K. Allen, residence of Barbara and Eugene Kovalenko, Long Beach, California.)

Figure 8.3 (*above, right*). The stationary glass wall looks onto an enclosed garden, which adds cheer to the room and expands space. Ripplefold draperies control light. (Courtesy of Kirsch Company.)

disadvantages, however, may be offset by the pleasure derived from the close relationship this type of window provides with the outdoors.

□ The bay window is a large projecting window that is either bowed or angled. The bow bay is a smooth, sweeping curve of multipanes, which often creates the room's focal point.

COMBINATION OF MOVABLE AND STATIONARY WINDOWS

Three windows composed of both movable and stationary parts are the following:

□ The picture window is a large stationary central section of either small panes or one large pane, and a double-hung window at either end.

□ The angled bay is made up of three or more windows that angle out of the room. The central pane may be stationary and the side ones movable.

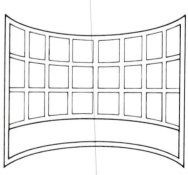

Bow bay

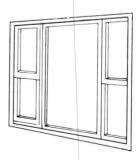

Picture

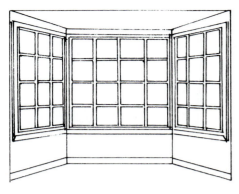

Angled bay

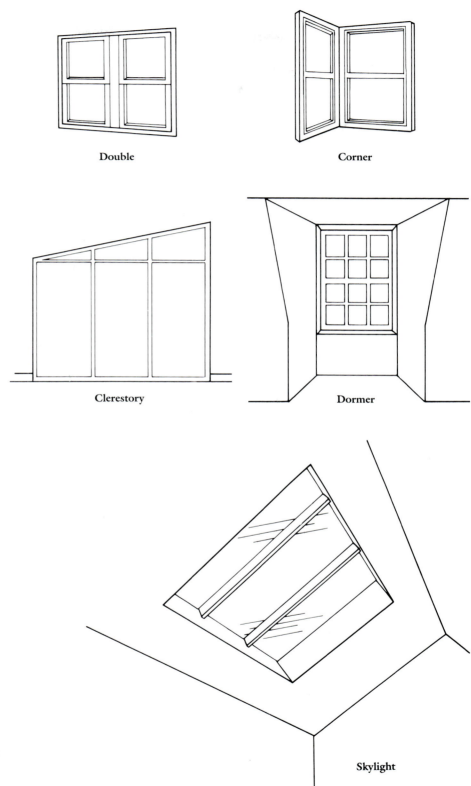

Double

Corner

Clerestory

Dormer

Skylight

OTHER COMMON WINDOW TYPES

Other common window types are movable, stationary, or a combination of both:

□ The single window may be standard size, high and narrow, or a small cutout in the wall. Panes may vary, but the double-hung is the most common.

□ Double and multiple windows refer to identical windows placed side by side. They may be separated by a strip of wall or only by their abutting window frames. Unifying them is usually the main objective.

□ The corner window consists of two windows that meet, or almost meet, in a corner. The angle should not present a problem. Corner windows should be thought of as double windows and treated accordingly.

□ Clerestory windows may be straight or slanting windows set at the ceiling or high in a wall between two roof levels. They are usually left bare.

□ Dormer windows are vertical windows that project from an alcove in the roof, usually filling the entire space.

□ Skylights may be single or grouped panels of glass or plastic, may be flat or domed acrylic, and may be fixed units or movable for ventilation (see Figure 8.4). Entire skylight ceilings in kitchens, laundries, and bathrooms have the special advantage of providing adequate daylight for inside rooms. In small areas, light from above can expand visual space and can make the greenery of trees part of a

Figure 8.4. This sun-drenched solarium, with its attractive angled bay, is the result of ingenious remodeling. Generous wall and skylight windows are softened by abundant foliage. An intimate fenced-in garden precludes the need for privacy. (Courtesy of Armstrong World Industries.)

room. Skylights have the unique ability to bring a new dimension into a room by highlighting elements previously ignored. Fascinating lights and shadows created by light from above can add hourly interest to a room. The skylight window has a number of disadvantages, however. Water seepage, insulation, and cleaning can present problems, and it presents a security problem unless protected by safety-wired glass.

□ Arched windows are those in which the upper part of a rectangular opening is topped by an arch.

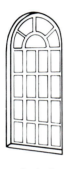

Arched

□ Beveled and stained glass is being used in many homes today, where it evokes a sense of the Victorian era (see Figure 8.15). Beveled glass refers to the angle ground into the edge of plate glass, which reflects the light in colorful ways. Pieces are often joined by zinc or lead to form a design. Today stock beveled and stained glass is available for doors, windows, sidelights, transoms (small windows placed over doorways or above larger windows), and skylights. Used for the latter, it brings a brilliant glow into a room.

WINDOW TERMINOLOGY

A knowledge of window terminology is essential to determine the type of treatment to be employed.

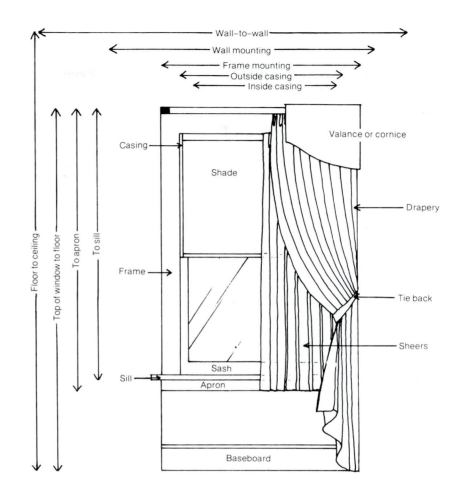

THE WINDOW ITSELF

The *casing* is that part of the window which fits into the wall. The *frame* is the wide molding that covers the casing and frames the glass. The *sash* is the part that holds the glass. **Mullions** are the horizontal bars separating the glass panes. **Muntins** are the vertical bars separating the glass panes. These terms are frequently used interchangeably. The *sill* is the narrow shelf at the bottom of the frame. The *apron* is the part of the frame beneath the sill. The *return* is the distance from the end of the outside drapery rod to the wall, which should allow room for undercurtains but ought not to exceed 6½ in. (see drawing).

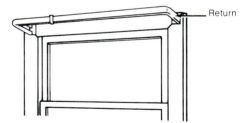

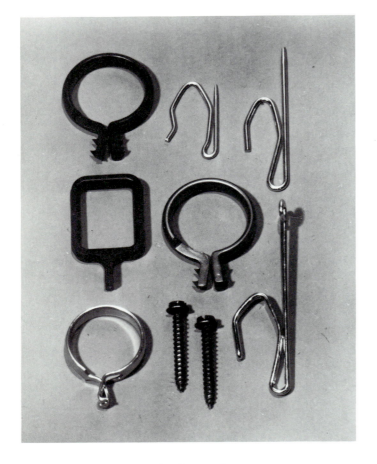

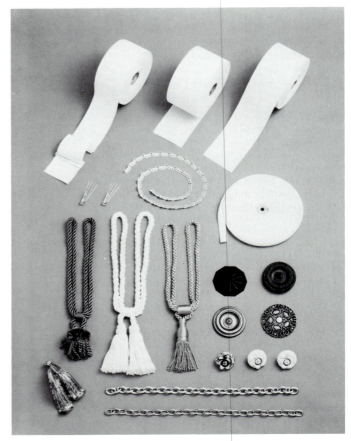

Figure 8.5 (*above, left*). Hooks, rings, and screws for drapery. (Courtesy of Kirsch Company.)

Figure 8.6 (*above, right*). Some necessary tapes, as well as decorative hardware including cord and tassel tiebacks, and metal chain, leaf, and rosette holdbacks. (Courtesy of Kirsch Company.)

WINDOW HARDWARE

Functional Purely functional hardware is inconspicuous and includes the following: *Sash rods* are flat rods attached close to the sash, often both top and bottom, on which curtains are shirred. *Extension rods* are used for stationary curtains and drapery. They extend to various lengths and are available in single and double sets. *Traverse rods* operate on a pulley system. They come both one- and two-way, and are used for drawing curtains and drapery. *Spring tension rods* fit inside the casing. *Swinging rods* are mounted on a mechanism that permits the rod to swing backward. These rods are suitable for in-swinging casements, dormers, and French doors. *Extender rods* extend outward to support stationary drapery beyond the window. *Ceiling tracks* with

ROD PLACEMENT ON WINDOW FRAME

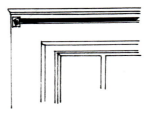

Desirable

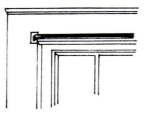

Desirable

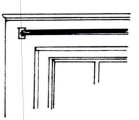

Less desirable

CURTAIN AND DRAPERY RODS

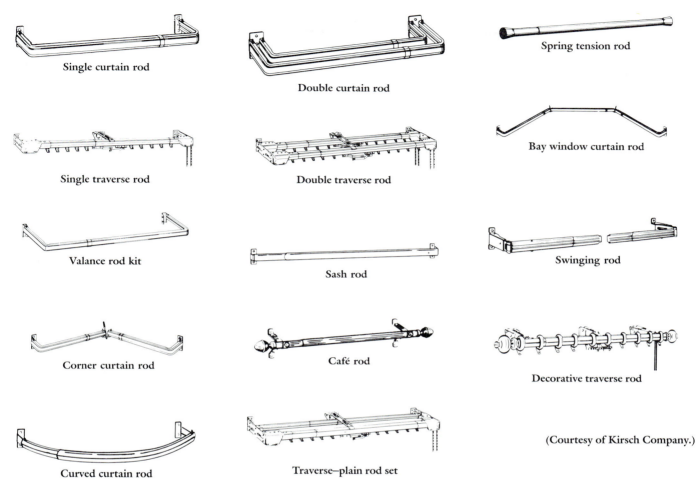

Single curtain rod

Double curtain rod

Spring tension rod

Single traverse rod

Double traverse rod

Bay window curtain rod

Valance rod kit

Sash rod

Swinging rod

Corner curtain rod

Café rod

Decorative traverse rod

Curved curtain rod

Traverse–plain rod set

(Courtesy of Kirsch Company.)

concealed drawing mechanisms are particularly popular in contemporary rooms. Small accessories such as hooks, rings, ring slides, brackets, and draw chords are all part of the unseen draw-drapery system.

Decorative   Decorative hardware is also functional, but provides decorative accessories for the room as well. Rods may be wood (natural wood, stained, or painted), metal, such as pewter, brass (shiny or in antique finish), chrome, or wrought iron, and are equipped with a variety of ***finials*** to accommodate any style. Draperies are suspended on rings and may be cord operated or hand

drawn. In the latter case, rings should be loose. Metal holdbacks that conform to the style of the rods can do much to add a finishing touch.

CURTAIN AND DRAPERY EMBELLISHMENT

The *heading* is the pleating or gathering at the top of curtains and draperies that forms the folds (which are essential to the beauty of the arrangement, and provide the necessary fullness for drawing). Headings are made in a number of ways. *French* or *pinch pleats* make up the most common type of heading. They are made by stitching together, about 3 in. from the top, three small pleats. The pleats, which are spaced 3½ in. to 4½ in. apart, are held upright by an interlining

of buckram. *Ripplefold* is a simple method of creating gentle undulating folds by means of a compact track containing snap carriers (see Figure 8.3). Folds are made from flat panels of fabric and are identical on both sides. *Accordion folds* are made by a combination of a compact track with snap carriers and a nylon heading tape. Trimly tailored pleats form architectural-like folds. *Easypleats* are made by a special tape that is attached to the inside top of the drapery. When pleater hooks are inserted in ready-made packets, folds are automatically formed. *Shirred headings* are most often used on kitchen, bedroom, and bathroom curtains. They are made by stitching a

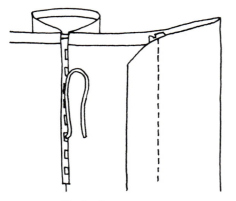

Single pleat with hook

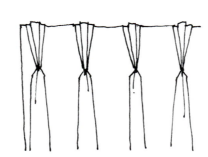

Pinch pleat detail

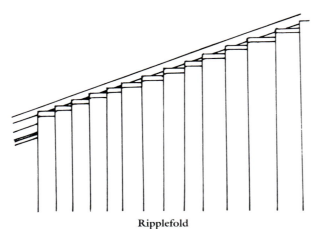

Ripplefold

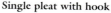

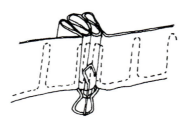

Accordian pleat

Easypleats made with heading tape and hook

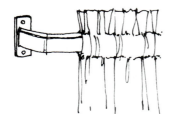

Shirred curtain on single rod

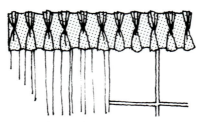

Valance with pinched pleats

pocket approximately 1½ in. from the top, in which the rod is inserted. By means of a series of additional pockets under the main rod pocket, which are gathered by inserting tape, one can create a puffy look.

The *valance* is a horizontal decorative treatment across the top of the window. It is used solely for appearance and does not change the function of the drapery. It may be straight or shaped. Shaped valances are held smooth by a stiff interlining and are usually attached to a dust board. If the fabric is patterned, the shape of the valance should conform to that pattern. If the fabric is plain, the valance should run the same way as the drapery. A valance screens hardware and gives the drapery a more finished look. It can appear to extend the height and the width of a window and can unify windows of different sizes, thus altering the room's visual proportions. In designing a valance, scale is important. A safe guideline is that the depth should be approximately 1½ in. for each foot from the top of the window treatment to the floor. The ends of the valance may drop lower.

A *swag* is a graceful window treatment devised to drape fabric over the top of the window and taper it to the corners. A *jabot* drapes down from the corners of the swag. It is usually pleated and may be of varying lengths. Swags and jabots may be hung over sheers, drapery, venetian blinds, miniblinds, or on an otherwise bare window. A *festoon* is a single draped member of a swag. A *cornice* is basically a valance made of wood. It may be stained, painted, covered with fabric or a mirror, or made of pressed metal. Both cornices and valances should have sufficient return to allow for draperies underneath. *Tiebacks* or *holdbacks,* which hold back stationary draperies, come in a wide variety of materials and styles. They may be of metal, glass, matching or contrasting fabric, or cord and tassels. The point at which the drapery is tied back should follow the proportion of the golden mean—somewhere between one half and one third from the bottom. *Trimmings,* which become fashionable from time to time, give a finished look to some draperies and can add a personal touch. They include a vast array of fringes, braids, edgings, cords, and tassels (see Figure 8.6).

TYPES OF WINDOW TREATMENTS

With today's freedom in window decoration, no longer does a problem window have to exist. If windows are too big or too little, too high or too low, too many or too few, badly proportioned or out of balance, concern need not be great. A window treatment is available for every window. The first step is to visualize the room's *desired* elevations, then proceed to *make* them that way. A window that is an architectural liability can often be turned into an asset. A wall that has no window can be treated as though it had.

Changing a window treatment can give a room a completely new look and need not strain the budget excessively. A nondescript room can take on glamour and beauty with an accent of an appropriate fabric at the window. A busy room can become quiet and a small room can expand when windows are inconspicuously draped or shuttered to blend into the architectural background. Easily accomplished is making small windows appear larger, low windows appear higher, or awkward, unnecessary windows seem to disappear.

With today's flexible interior design, window treatments have no absolutes. While living spaces become smaller, however, the tendency is toward simplicity.

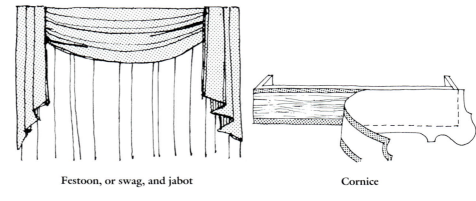

Festoon, or swag, and jabot

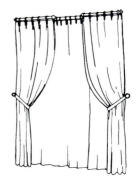

Cornice

THREE WAYS TO HANDLE A WINDOW PROBLEM

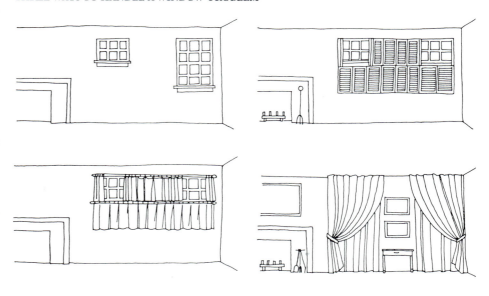

One window—four ways

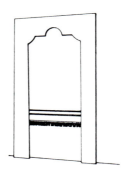

Bare windows and simple, unobtrusive treatments are increasingly in use, since they can visually expand space. When deciding on a window treatment, the principles of design should always be kept in mind. Proportion and scale are of utmost importance, and emphasizing the vertical line is almost always desirable.

Armed with these considerations, deciding on appropriate window treatments from the almost unlimited options available ought to be a pleasurable experience. The following are the most common types of window treatments in use today.

CURTAINS AND DRAPERIES

□ Underdraws or blackouts are plain, purely functional draperies that are drawn next to the glass for privacy and warmth. When not in use, they are stacked against the wall out of sight.

□ Glass curtains or sheers are used primarily to diffuse light and to provide daytime privacy. They may be hung permanently against the glass or drawn back. Much of their beauty and efficiency is dependent on their fullness, which should be three times the width of the window. When nighttime privacy is desired, sheers should be combined with draw draperies, blinds, or underdraws.

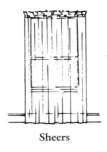

Sheers

□ Semisheers (also called casements or drapery, and sometimes used interchangeably with sheers) are most often used singly and are drawn to control light and to provide nighttime privacy. Semisheers that emit some light are the most common choice for large areas of glass.

□ Side draperies are stationary at the sides of the window. They may be hung straight or tied back. Their principal purpose is to bring beauty into the room. For daytime privacy, sheers may be combined, and for nighttime privacy and warmth, underdraws, louver blinds, or roller shades may be added. When plain side draperies are used, a patterned underdraw can sometimes create a pleasant effect.

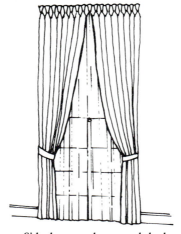

Side drapery, sheers, and shade

□ Draw draperies are made to draw over the window to control light, heat, and cold, and to provide privacy. They should

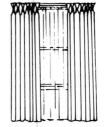

Draw drapery and sheers

hang straight and may be used alone or combined with other curtains or blinds. With a combination of draw sheers and draw drapery—which is the most common usage—the view can be exposed, and light, sound, heat, cold, and privacy can be controlled in an effective manner. All curtains and drapery should be hung to one of three lengths: the sill, the bottom of the apron, or the floor.

CURTAIN AND DRAPERY LENGTHS

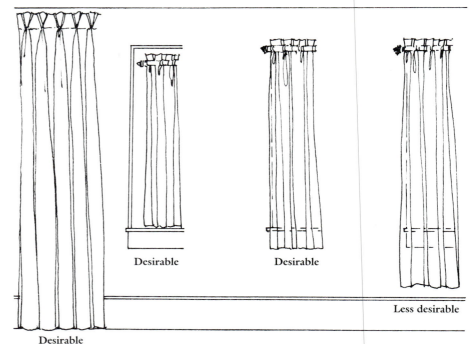

Desirable

Desirable

Desirable

Less desirable

□ Fabric panels are flat panels of fabric attached to sliders in a multichannel track with Velcro nylon fastening tape. When covering the window, panels reveal the full dimension of the fabric; when drawn back, they fold conveniently against the wall. In rooms in which a tailored look is preferred, panels of fabric that slide on a track can often be the solution.

□ Café curtains or tiers are any curtains hung over the lower part of the window. Usually used for privacy, they may draw or be stationary. Two or more tiers are sometimes hung to cover the entire window, in which case the rods are concealed. Café curtains may be complete in themselves or may be teamed with draw or side draperies.

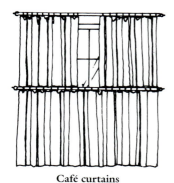

Café curtains

Tiered curtains

□ Sash curtains, which are usually sheer, are hung close to the glass and shirred top and bottom on sash rods. They are used mainly on in-swinging casements and French doors.

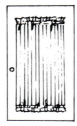

Sash curtains

□ Ruffled tiebacks are well known and are used mostly in cottagelike dwellings, and in kitchens and bedrooms almost anywhere. They are usually made of light, sheer fabric and add a fresh, informal air to any room.

Ruffled tiebacks

□ Ready-mades are curtains and draperies made to standard lengths, and are available in most drapery departments. Although less full than custom-made curtains and draperies, the effects of ready-mades often belie their modest cost.

Important to keep in mind is that windows are viewed from two perspectives: outside and inside. Many people see windows from the outside; comparatively few see them from the inside. Patterned fabric should always be lined if the windows look onto the street. Unless

the house is a dark color, a plain, off-white lining will make windows unobtrusive. When several windows face the street, they ought to look as much alike as possible, especially those that are on the same level.

OTHER WINDOW TREATMENTS

□ Shutters, which have been used since ancient times, are having a resurgence of popularity. They can substitute for drapery, can be adjusted for light and air, and are remarkably versatile. They come in standard sizes and can be custom-made to fit any window. Light colors are more practical, since dark colors show dust more readily.

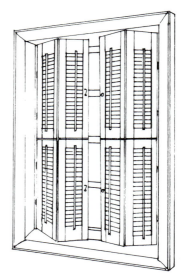

Shutters

Figure 8.7. Shutters that are at home almost anywhere enhance this traditional living room. Light and privacy can be easily controlled by the double row of folding panels and moveable louvers. (Courtesy Henredon Furniture Industries.)

Figure 8.8. Ever-versatile and timeless shutters are suitable in any style of decor and on any window. In this contemporary setting, they cover almost the entire expanse of a two-story window to shut out heat, cold, and light, and to provide privacy and a handsome backdrop. (Photograph by Mark K. Allen, residence of Mrs. J. Hamilton Calder.)

Figure 8.9. The same setting as in Figure 8.8, but shutters are opened at the bottom, with only the louvers opened at the top to bring the outside in. Unlimited effects can be achieved through the adjustment of shutters and louvers. (Photograph by Mark K. Allen, residence of Mrs. J. Hamilton Calder.)

□ Venetian blinds (or shades), another carry-over from ancient times that previously was purely functional, have with modern adaptations become popular window treatments in both traditional and contemporary style homes. In most cases, aluminum, stainless steel, or plastic has replaced the heavy wooden slats. Used both horizontally and vertically, venetian blinds can adjust precisely for light and privacy.

□ Miniblinds or louvers are made on the principle of venetian blinds, but the metal or plastic slats are narrow, creating

Miniblinds

a sleek, trim look that has become high fashion (see Figure 8.1). Miniblinds come in a wide range of colors and wood grains, and are lightweight, easily maintained, and complete, requiring no supplementary hardware. Used alone, they can add sophistication to the most formal interior and can be at home in the most modest room. They can be combined with a wide range of draw and side draperies for a more traditional look.

□ Vertical blinds, also based on venetian blinds, are made of vertical strips that pivot at the top or at the top and bottom. When drawn, the strips overlap to provide maximum privacy and light control. Vertical blinds may have a dif-

Figure 8.10 (*top*). Floor-to-ceiling vertical shutters control light and privacy on this glass wall, high above the city lights. (*Courtesy of Levalor Lorentzen Company.*)

Figure 8.11 (*bottom*). Sill-length vertical shades add architectural interest, provide privacy, and control light. Dramatic lighting illuminates the bookshelf below the sill. (*Courtesy of Levalor Lorentzen Company.*)

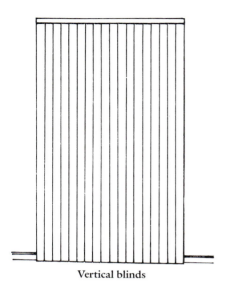

Vertical blinds

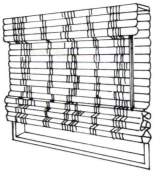

Woven wood Roman shade

ferent color on each side, may be covered with wallpaper or fabric, or may be made of fabric.

◻ The Roman shade has a flat surface when down. When drawn up from the bottom by a cord, it pleats up in horizontal folds made possible by a precreased rigid lining or by rings (or ring tape) and cords attached to the back of the shades.

◻ Woven blinds are another version of venetian blinds, in which slats of wood, bamboo, or metal are interwoven with colored yarn. They can be drawn up like a Roman shade, can operate on a spring roller, or can be made to operate vertically. Woven blinds add an element of texture and color, are easy to maintain, absorb noise, and are good conservers of energy. Since woven blinds tend to attract lint and grease, however, their use near stoves and washers should be avoided.

◻ The roller shade, an old favorite, is an effective and inexpensive window treatment. It may be installed between window casing or on the outside of the frame. The most common material is vinyl that comes in a variety of weights and is usually in white or in shades of off-white. Originally thought of as purely functional, the simple roller shade is now laminated with fabric or wallpaper and is trimmed in a variety of ways. The once common shade has assumed a role of decorative importance. When hung in a bottom-up manner, it is especially effective for privacy. Roller shades may be light filtering or room darkening. They are easy to maintain, and insulate against heat and cold.

Figure 8.12. Woven Roman shades are the perfect window treatment in this handsome setting. (Courtesy of Kirsch Company.)

Figure 8.13. Balloon shade made of permanently pleated polyester has an ethereal appearance. (Courtesy of Jack Lenor Larsen.)

□ The Austrian shade consists of rows of lightweight fabric seamed in such a way that they fall into deep scallops. The shade is operated by a draw cord.

□ The balloon shade is made of panels that hang flat but balloon at the bottom when they are drawn up.

□ Bamboo and split-wood shades emit some light, and their warm, natural texture is appropriate for most informal rooms. They may be used alone or combined with draperies, but are inadvisable on large windows because of their weight.

□ Screens can work wonders for windows. Widely used in Spain and the Middle East for centuries, the pierced or grillwork screen can be an exotic window treatment and has become popular in

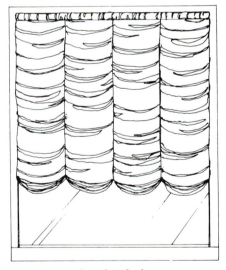

Austrian shade

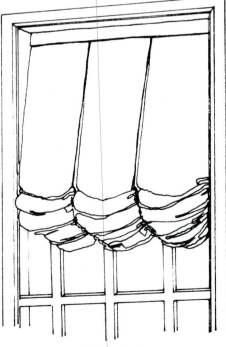

Balloon shade

America. Privacy can be secured while light is filtered through, creating an atmosphere of uncluttered appeal. A screen can conceal an unsightly view, a group of poorly designed windows, an architectural defect, or a windowless wall. Sheers can be hung behind from top to bottom, and in the absence of a window, an indirect light behind the sheers will create a new dimension. *Shoji* screens, either sliding or stationary, may be used to establish an oriental theme.

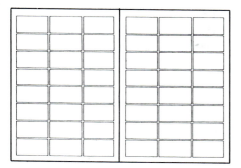

Shoji screen

□ Plants can successfully be used in lieu of other window treatments (see Figure 8.4). Hung at varying heights and placed on pedestals, plants can form a bower of greenery that will soften hard-edged architecture, filter the light, and afford privacy according to the amount used. The built-out window can become a greenhouse and can contribute to passive solar energy.

□ The bare window is sometimes beautiful in and of itself, and to muffle it in layers of drapery can be a mistake. Triple glazing can control energy, and if privacy is not a problem, the maximum benefit from nature can be obtained by leaving the window bare. Miniblinds with outside control can be used outside or between double-paned windows.

Figure 8.14. Beautiful windows speak for themselves, and in this setting need no drapery or blinds. Graceful plants provide a pleasing contrast to hard edges. White wall, wood floor, and a dhurrie rug complete the background for the handmade furniture in this striking contemporary room. (Courtesy of the McGuire Company.)

WINDOWS AND WINDOW TREATMENTS THAT CONSERVE ENERGY

With the present energy consciousness of the American public, ways to insulate windows from seasonal elements are of major concern to people everywhere and cannot be overemphasized. Manufacturers are making multiple-glazed windows with a special antireflective coating that directs the sun's heating energy inward. Set in wooden frames, these windows are attractive and highly energy efficient. Curtain and drapery manufacturers are producing a variety of insulators for windows to save energy, such as double-woven multilayered fabrics that trap warm air in the room, and insulated drapery and linings that insulate against heat and cold, thus cutting down on utility bills.

Few things do a better job of insulating than natural materials. The more yarn used in the fabric, the tighter the weave and the bulkier the material; and the fuller the drapery, the more air it will trap. Layered window treatments are effective insulators. One efficient combination is woven wooden shades placed near the glass, with drawn sheers and lined draw draperies. To trap cold or hot air, the sides of the drapery may be anchored to the window frame or wall by two-faced fabric tape. Other effective energy-saving window treatments are quilted blinds, *lambrequins* and cornices sealed at the top and sides, and window shades equipped with side channels to seal the cracks, which can be operated by a mechanical device. Edge sealing is the most critical point for effective energy saving in window treatments.

With the rapid changes occurring in housing and technology, and the long-range need for energy conservation, what windows will be like in the coming decades is speculative.

Doors

As an essential part of a room's architectural background, doors allow passage into the house and from one room to another. Their location is important in

Figure 8.15. Exquisitely designed beveled glass lends distinction to a window or an entrance door, and combines the protection of insulated glass with the appearance of antique leading. (Courtesy of Weather Shield Manufacturing.)

controlling the flow of traffic and the arrangement of furniture. Doors can also provide privacy or a two-way view, depending on their structural materials. They can allow ventilation, help control temperature, and provide sound barriers and safety.

The main entrance door is the most important element and the focal point in the facade of the house. Over the years, this door has been given special attention. Paneled period doors are not commonly made today, but salvaged ones are highly prized, and leaded glass panels, popular in the nineteenth century, are again finding favor with many people. Most exterior and interior contemporary doors are plain and flush, sheathed on both sides with plywood. Metal interior doors with insulating cores are effective in saving energy and are used increasingly.

TYPES OF DOORS

The three basic types of doors are swinging, folding, and sliding. They may be constructed of a variety of materials, such as wood, aluminum, plastic, and glass, or a combination of a number of these, depending on location and use.

Swinging Swinging doors are most commonly used. They are easy to install and operate, and come in standard sizes. They may be single or double hinged at one side. Most doors are *single hinged* and swing one way only; the *double-hinged* door swings both ways. The latter is convenient in areas where people frequently carry things, such as between kitchens and dining rooms. A swinging door placed near a corner, with the arc swinging toward the adjacent wall, preserves wall space and directs traffic along the side of the room. *French* doors are pairs of glass-paned single-hinged swinging doors that open the same way (usually inward), leading to a private outside area. On rare occasions, they are used between rooms. The **Dutch door** is a single-hinged door divided horizontally, making it possible to have ventilation from the upper area while the lower half is closed. Some tall, modernized versions are seen in contemporary houses.

Folding Folding doors are a practical solution to saving space. They are available in sizes from a single door to a full wall divider, and may be attached at both top and bottom or at the top only. Made in a wide variety of styles and materials, which include plastic, fiberglass, and louvers, they are flexible and relatively inexpensive.

Sliding Sliding doors used on the exterior may be part of a glass wall or may be installed in pairs that slide one behind the other. Popular in contemporary houses in making the patio or garden a part of the living area, sliding glass doors have been found to present a safety hazard. Because of this hazard, they are being replaced in many homes by types of safety glass.

Dutch door

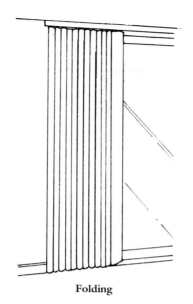

Folding

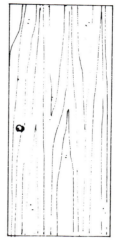

Flush

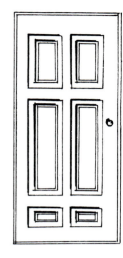

Traditional

Figure 8.16. Wood folding doors are the solution when space is limited and in areas where swinging doors may obstruct. The doors furnish privacy for the dining area when necessary and fold back against the wall when not needed. (Photograph by Mark K. Allen.)

Figure 8.17. Sliding glass doors make the brick patio accessible for outdoor living. (Photograph by Mark K. Allen, residence of Barbara and Eugene Kovalenko, Long Beach, California.)

Interior sliding doors usually slide into a pocket installed in the wall. Although not as flexible as folding doors, sliding doors are great space savers and can provide complete or partial privacy, depending on the materials used. The traditional Japanese shoji sliding panel is at home in both traditional and contemporary interiors, and can serve multiple uses.

PLACEMENT OF DOORS

If doors are well placed to preserve wall space and direct traffic in the most efficient manner, they present no problem. If a room has a surplus of doors, the unnecessary ones can be camouflaged in a number of ways. One way is to remove the molding, cover the opening, and paint or paper it the same as the wall. Another option is to remove the hinges and fill the opening with shelves for books and small art objects. For a number of reasons, relocating a door is sometimes possible and desirable, and the expense may be worth it.

TREATMENT OF DOORS

The treatment of doors depends on the design and decor of the room. Doors are most often painted to blend with the walls. If a door has a particularly good design, however, or if it is needed to balance another architectural feature or an important piece of furniture, painting the door a contrasting color can aid in the room's decoration. When walls are paneled, doors may conform to the walls or may be painted in a contrasting color. In adapting to the prevailing emphasis on height, many of today's doors are dramatically tall, sometimes fitting into arched openings.

ASSIGNMENT

Using Plate 11 in the Student Work Packet, carefully examine the window at the top of the page and design an appropriate treatment for this window in each of the following three conditions:

1 The window has an unsightly view, but it must provide light during the daytime. Since the room is near a public highway, it must have day- and nighttime privacy as well as noise control.

2 The window has a pleasant view onto a private enclosed garden, but needs nighttime privacy and energy control.

3 The window has a dramatic hilltop vista both night and day. Privacy is not a problem. Since the window faces west, however, faded furnishings and wind and energy conservation are major considerations.

CHAPTER NINE

Furniture

Fashions and fads in home furnishings come and go. With each change of fashion, only a few select items survive, while others become dated and fall by the wayside. With the changes of time, the good elements of each period will be updated by new components, but the basic character of the design will remain the same. To be able to choose the good from the faddish should be the aim of every purchaser.

Before buying furniture

Furnishing one's first home is one of life's real pleasures. The pride of ownership adds a new dimension, and each step should be taken with the future in mind. The first furniture purchase should be made only after careful study and planning. To become a discriminating customer takes time and effort, but it will pay big dividends. If one becomes

Figure 9.1. Timeless and versatile wicker contributes to the comfortable and airy feeling in this attractive room. The sisal rug, wood shades, and abundance of greenery are in harmony with the outside, which becomes part of the interior environment. (Courtesy of the McGuire Company.)

knowledgeable about the principles of design and what goes into the making of a fine piece of furniture, selection will be made wisely.

Seldom do young people decorate their first apartment with a specific style of furniture in mind, and this is not important. What is important is that the first purchase is made with a plan—a general theme that can eventually be achieved. Simple but well-designed pieces can be blended into a more definite scheme later on. Buying a roomful of advertised "economy" furniture should be avoided. At best, it will be mediocre and will likely be dated in a few years. Instead, one good piece of wood furniture is a wise start, filled with an assortment of temporary items, candidly retrieved from a variety of sources.

The first piece might be a basic article that will serve many functions over a lifetime. For example, a chest or cabinet, the ancestor of all case furniture, is a good piece to begin with. It can be a mood setter in a one-room apartment, and later it can be moved to the entrance hall, a bedroom, or even the dining room. After years of use, it may finally return to the favored place in the living room. Its mellow patina, resulting from years of care and rubbing, will add warmth and character to whatever decor has been developed.

After the indispensable storage piece, the next essential should be a bed. The best set of mattress and springs that the buyer can afford is the wisest investment, since much of one's general health and feeling of well-being are dependent on the quality of sleep. A standard metal frame or four improvised sturdy corner posts will suffice to support the springs. A headboard can be purchased later. For the more affluent, the market abounds with elegant traditional and sophisticated contemporary styles. Also of necessity are a table and chairs. A wooden drop-leaf table that serves a multitude of purposes and takes little space is a practical choice. With reasonable care, it will give a lifetime of service. The versatile parson's table is a good starter piece that will serve many needs. Sturdy but small-scaled wooden chairs that can easily be transported will satisfy inumerable needs and may become family heirlooms.

Aside from these necessary pieces, furniture purchases are dependent on individual circumstances such as available space and financial status. Interior design

Figure 9.2 (*above*). This striking wall cabinet, which serves here as a focal point, could be used in many places to serve many needs. Its simple, sleek lines are echoed in the coffee table and are set off by the curved lines of the sofas and the vase. (Courtesy of Frederic Williams Interiors.)

Figure 9.3 (*facing page, top*). The versatile drop-leaf table serves here as a desk. (Courtesy of Armstrong World Industries.)

Figure 9.4 (*facing page, bottom*). When guests are expected, the table is used for formal or informal dining, and the stereo becomes a serving center. To further change the room's aspect, a sliding wall panel covers the open shelves. (Courtesy of Armstrong World Industries.)

Figure 9.5. Indispensable parson's tables can be used for an end or a corner, for coffee, cocktails, or snacks, or backed up to a sofa. (Courtesy of Founders Furniture.)

Figure 9.6. Small tables of chrome or brass with glass tops take little space, can serve many needs, and add a cosmopolitan touch to a room. (Courtesy of Thayer Coggin.)

is a continuing process; as circumstances change, more furniture will be required. If one piece is chosen at a time, each piece with the overall plan in mind, the rooms will likely have more appeal and personality. The temptation to purchase something that is momentarily appealing but in no way related to the other furnishings should be resisted, as should overwhelming salespeople and so-called bargains. No matter what the cost, if a piece of furniture does not meet individual needs and does not seem right in the room, it is not a bargain at any price. If furniture is good design when purchased, however, it will *always* be good.

Furniture marketing methods

Some understanding of furniture marketing methods will be helpful in making a purchase. To begin with, furniture is often presented to the customer in suites, groups, and collections.

A *suite* of furniture consists of pieces of furniture designed to be used together in a specific room. All pieces look alike and are priced as a unit, and as a rule they cannot be broken up. Two such units are a dining room suite consisting of a table, chairs, and a buffet, and a bedroom suite consisting of a bed, a chest, and a dresser.

A *furniture group* is a large ensemble or collection correlated by the same design. A group may include suites for bedrooms, dining rooms, and living rooms, with many extra pieces. The advantage in purchasing from a group is that pieces are coordinated, and additional items are usually available later on to complete the starter set. A danger here, however, is that a look-alike design may become monotonous. Designing rooms in which everything matches should be avoided. Such rooms are often set up in furniture stores, and they lack interest and personality.

A *collection* has a look of individuality and is usually in the higher-priced market. The impression is one of a mixture of pieces thoughtfully collected over a period of time. Designs are not the same, but all will have a feeling of compatibility.

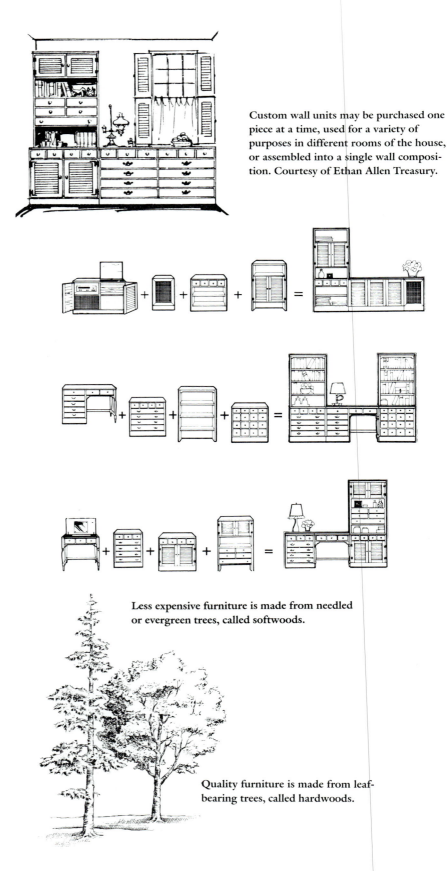

Custom wall units may be purchased one piece at a time, used for a variety of purposes in different rooms of the house, or assembled into a single wall composition. Courtesy of Ethan Allen Treasury.

Less expensive furniture is made from needled or evergreen trees, called softwoods.

Quality furniture is made from leaf-bearing trees, called hardwoods.

Buying wood furniture

The actual value of wood furniture is determined by (1) the wood used, (2) the quality of construction and craftsmanship, (3) the finish, and (4) the design. The price of a piece of furniture is related to these values. Beyond these, the buyer pays for various refinements such as hand carving, unusual veneers, exotic woods, and luxury fabrics.

WOOD

The wood used in furniture, which is of major importance, is better appreciated through an understanding of wood terms: *solid, genuine,* and *veneer.* When a piece of furniture is marked "solid," it indicates that it is made from solid hardwood. The label "genuine" shows that the furniture is made of a single hardwood, with veneer on flat surfaces and solid structural parts such as the legs. Veneer is a thin layer of finishing wood applied to the body of a less refined wood. Some people still cling to the old notion that furniture with veneer is of inferior quality. The contrary, however, is true. With the new methods of cutting and laminating veneers, a piece of veneered furniture today can be stronger and more resistant to warping than a solid piece. Only veneering permits the beautiful effects achieved by the different methods of matching wood grains.

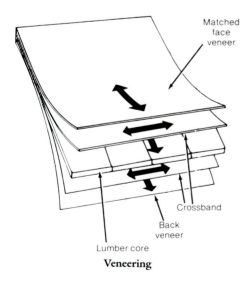

Matched face veneer

Crossband

Back veneer

Lumber core

Veneering

Furniture is made from both hard- and softwoods. Hardwoods come from deciduous trees (those that drop their leaves), such as oak and maple. Hardwoods are more durable and dent resistant than softwoods, and they are more costly. Hardwoods are more attractive than softwoods, however, and they are preferred for fine furniture. Softwoods come from coniferous trees (those with needles that are mostly green the year round), such as pine and spruce. Softwoods are used for less expensive furniture and are also used in combination with hardwoods. The woods most widely used in furniture construction today are pine, birch, maple, oak, cherry, walnut, mahogany, pecan, and teak (see "Color in Wood," Chapter 5). Labels that describe the finish, such as "fruit wood finish" or "walnut finish," refer to the color only, not to the species of wood used.

QUALITY OF CONSTRUCTION

The quality of construction and craftsmanship are often easily apparent. Through a knowledge of what constitutes quality in these areas, one can be assured of getting well-made furniture. Some of the construction features that can be discerned are the following:

□ All sections of furniture should be joined firmly and securely. The most common terms for joining wood are: (1) mortise and tenon, (2) dowel, (3) miter, (4) dovetail, and (5) tongue and groove.

□ A well-constructed chest or table will remain rigid when an attempt is made to rock it.

□ Back panels should be recessed and smoothly finished.

Inner characteristics of furniture determine durability: (1) selected hardwoods; (2) mortise and tenon joints; (3) heavy-duty center drawer guides; (4) drawers dovetailed front and back; (5) durable dust panels between drawers; (6) durable drawer bottoms held rigidly in grooves; (7) strong case backs recessed into ends; (8) well-mounted top and sides; (9) drawer interiors sanded and sealed. (Courtesy of Stanley Furniture.)

Mortise and tenon

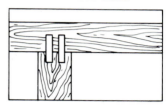

Dowel

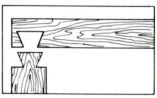

Miter

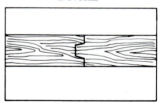

Dovetail

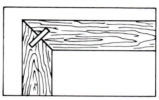

Tongue and groove

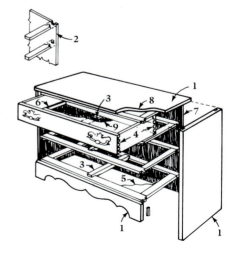

A

B

C

D

E

F

Figure 9.7. Chairs add interest to a room's decor. *A,* Windsor armchair; *B,* Early American ladder-back armchair; *C,* Queen Anne armchair; *D,* Chippendale ladder-back side chair; *E,* French provincial chair; *F,* cane-back neoclassical side chair. (*A, B, C, D, F,* courtesy of Ethan Allen; *E,* courtesy of Drexel Heritage Furnishings.)

▫ Unexposed parts need not be the same quality as exposed surfaces, but should be sanded smooth and stained to match the piece.

▫ Drawers and doors should operate with ease and should be flush with the surface when closed.

▫ Drawers should have solid sides, three-ply nonwarp bottoms that are sanded and sealed against snags, dovetail joints, and should be separated by dust barriers.

▫ Chairs should be sturdy, well proportioned, and comfortable.

The quality of construction, which ranges from poor to excellent, must often be left to the integrity of the manufacturer and the word of the salesperson. A good manufacturer takes great pride in the skilled workmanship that goes into the product, since the company's reputation depends on it. A reliable merchant will be honest in evaluating the furniture he or she sells.

FINISH

The finish on a piece of wood furniture is not always evident, but with a little study, one can be a fairly good judge of its appearance. Good furniture has a mellow patina that results only from much rubbing, a practice that requires time and effort and therefore adds to the total cost. A number of finishes used on furniture today help maintain the beauty of the wood and protect it against the hazards of daily use. Finishes make woods highly resistant to marks from glasses, spills, scratches, and abrasions. Even cigarette burns are no longer the catastrophe they once were. These wonder-working finishes are often completely invisible and let the beauty of the wood grain and color shine through. The salesperson should be qualified to explain the type of finish on the furniture that is being considered for purchase. Poorly constructed furniture often has a hard shine produced by varnish, which may cover inferior wood but will quickly show scratches.

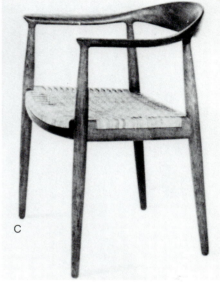

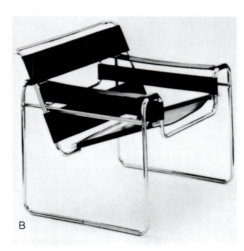

Figure 9.8. Some chairs that have become modern classics. *A*, Thonet's bentwood armchair; *B*, the Wassily armchair, designed by Marcel Breuer; *C*, Hans J. Wegener's The Chair; *D*, Eero Saarinen's plastic pedestal chair. (*A* and *B*, courtesy of Thonet Industries; *C*, courtesy of Frederick Lunning; *D*, courtesy of Knoll International.)

A

B

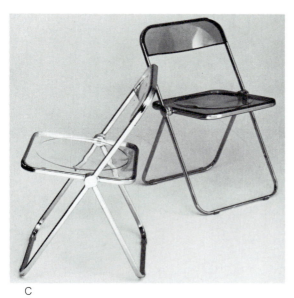

C

Figure 9.9. More modern classics: *A*, the Barcelona chair, designed by Miës van der Rohe; *B*, Charles Eames's lounge chair; *C*, the famous Plia folding chair with aluminum frame and plastic seat and back, designed by Carlo Pirelli. (*A*, courtesy of Knoll International; *B*, courtesy of Herman Miller; *C*, courtesy of Castelli Furniture.)

DESIGN

Design, or style, is a personal consideration, and the design of furniture is usually chosen on the basis of individual taste. If taste is formed on an understanding of the general principles of design, and if suitability and comfort are kept in mind, each furniture purchase should be satisfactory. In general, simple, unadorned items are wise purchases. They will likely be a better value than ornate pieces. Purchasing cheap imitations of more costly hand-carved items should be avoided. The buyer should know what is good design, what he or she likes, and what is right for his or her needs. If a piece of furniture does not have personal appeal, the buyer should not be pressured into a purchase—no matter how popular the style. One does not always have to pay a lot for good design. If the buyer is willing to forego unnecessary extras, he or she can have desirable and well-designed furniture for a modest price. Money should be invested in quality and in good but simple design. Makers of fine furniture have pointed out that only the rich can afford to buy cheap furniture.

Buying upholstered furniture

In the purchase of upholstered furniture, fabric is usually the first consideration, since it is an important step in interior design and is an expression of personality and individual taste. In selecting the fabric, *use* should be the determining factor. The buyer should consider where and by whom it will be used, and the kind and amount of use it will get. When the color, pattern, weave, and feel (or "hand") of the fabric are satisfactory, the tailoring should be inspected. Precise tailoring is necessary for a well-finished

appearance. Seams, welts, and cording should be smooth, straight, and firmly stitched. Hems and pleats should hang evenly. Large patterns should be centered, and patterns should be matched. Quilted fabric should have close, secure stitching to avoid catching. Cushions should fit snugly, and the area under the cushion (the platform) should be covered with a sturdy, coordinated fabric. The back panel should be firmly and neatly tacked or stitched.

Hidden beneath the cover of upholstered furniture are the elements that should produce durability and comfort. Durable, high-quality upholstered furniture has a number of important features:

□ The frame is of strong wood such as oak or elm, and has been dried and conditioned with strongly reinforced joints.

□ The seat and back bases, depending on the type of spring construction used, may be (1) burlap or canvas, (2) steel strips, or (3) 3- or 4-in. strips of closely woven webbing of jute, plastic, or rubber.

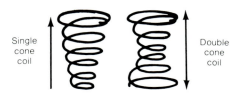

Single cone coil　　Double cone coil

□ The spring construction may be of either sinuous wire or coils. The sinuous wire is the simpler, and by some criteria, better. It is particularly desirable for slim-line modern designs and tight-seated occasional chairs. The cone coil comes in both single and double cone. The *single-cone coil* is a prefabricated unit for standard styles. It is an all-wire unit with coils tied to each other and attached to top and bottom border wires. *Double-cone coils* are mounted and affixed on a resilient base such as strips of webbing or metal, and are hand tied at the top. This construction provides maximum comfort and is used in more expensive deep-seated upholstery.

□ The cushioning should be comfortable, resilient, able to take hard usage, and should stay in place. Since new materials are being added continually, and older ones are being improved, meaningful questions should be asked: What kind of cushioning does the chair or sofa have? Will it retain its shape? Can it be cleaned? Is it odorless and nonallergenic? Is it light enough to make the furniture easily movable? What kind of springs does it have?

□ Filling materials of various types and qualities are used for cushioning, either alone or in combination. These materials, but not the quality, will be listed on the attached label. *Polyester* is a commonly used filler. It is lightweight, resilient, odorless, and resists mildew and moths. It may be used alone or combined with cores of foam or innersprings. *Foam rubber,* which may be used alone or over springs, is durable, resilient, and lightweight, and retains its shape. *Urethane* foam is a synthetic material of great versatility. Its extreme lightness and resiliency are particular features. It resists liquids, moths, and mildew. *Rubberized fibers* such as sisal, which have less resiliency than the previous filling materials, are used in moderately priced furniture. *Shredded fibers* from natural sources such as some leaves are generally used in low-priced furniture. *Cotton felt* is used to protect springs and other filling materials, and is used alone on inexpensive furniture.

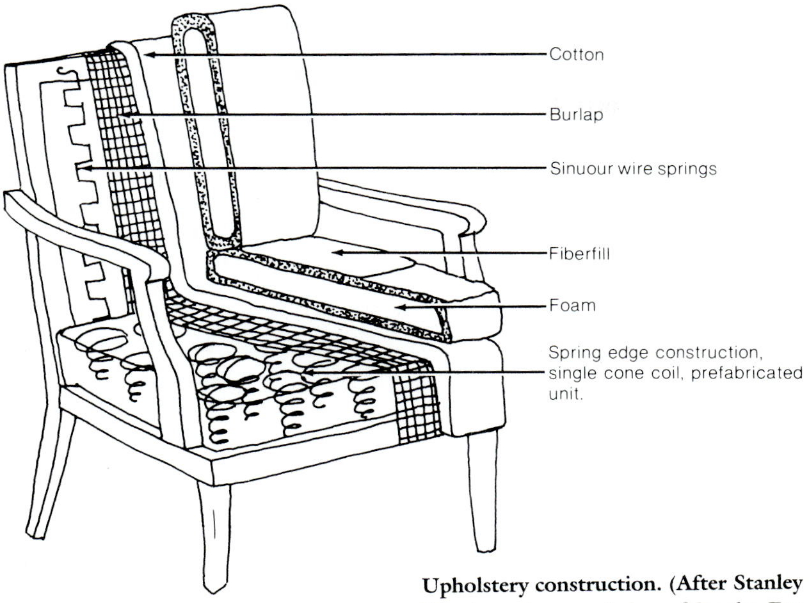
Cotton
Burlap
Sinuour wire springs
Fiberfill
Foam
Spring edge construction, single cone coil, prefabricated unit.

Upholstery construction. (After Stanley Furniture, by permission of Stanley Furniture Company.)

To be assured of the comfort of a chair or sofa, one should sit on it. The depth of the seat and the height of the back and arms should be checked. If a lounge chair is being chosen for a particular person, that person should try it out. A chair that is comfortable for one person may not be right for another. Every person deserves a chair that fits his or her proportions.

To get the best service from upholstered chairs and sofas, one should select those with loose cushions on the back and seat. They can be turned and used on both sides, thus doubling the life of the fabric. Square seat cushions wear better than T-shaped ones; the middle and end cushions may be exchanged to increase the wear. Dining room chairs with slip seats that are easily removed and recovered take less material and wear longer. Quilted fabric will wear longer than plain.

When buying the first pieces of upholstered furniture, a wise choice is a basically simple, well-proportioned design that is not limited to any specific style or period. When covered in the appropriate fabric, such a piece will fit into any decor used later on. Wicker comes in a wide price range, can be used almost anywhere and is never out of style (see Figure 9.1).

Because so many hidden features are in upholstered furniture, and quality varies from poor to excellent, relying on the integrity of the manufacturer and the word of the salesperson is often necessary. Buying from a reputable dealer is therefore important. Whenever possible, one should choose brand names that have an established reputation for superior quality. Most manufacturers supply information tags, warranties, and helpful literature with their furniture. The buyer should read these carefully, as they are a guarantee of satisfaction.

Furniture styles

Throughout history, the diversity of people everywhere has found expression in many ways, including the way people lived in their homes and the things with which they surrounded themselves. Invariably the most basic piece of furniture in all Western countries was the "seat," the evolution of which is a fascinating study. The differences in designs of seats, or chairs, and other items of furniture as well as the decorative arts, were the result of a number of factors including climate, politics, religion, and customs, which varied from one country to another.

In the past, Americans have shown little reverence for historic design. Too often the latest trend in home furnishings has been held in highest esteem, with little regard to quality. As interest in America's cultural heritage has grown, however, a concern for ancestral homes has come into focus, with furniture being an important element. Today few restraints are imposed on how furniture is combined, and the alternatives are many. Effectively integrating the past with the present, however, requires pertinent information. Although an understanding of period styles of furniture is not necessary to create an attractive home, a knowledge of historic furnishings will deepen the aesthetic appreciation of one's design heritage, will broaden one's concepts of interior design, and will foster creative energies. A working knowledge

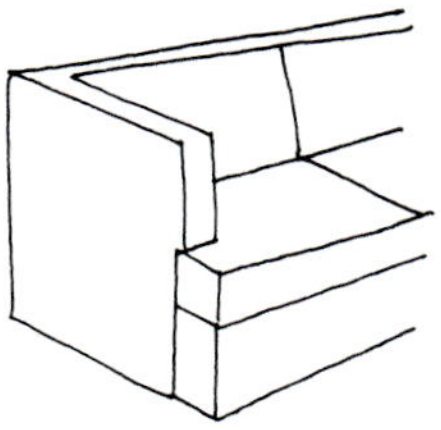

T-shaped cushion

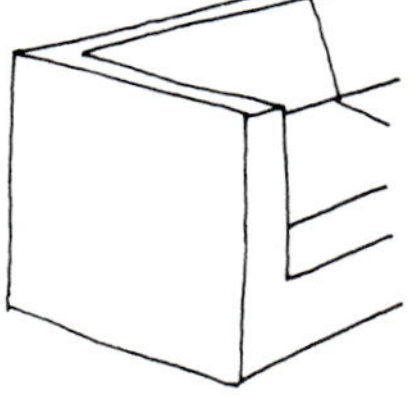

Square cushion

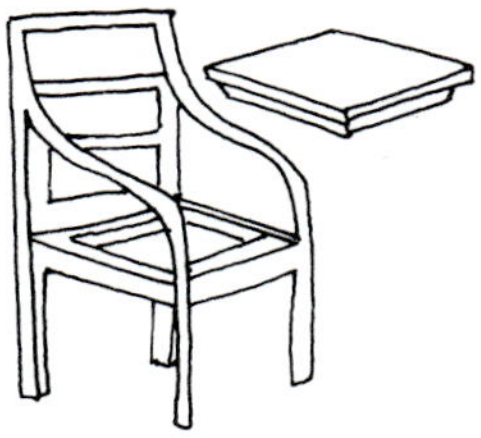

Slip seat

of the most commonly used styles of furniture, both traditional and modern, is essential to the interior designer. For the person interested in designing his or her own home, this knowledge will instill confidence in his or her designing ability, will provide a basis for making valid choices, and may be the source of an exciting and continued interest.

A clarification of the terms *antique, reproduction, adaptation,* and *period style* may be helpful. An antique is a piece of furniture or a work of art that according to United States law must be at least 100 years old. A reproduction is a copy of an original. Some are done so meticulously that only the well-trained eye can detect the difference; yet some modern reproductions are far from exact copies. An adaptation is an article in which only some elements from the original have been adapted to a contemporary design. *Period style* is a term used to designate a single item or a complete interior, including the architectural background, furniture, and decorative arts that were prevalent in a specific country at a particular time in history. Some people refer to this style as *traditional.* Sometimes furniture styles are lumped into two general categories: *period* and *modern.* Some authors use the term *contemporary* to include today's modern; others separate the two. Some confusion and much overlapping exist. Since no official body has established what term refers to what style, this text will group today's most commonly used furniture styles into three general categories: (1) informal provincial, (2) formal traditional, and (3) contemporary and modern, followed by a number of other styles in use today.

In the belief that a detailed consideration of furniture styles is beyond the scope of a beginning course in interior design, an effort has been made to briefly characterize the furniture styles that have had the greatest impact on American lives. This effort is made with the hope of stimulating curiosity in, and further study and a better understanding of, the values of America's cultural heritage, with the knowledge that to know the past is to lay a sound foundation for the present and for the future.

INFORMAL PROVINCIAL

Informal provincial is the handcrafted look in America. To achieve this style, one may use only one ethnic style or may combine furnishings from many sources, so long as the feeling is one of lived-in, unpretentious homeyness. Whether part of the architectural background, movable furniture, or the arts and crafts, furnishings that come from the same country will share a natural affinity and will combine well. Much of the provincial charm is a result of bringing together items from different areas at home and abroad.

One popular style in this category is the look of seventeenth-century America—commonly called "Early American." This style can be created by using a pine wall, simply paneled, a wallpaper with an authentic pattern, or warm off-white painted plaster. With any of these treatments, a dado is appropriate. Braided or hooked rugs on plank floors or textured wall-to-wall carpeting will add to the homey look. Pine or maple furniture is appropriate for this style and might include a corner cupboard, an open *hutch,* a ladder-back chair with a rush-bottom seat, a Windsor chair, a painted *Hitchcock* rocker, a spindle-armed sofa, a *dough-box* end table, and a cobbler's bench for a coffee table. Fabrics with a handcrafted look, coarse weaves, tweed, and old-fashioned designs are appropriate. Colors are typically warm, earthy tones with a predominance of blue.

Early American

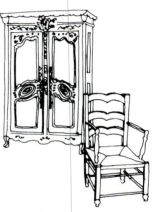

Country French

Capturing the rustic feeling of country French can be accomplished by using a pictorial *toile de Jouy* fabric on walls, at the windows, and in upholstery. Sturdy *distressed* furniture with a combination of straight and gently curving lines is appropriate. Such items as a *salamander-back chair,* an *armoire* with molded panels, a small *commode* with open "chicken-wire" grills, and a handsome *panetiere* (bread box) will create an air of authenticity. Accessories are virtually unlimited and are important in setting an informal provincial mood. Pewter, copper, wood, and painted tin items are suitable. ***Primitive paintings,*** silhouettes, pictures of songbirds, brightly decorated pottery, and ***tole*** lamps are only a few of the items that are appropriate for the informal provincial look. One or more original pieces that echo the history of any of the styles used will add distinct character and appeal to a room.

Historically, furnishings with a rustic, handcrafted look were considered for use only by the poor and peasant classes of every country, and more ornate, refined furniture, smooth textures, and shiny surfaces were considered the prerogative of the wealthy. This is no longer the case. The informal provincial style is the choice of many people and no longer reflects social or economic class.

FORMAL TRADITIONAL
(French and English)

The term *traditional* may refer to interior furnishings from any country so long as it is one of the more formal styles. Many of the favorite traditional designs come from the eighteenth century, an age of great prosperity and a flourishing of the arts in the Western world. The furniture styles of this period from both France and England have been great favorites with many Americans who enjoy their warmth, grace, and elegance. Some of these styles have been adapted and scaled to meet present-day requirements without losing their true character.

FRENCH

From eighteenth-century France comes the excessively ornate rococo style of Louis XV and the lavish delicate neo-classic style of Louis XVI. Excellent reproductions of these lavish styles are being made today, sometimes with a surprising degree of authenticity.

The furniture of the Louis XV period has been simplified to produce an extremely popular and versatile style that Americans have termed *French provincial*. Although most Americans have preferred to use this style in a formal setting, it

FRENCH

Louis XV

Louis XVI

may successfully be dressed up or down. The choice of fabric will determine the degree of formality. Accessories may be as formal as personal taste dictates. French provincial is an ideal choice for those who want casual comfort with an air of elegance.

The neoclassic style of Louis XVI, which is the choice of many Americans who desire delicate urbanity, has been simplified for wider use and has been termed *Italian provincial*. The style is characterized by restrained and dignified richness. Appropriate for this furniture are fabrics such as damasks, brocatelles, and cut velvets in soft colors of green, gold, venetian blue, and white, with stripes and classical designs of late eighteenth-century France and Italy. Formal paneling, architectural paper, Japanese grass cloth, and flocked paper in classical

designs are appropriate for walls. Plain-weave wall-to-wall carpeting and Aubusson, Savonnerie, and faded oriental rugs are suitable for both French and Italian provincial.

ENGLISH

English furnishings of the eighteenth century, commonly known as Georgian, have a different look from the French of the same period. English furniture was more sturdy and more restrained. The style known as Queen Anne, introduced around 1700, was based on the curve and assumed a grace and refinement formerly unknown in English furniture. The Queen Anne style had an immediate and lasting influence on Americans, who found in its timeless and versatile design a practicality that combined well with most styles. Although its popularity has waned over the years, the 1970s witnessed a resurgence of Queen Anne furniture, which has gained momentum in the 1980s.

Those who desire a less formal look might choose earlier, less ornate Queen Anne furniture forms such as a simple fiddleback side chair, a chintz-covered wing chair, a bonnet-top ***highboy,*** and a rectangular tea table. These forms can be placed against a background of plain painted walls with a darker colored dado, hardwood or simulated hardwood floors,

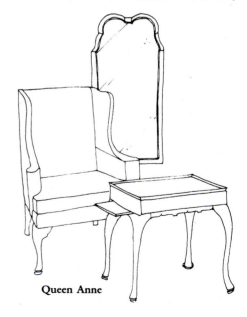

Queen Anne

hooked or oriental rugs, and informal chintz-draped windows. For a more formal look, the later, more ornate Queen Anne furniture may be dressed up and placed in the most dignified setting.

Chippendale furniture, which was first produced in England in the eighteenth century during the golden age of the great cabinetmakers, graced the newly acquired mansions of the new affluent society in America during the mid- and late eighteenth century. Chippendale fur-

Chippendale

niture is a product of a "school" rather than the work of a single man, and incorporates designs from Queen Anne, Gothic, French, Adam, and Chinese. It uses both straight and curved lines, and is large in scale, sturdy, and elegant. The most characteristic pieces are the *yoke-back* side chairs, flared wing chairs, large *case* pieces such as *breakfronts* and highboys, desks, and small tables, of which the piecrust tilt top is a furniture gem. Typical room settings have formally paneled walls and hardwood floors with oriental rugs. Fabrics are damasks, taffetas, brocades, and velvets in rich primary colors.

Furniture in America from about 1790 to 1815, known as federal, was dominated by the styles of English cabinetmakers Hepplewhite and Sheraton,

Federal furniture of Duncan Phyfe

whose designs grew out of the Louis XVI taste. Both styles were more delicate than Queen Anne and Chippendale, and the emphasis was on color and surface decoration rather than on form. Dining room furniture in the new style was particularly popular, since the smaller scale made it suitable for most homes. Fabrics with a French look are suitable for this style, as well as light-colored wallpapers, painted wood trim, and French or oriental rugs. Although federal furniture has not been in popular demand in recent years, its design will always be good. During the federal period America produced its most famous cabinetmaker, Duncan Phyfe. Phyfe interpreted the English forms, but also developed a style of his own. He is the only American cabinetmaker whose furniture is called "period" furniture.

Rural English

In the 1960s a trend toward the new English look in America occurred, which has continued into the 1980s and promises to remain for some time. The new English look is varied, versatile, and spans centuries of history. It is a country look with a quality of lived-in opulence and a svelte strength that is more manor than farmhouse. Much of the beauty of the English look is in the furniture itself, which for the most part is scaled to today's homes and has a well-bred look that combines a robust structure with a mellow finish. It covers a wide gamut of moods in varying degrees of formality and informality, but always with an eye to authenticity of design. Appropriate for this furniture are deep, rich colors in muted shades of green, red, blue, and gold. Fabrics may be velvets, brocatelles, and damasks in Renaissance designs, or printed linens and crewel embroidery for a less formal mood.

CONTEMPORARY, MODERN, AND POSTMODERNISM

CONTEMPORARY

The term *contemporary* is commonly used to designate a broad category of design used today. Some manufacturers have called it "classic contemporary"; others

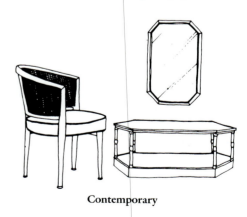

Contemporary

refer to it as "transitional." By any name, contemporary is a modified modern. Furniture is modern with a flavor of a historic style marked by a new elegance. In achieving this elegance, designers have returned for inspiration to classical and traditional forms, which they have adapted to fit today's homes. Many use authentic motifs and carving. The grace and dignity of Old World artistry is combined with contemporary originality to produce fine furniture that has beauty and appeal and the usefulness and sturdiness needed for present-day living. Many storage pieces have been made high and narrow to use limited space, and many dual-purpose pieces are filling a practical need. Contemporary mixes well with modern or with reproductions of period styles. When planning the general scheme of the room, personal preference should determine one's special "mix."

MODERN

At any time in history when a new art form emerges that breaks all ties with previous design forms—whether it is in music, architecture, or furniture—it is referred to as "modern." In each era it has been an expression of the times. Today's modern furniture design is an expression of the twentieth century and aptly suggests the tempo of modern Americans. The key word in modern design is *functionalism*. Function determines the form of each object with an emphasis on line, proportion, color, texture, and finish. Furniture is designed for comfort, convenience, and durability, and has a tendency to be lower than other styles. Common features of modern furniture are simplicity of planes and surfaces, and the use of plastics, metals, and glass. Molded plastic chairs are sturdy, light, durable, and relatively inexpensive. Plastic-laminated surfaces are impervious to moisture, may simulate natural wood grains, and are easy to maintain.

Inflatable plastic furniture is practical for Americans on the move, and when in use seems to float, making it a good choice for rooms with limited space. Items of brass and steel combined with wood are popular. For hard-use areas, either residential or commercial, versatile modern furniture is practical and comes in a wide price range. Modern is many

Modern

things: sleek and functional, puffy and comfortable, formal and informal, expensive or priced to fit the most modest budget. Modern is stimulating, youthful, flexible, and easy to care for.

Backgrounds are often stark white with strong architectural emphasis on verticality and height to expand space, with some areas dramatically papered. Woods are prominent, usually in a natural state. Fabrics emphasize texture and contrast, with vinyls playing an important role. Pattern may be bold in abstract or conventional design, with motifs drawn from any source. Color schemes range from sophisticated white, and neutral monochromatics, to sharp contrasts with unusual combinations. Wooden or tile floors with area rugs of handwoven dhurries or orientals are favored.

Modern furniture should be chosen with an eye to good design. New advances in technology are bringing about frequent changes in materials and methods of production, which make modern furniture vulnerable to a sudden turn in fashion.

Since the early twentieth century, modern design has gone through many stages, each contributing something of lasting value. Some of the furniture designs, which have become twentieth-century classics, and their designers should be well known to every student of interior design.

The focal point of modern design from 1919 to 1933 was the Bauhaus in Weimar, Germany, and the new philosophy—that aesthetically pleasing objects could be created by mechanical means—was the impetus that set it in motion. At the Bauhaus the two great furniture pioneers Marcel Breuer and Ludwig Miës van der Rohe developed the *cantilevered* steel chair, which has been the model for thousands of variations throughout the world. Miës van der Rohe is best known for his *Barcelona* chair, which has a timeless elegance.

Other modern classics are Michael Thonet's well-known bentwood chair, Hans Wegener's *The Chair*, which is characterized by refinement of shape, sculptural details, and an understanding of the inherent qualities of wood, Charles Eames's famous molded rosewood chairs, Eero Saarinen's much-copied molded plastic pedestal chair, Le Corbusier's *Grand Confort* chair, Alvar Aalto's popular *pension* chair, and two Italian chairs of the 1970s: Soriana's upholstered chair, designed by Tobia and Afra Scarpa, and Castelli's budget chair, the famous Plia, designed by Carlo Pirelli (see Figure 9.9). Any one of these chairs can add an air of distinction to a room and should be familiar to every discerning American.

POSTMODERNISM

A new direction in architecture and interiors, referred to as "post-modernism," promises to bring about profound changes in design of the eighties. Many top designers in the field believe that this new and freer spirit of design will have a liberating effect and will add a fresh inspiration to the design community. They foresee a transition movement that will be historically aware and sensitive to the changing needs of today's families while communicating new concepts. How and by whom this new movement will be interpreted is yet to be determined, but some anticipate that the more adventurous furniture manufacturers will respond.

OTHER STYLES IN CURRENT USE

ORIENTAL

The Oriental influence is part of America's early tradition, since it was known to our ancestors in Europe. Principles and elements of Japanese architecture, which include the predominance of the horizontal line, the use of natural materials, asymmetry, open planning, simplicity, and the absence of ornamentation, were used by Frank Lloyd Wright in his buildings and are an integral part of the Japanese house in America today. The interior of the Japanese house is open and uncluttered, wood floors have tatami

Figure 9.10 (*top*). The Grand Confort chair and matching sofa, designed in 1928 by Le Corbusier. This chair was the first to eliminate the standard frame. (Courtesy of Atelier International.)

Figure 9.11 (*bottom*). The Modu Form oak sectional group allows flexibility of arrangement for high-traffic environments. (Courtesy of Modu Form, AG&W Industries.)

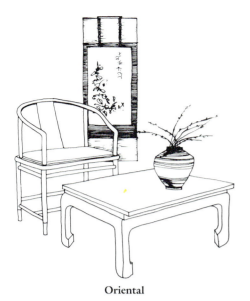

Oriental

The Southwest look

Victorian

mats, ceilings are beamed, walls are plain, and shoji screens, often used for both walls and windows, open onto the gardens. Furniture is sparse, usually in a natural finish, built low, and supported on brass feet. Color schemes used in fabrics for drapery and upholstery are shibui—taken from nature (see Chapter 5). Only a few treasured items are displayed. The entire scheme is unobtrusive, easy to live with, and has a sense of refinement.

THE AMERICAN SOUTHWEST

The American Southwest style was never fully appreciated until the decade of the seventies, although the adobe house was probably the earliest in America's history. Composed of a blending of Spanish and Indian cultures, the Southwest look is exemplified in a casual, unpretentious interior of timeless style and charm. White rough-plastered walls, dark wood-beamed ceilings, Mexican tile floors, a corner fireplace, and built-in benches provide an uncluttered background against which the simple, hand-carved, painted furniture and colorful, hand-

crafted arts provide an exciting contrast. Rush-bottom chairs, a trestle table, a chest, and the indispensable *trastero*, or great cupboard, make up the principal items of furniture. Through the use of geometrically designed Navajo rugs, brilliantly colored wool embroidery, gleaming tinware, Indian pottery, and folk images, the unmistakable Southwest look is firmly established with an originality and distinctive beauty that has universal appeal.

VICTORIAN

Victorian is not a style but is an era that spanned the 64-yr reign of England's Queen Victoria (1837–1901) and the first two decades of the twentieth century. During that time, styles from Gothic to Greek revival were revived with considerable exaggeration and overlapping. Much Victorian furniture, which for so long was maligned and considered no better than junk, is now being sought after as valuable antiques. Many of Victorian furniture's admirers are enthusiastically repairing, refinishing, and putting it to work, often in new ways. After moving from parlor to attic to junkyard to antique shop, Victorian furniture has returned to the living room.

Although Victorian furniture was a combination of many things, the image most commonly evoked by Americans is

the lavish *Belter Parlor* with its florid walls and carpets, marble-topped tables, and excessively carved suites, which included a love seat, a lady's and a gentleman's chair covered in red velvet, plus a generous supply of fringed and beribboned "fancy" chairs. Lest the room seem bare, several whatnot shelves laden with bric-a-brac, dried flowers under glass domes, small statuary, and a mantelshelf overburdened with rococo ornaments completed the symbol of Victorian affluence. Victorian furniture today has been greatly moderated from the stereotype of a century ago. Both young and old are finding that nineteenth-century furniture is a good mixer, and to the surprise of many, it is often at its best when placed in a modern setting.

THE COUNTRY LOOK

The term *country look* came into popularity during the early sixties. Shortly thereafter it became a catchall term for almost anything from rustic to manor. Today, however, it is becoming a viable style. The look is cloistered and comfortable, and may incorporate furniture from a number of countries so long as designs are rooted in the past and have an aura of quality and character. Two examples are the country French and the English manor look. Furniture may be adaptations or reproductions, but an antique or two will add much to the feeling of authenticity.

Living with and nourishing old furnishings of warmth from centuries past does not mean being old-fashioned. The country look today can be found in an apartment on Park Avenue, a hillside home in California, or anyplace in between. A successful country look takes careful study and planning. Fabrics and accessories play an important part in setting the theme. If each item is chosen with discrimination, the result can be an environment of casual sophistication that is warm and familiar and has a feeling of both nostalgia and comfort for modern living.

A review of fashion trends in home furnishings shows that from time to time, certain foreign influences become popular. Some are short-lived, and others have persisted over a long time. The most popular influence in recent years was Mediterranean, which came into vogue in the sixties for a brief period.

MIXING STYLES

Today, fewer families than before buy matched items of furniture, and they no longer maintain the same style of furniture throughout the house or even throughout the same room. The eclectic look—which is a mixing rather than a matching—is in vogue. Eclectic does not mean a hodgepodge, however. Pieces should be related in scale and chosen with a final goal in mind. Success will be more surely achieved if a common theme runs through the entire scheme—some element that ties the pieces together. For example, to achieve the provincial look, informality is the key, and all country furniture, regardless of the source, is

Eclectic

compatible. For the traditional look, dignity is the key, and refined pieces of almost any style can be combined together with pleasant results. The modern look allows for more daring and imagination.

Whatever the general theme of a room, it ought not dominate so as to create a feeling of monotony. Interest can often be brought into a room by the unexpected. For example, a pair of Victorian chairs placed in a modern setting will bring something special to the room. A modern sofa will give a period room a fresh, updated look. An up-to-date arrangement of traditional furniture can reemphasize its beauty. The clean sweep of modern decor may serve as the most effective background for a highly prized antique.

Today, more than ever before, people are taking a more mature look at furnishings of the past and the present, and are finding new ways in which they can be used. People have discovered that much can be borrowed from furnishings of the past to enrich present-day living and that much from the present can add new life to the old. As new foreign influences come along, each can be adapted to meet present-day needs without discarding everything from yesterday. In this way, people are developing a more mature attitude toward interior design.

Intelligent shopping

When selecting furniture, style names should not be of great concern. They should be used only as guidelines. The buyer should determine what features distinguish one style from another, what mood is created by each, and which styles can and cannot compatibly be used together. The buyer should learn what constitutes a genuine antique, a reproduction, and an adaptation. The library, a variety of good magazines, and model rooms in stores are sources for information and ideas. The buyer should pay particular attention to homes he or she likes and should consult a professional interior designer. These guidelines will help the buyer to shop with more discrimination and to get the best value for his or her money.

Too many people today are buying elaborate furniture because they mistakenly think it looks expensive. They are influenced by the high percentage of bad household furnishings available. Although in the much-publicized warehouse operations the preponderance of furniture design is poor to mediocre, good design can be found there at reasonable prices by one who shops with a trained eye. Avoiding the selection of a definite period style is usually wise for young people furnishing their first home. Their tastes frequently change after a few years, and replacement of furniture is a major expenditure. Always available is well-designed nonperiod furniture that adapts to any style, and only the appropriate use of fabric is necessary to create a definite mood.

Since purchasing furniture is a long-time investment, it should not be done hurriedly. The interior designer should shop until he or she finds what will appeal to client tastes; the home owner until what will appeal to his or her family's tastes. One piece at a time should be purchased and then lived with awhile. In the home, the piece will appear different from the way it appeared in the store, and ideas for interior design may change accordingly. No matter what style is preferred, furniture that is well designed with simple, uncluttered lines will give satisfaction for a long time.

To shop intelligently, one should become familiar with the style names of the most commonly used pieces of furniture. Certain identifying names have been given to different styles of furniture, and although details such as legs, arms, and backs will vary widely, the general shapes can easily be recognized.

Upholstered chairs and sofas are identified by their general shape, height from the floor, types of backs, arms, and legs. Although some details such as cushion treatment and trim will vary with the individual designer, they can usually be identified.

Many different kinds of tables are used today. Decorative details such as legs, feet, and points of design will vary according to the style of the period, but the general characteristics remain the same and can be recognized.

Case furniture is a general term for pieces of furniture used for holding things. In cabinetwork it refers to the shell of a piece of furniture, such as a chest of drawers, or any type of cabinet. As with chairs and tables, the details in case pieces will differ depending on the period design, but the major charac-teristics remain the same. For a number of the most common styles of chairs, sofas, tables, and case pieces, see Figures 9.12 and 9.13.

Many furniture firms use plastic where they once used wood. See-through acrylic furniture can be attractive and seems to occupy no space, but it scratches easily. Many molded plastic chairs and tables are of excellent design, are practical and durable, and come in a wide price range. The famous pedestal chair of Eero Saarinen has become a modern classic. The design will always be good, and the chair may be used almost anywhere.

For some purposes, such as for tabletops that get hard usage, plastic may serve the purpose better and will be more durable than wood. Plastic can have a look and feel near to that of wood, needs no wax, stain, or varnish, resists scratches and most household liquids, and is easy to maintain. The veneer may be a vinyl laminate that contains a thin veneer of wood, a vinyl that simulates wood grain-ing through a photographic process, or a combination of both vinyl laminate and simulated wood graining.

Plastic is sometimes used on the face of furniture pieces to simulate intricate carv-ing. Although plastic on flat surfaces can be a practical and wise choice, its use in simulating hand carving should be avoided, since this smacks of pretense. Manufacturers and salespeople do not refer to these pieces as plastics, but as vinyl veneers, high-pressure laminates, or molded components. If used where they serve a definite function, man-made ma-terials may be a better choice than wood.

Care of fine furniture

Elementary as it sounds, regular dusting and polishing are the best guardians of the beauty of a fine furniture finish. Grandma with her feather duster under-stood the secret of preventing the ac-cumulation of surface soil, often abrasive and harmful to a carefully rubbed finish. Today excellent waxes and polishes, if used regularly, can deepen the luster and clarity of fine finishes as they maintain an important protective film. Accidents will occur, and for the treatment of these, the following suggestions are presented courtesy of Ethan Allen, Baumritter Corporation.

Minor scratches A wax stick in a match-ing color should be used to fill the scratch. Wax sticks are inexpensive and are usually available at paint, hardware, or furniture stores. The wax should be rubbed in well, then the furniture should be wiped with a soft, dry cloth, followed by an application of polish.

White spots—cause unknown The blemish should be rubbed with cigar or cigarette ashes, using a cloth dipped in wash, lubricating oil, vegetable shorten-ing, lard, or salad oil. The area should be wiped off immediately and rewaxed with polish.

Alcohol spots Method A—The spot should be rubbed with a finger dipped in paste wax, silver polish, linseed oil, or moistened cigar ash. The area should be rewaxed with polish. Method B—On some finishes a quick application of ammonia will do the trick. A few drops should be placed on a damp cloth and rubbed on the spot. An application of polish should follow immediately.

Watermarks Marks or rings from wet glasses are common on tables, especially if these surfaces have not been waxed. Wax cannot prevent damage when liquids are allowed to stand on the finish indefi-nitely. The wax will, however, keep liquid from being absorbed immediately, thus allowing time for the liquid to be wiped up before it damages the finish. If watermarks appear, the following meth-ods should be tried. Method A—Wax or polish should be applied with fine 3/0 steel wool, rubbing lightly. Method B—A clean, thick blotter should be placed over the ring and pressed with a warm (not hot) iron. The process should be re-peated until the ring disappears.

FURNITURE IDENTIFICATION

Nested tables

Tea table

Harvest table

Pedestal table

Tilt-top pedestal

Tier table

Butterfly table

Console

Pembroke

Gateleg

Lamp table

Hutch

Secretary

Breakfront

Armoire

China cabinet

Double chest

Chest on chest

Chest of drawers

Kneehole desk

Buffet

Student desk

Grand piano

Four-poster bed

Canopy bed

Ottoman

Console piano

Figure 9.12. Furniture identification: tables, case furniture, desks, beds, and pianos.

FURNITURE IDENTIFICATION

Side chair

Open-arm chair

Wing chair

Channel-back chair

Tub chair

Ladder-back chair

Spoon-back chair

Skirted club chair

Occasional chair

Lawson lounge

Recliner

Camelback

Lawson

Tuxedo

Studio couch

Studio couch opened to bed

Chesterfield

Love seat

Convertible sofa

Rollaway bed

Chaise lounge

Convertible sofa open to bed

Figure 9.13. Furniture identification: seating pieces and beds.

Candle wax   An ice cube should be held on the wax for a few seconds to harden it, but melted ice should be wiped up immediately. As much wax as can be removed with the fingers should be crumbled off, then the area should be scraped gently with a dull knife. A brisk rub with a clean cloth saturated with liquid wax is the next step. The area should then be wiped dry with a clean cloth. The process should be repeated until the mark disappears.

Milk spots   When milk or foods containing milk or cream are allowed to remain on furniture, the effect of the lactic acid is like that of a mild paint or varnish remover. The spilled food should be wiped up as quickly as possible. If spots show, they should be cleaned with wax. Then the procedure for alcohol spots should be followed.

ASSIGNMENT

Visit a wide range of furniture stores, from the economy-priced factory outlets to the most prestigious showrooms, and make the following observations:

1 Compare the quality of design and craftsmanship and the prices. Make notes of findings at different price levels.

2 Observe room setups for the overall effect, then make a detailed examination of the floor coverings, wall and window treatments, individual pieces of furniture, and accessories.

3 Feel the wood and inspect the upholstery and drapery fabrics. The things that appeal repeatedly will indicate personal preferences.

CHAPTER TEN

Furniture and Wall Arrangement

The arrangement of the furnishings in a room constitutes a composition in spatial design, and if successful, it will have incorporated certain art principles and elements. Since a room is planned for particular people and for their unique way of living, however, furnishing a room should be approached from a practical, commonsense point of view, using the principles of design merely as guidelines.

Furniture

SPATIAL DESIGN IN FLOOR COMPOSITION

New economic standards, contemporary trends in architecture, new furniture styles, and changes in manner of living that place an emphasis on different activities within the home—all have an influence on the use of space, not only throughout the house as a whole but also within individual rooms.

With the increase in building costs, space is at a premium, and its distribution within the home has changed to meet today's needs. During the early years of the century, the parlor was a small, often austere room used only for special occasions. The dining room was the gathering place for families three times a day, and the kitchen was big and homey—the heart of the home. In the late twenties, open planning became the vogue, with the entrance way, the living room, the dining room, and often the kitchen as one open space, with areas of activity defined by rugs, by furniture placement, and through the use of color and fabric. The past decade has seen a return to more privacy but with an easy feeling of flexibility. Little need exists for the parlor today, although a living room off bounds to household activities is once again in demand. The dining room is back, but it is smaller and is used as dual-purpose space, since three-times-a-day togetherness is seldom possible. The kitchen expanded into a family room, has again taken on the main burden of household living.

The key word today in furniture arrangement for every room is *efficiency*. Strict adherence to any set of rules will most likely be inappropriate in furnishing today's home. When arranging furniture in any room of the home, first priority should be given to the household and its life-style. Beauty and good design are important, but comfort and convenience are the most essential. A room can be pleasant in appearance but impractical for living.

In spite of the differences in life-styles, certain guidelines in the arrangement of furniture should provide some help.

Figure 10.1. When well integrated into a corner grouping, the sofa need not be placed parallel to the wall. In this room, the corner space behind the sofa accommodates triangular tables and secondary seating, resulting in an ingenious overall arrangement. (Courtesy of Michael G. Merle Associates.)

GUIDELINES IN FURNITURE ARRANGEMENT

▫ Each room should be planned with a purpose in mind. A decision should be made on who will use the room and for what purpose.

▫ Furniture should be in keeping with the scale of the room. The overall dimensions and the architectural background should determine the size and general feeling of the furnishings.

▫ Space for traffic should be provided. Doorways should be free. Major traffic lanes should be unobstructed by furniture. Redirecting traffic is sometimes necessary, which can be accomplished by skillful furniture placement and by the use of screens and dividers.

▫ Furnishings should be arranged to give the room a sense of equilibrium. Opposite walls should *seem* balanced so that the room will be at rest. When neither architectural features nor furniture distribution can create this sense, it may be achieved through the knowledgeable use of color, fabrics, and accessories.

▫ A good balance of high and low and angular and rounded furniture should be achieved. When furniture is all or predominantly low, the feeling of height may be created by incorporating shelves, mirrors, pictures, and hangings into a grouping.

▫ Architectural and mechanical features should be considered. Nothing should interfere with the opening of windows, swinging of doors, or heating or air-conditioning devices. Lamps should be placed near electrical outlets.

▫ A room should not be overcrowded. Underfurnishing a room is always better than overfurnishing. Some empty space between groupings helps to give an uncluttered effect. An occasional open space or empty corner may enhance a room and may give the occupants breathing space. On the other hand, an underfurnished room may be too stark and uninviting. Either extreme should be avoided.

▫ Large pieces of furniture—particularly case pieces—are usually better placed parallel to the walls. In some contemporary rooms, however, the major seating arrangement based on a diagonal plan can be effective.

▫ Pushing large pieces tightly into a corner, or close against floor-to-ceiling windows should be avoided.

▫ The heaviest furniture grouping should be arranged along the highest wall in rooms with slanting ceilings.

ROOM FURNISHING PROCEDURE

In thinking through and carrying out the furnishing of a room, the following suggestions may be useful.

Seldom should a room be completely furnished all at once; it should grow according to a well-organized plan. Whether the room is being furnished for the first time or is undergoing some minor modifications, the mood and function of the room should be determined. Once the completed room has been visualized, that picture should always be kept in mind. Inappropriate or faddish ideas should not be allowed to divert the unified atmosphere that is desired. No rooms, however, should adhere so rigidly to a theme that it becomes monotonous. Harmony with diversity should be the ultimate goal.

The room's size, shape, assets, and possibilities should be assessed. After the room assets and defects have been studied, the following questions should be

Figure 10.2 (*facing page*). Arranged for comfort and conversation, this pleasant cross-corner arrangement faces a diagonally placed fireplace and away from the light of the high, arched window. (Photograph by Mark K. Allen, residence of Arta and Ariel Ballif.)

asked: Are the dimensions of the room pleasing, or will altering the apparent height, width, or length be necessary? Are the openings well placed for balance and convenience? Are there jogs, niches, or other features to be minimized or emphasized, or would the addition of some architectural feature add interest? Will it be necessary to redirect traffic? What is the exposure? How much will the quality and quantity of light affect the choice of colors? These and other questions should be considered before you proceed.

The room should be drawn to scale on graph paper (¼ in. equals 1 ft). The exact position of all architectural features such as doors, windows, radiators or heat vents, and electrical outlets should be marked. Major traffic lanes (lanes in which traffic must pass from one door to another) should be indicated, and areas of activity should be marked. Experiments with different furniture arrangements can be made within the area drawn. Through the use of furniture *templates,* pieces can be moved around until the desired functional and decorative effects are achieved.

Furniture should be grouped according to function. Especial attention should be given to the room's focal point. Large pieces should be placed first and parallel to the wall, except in particular cases such as one in which the room lends itself to a diagonal arrangement. Also, a large reclining chair is usually more pleasing and inviting when placed at an angle. Although this procedure will not be the complete solution to furniture arrangement, moving templates around on paper is much simpler than pushing heavy pieces around the room and can save time and energy.

Sound systems
TV's

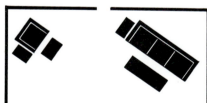

A large chair is often better across a corner.

Except in specific cases, a sofa or straight-wall piece of furniture should generally not cross a corner.

In a room with a slanted ceiling, the heaviest furniture grouping should be arranged against the highest wall.

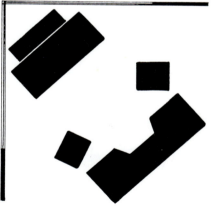

In some cases, a sofa may cross a corner. This room arrangement is pleasant.

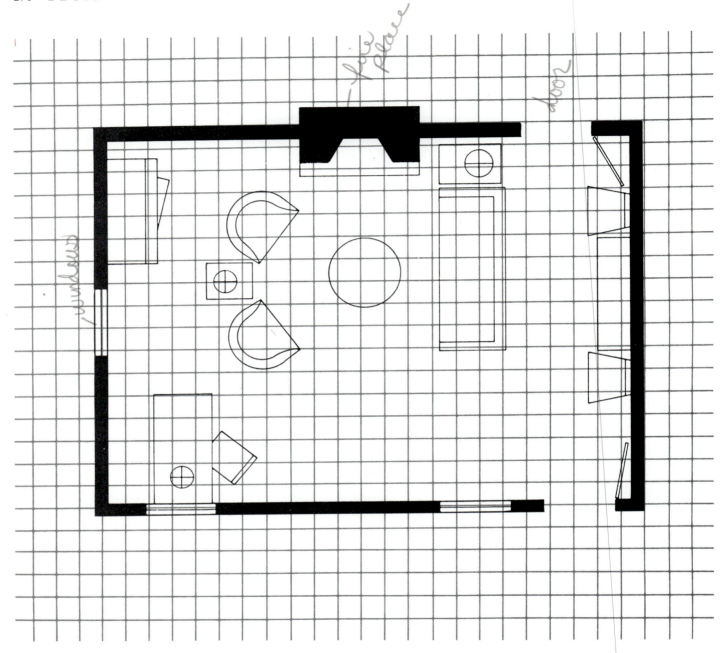

fire place

door

window

1/4" = 1'

A room drawn to scale. Large pieces should be placed first.

TRAFFIC

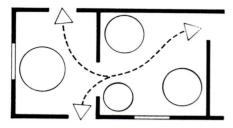

Traffic lanes and areas of activity should be indicated.

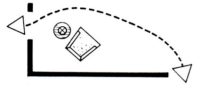

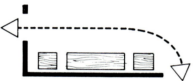

Blocking doorways should be avoided.

The final template arrangement should be duplicated in the room. Rarely is a piece of furniture complete in itself, because it calls for related pieces for function, comfort, or both. For example, a desk needs a chair, a piano needs a bench, a lounge chair and sofa need a table. Since most groupings need lighting, the appropriate lamp or lighting fixture should be chosen to provide adequate light for the particular purpose. Last is the placement of the small accessories that add a personal touch to the room.

Space should be allowed for people to move about easily. People also need legroom when sitting. The space within a group should be less than the distance between groups. A spotty appearance should be avoided. Occasional chairs are placed in convenient locations—usually against the wall.

SPATIAL PLANNING FOR ROOMS OF VARIOUS SHAPES

The square or nearly square room is the least pleasing proportion. To give the room a new dimension, the principles and elements of design will need to be brought into use. Some suggestions are: (1) Two opposite walls may be expanded by using a light, receding color, and a darker tone on the two remaining walls will pull them in (see Chapter 5). (2) One wall can be "extended" by running bookshelves the entire length. (3) An area rug the full length of the room, but less than the width, can be placed with the long side parallel to the bookshelves. (4) Furniture can be arranged to create a rectangular effect. The wall opposite the bookshelves should have some interest to provide weight and to pull it in. The result should be a room that *seems* rectangular (see drawing). These are only some of the ways in which the proportions of a square room may be altered.

The rectangular room, if well proportioned, is the easiest room to arrange. Comfort and beauty should be the main concerns.

The long, narrow room may present a problem, but a knowing use of a few principles of optical illusion can modify the apparent proportions of the room. First, the activity centers should be determined. Then, if the goal is to maintain the visual appearance of one large, flexible room, the furniture that stands out from the wall should be kept low. If the goal is to make separate compartments, some high pieces can be used as dividers. Furniture at right angles to the long wall will cut the length. Sectional furniture may turn a corner to create a cross-room

Skillfully planned furniture arrangements can change the apparent proportion of a square room.

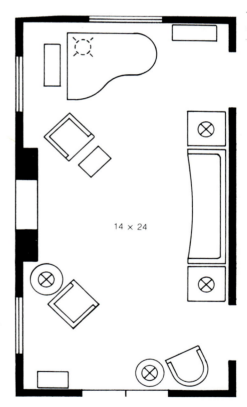

14 x 24

The rectangular room, if well proportioned, is the easiest room to arrange.

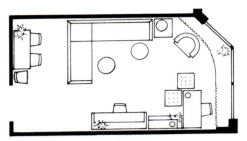

Principles of optical illusion can alter the apparent proportions of a long, narrow room. The curved line of drapery, the angled sofa, and the desk placed at a right angle to the long wall make the room seem wider.

A divider provides storage and privacy in an L-shaped room.

grouping (see drawing). Rugs can be used to define areas, and should preferably be placed at right angles to the long wall. Dividers and screens can create activity centers that will cut the length of the room. Ceiling fixtures hung low will draw groupings together. A platform partition that creates a new level at one end of the room can shorten the room's appearance. Color can work magic if used skillfully. Light colors expand space, and dark colors reduce space. Distinct changes of color for large areas, such as a dining area, will further alter the apparent room dimensions.

The L-shaped room lends itself naturally to a division of activities, particularly living and dining. Area rugs, dividers, and furniture placement can easily create livable space in the L-shaped room.

The room with a jog need not be a problem. The offset area can be used in such a way that it becomes a feature of and an asset to the room.

FURNITURE ARRANGEMENT FOR SPECIFIC ROOMS

Each room of the house presents a unique problem according to its function, and since the functions of different rooms vary greatly, each room should be considered separately.

ENTRANCE HALL

An entry is a passageway and should not be cluttered. Empty space permitting an easy flow of traffic is essential. The size of the room will necessarily determine the amount and scale of the furniture that should be placed against the wall (see Chapter 11).

During the past three decades, many houses were built without an entrance hall. In houses where the front door opens directly into the living room, a usually desirable plan is to create an unobstructed entrance to redirect traffic and to provide some privacy. This arrangement may be accomplished in a number of ways, depending on the space available, the placement of the door, and the arrangement of the rooms to be reached.

A successful way to set off an entrance is by the use of a built-in or freestanding storage wall. This wall will require slightly more room than a screen or a single wall divider, but has important advantages. If space is available, a deeper storage wall may provide closet space for outer garments on one side and open shelves for books or display on all or part of the opposite side. The storage divider may be planned with numerous combinations, depending on personal needs, and may be a decorative as well as a functional element in the home.

A standing screen creates a foyer and a backdrop for a desk.

Where space does not permit a heavy divider, a screen, either freestanding, with a track, or with a panel attached to the wall—the remaining panels free-swinging—may serve as a partial divider. In a small room where any type of divider would disadvantageously cut the space, the furniture may be arranged to redirect traffic by turning a sofa, a piano, or chairs toward the room and at right angles to the door, leaving a passageway for traffic. Such devices will provide limited privacy and will create the feeling of an entrance way (see drawing).

THE LIVING ROOM

The conversation area is the most important group in the living room and usually enhances and is combined with the focal point. In some cases the conversation area itself is the focal point of the room. Most important to keep in mind when planning the conversation area is that its function is to provide an intimate grouping, out of the line of traffic, in which people can hear and be heard in a relaxed atmosphere. The optimum distance across this area is about 8 ft, but plans should be made for enlarging the area by including occasional chairs that have been located at convenient points.

Built-in seating is usually not as comfortable nor as flexible as movable sofas and chairs, which may be regrouped for more intimate occasions or opened out to invite more participants. The sunken

TRAFFIC SHOULD BE REDIRECTED
WHEN NECESSARY.

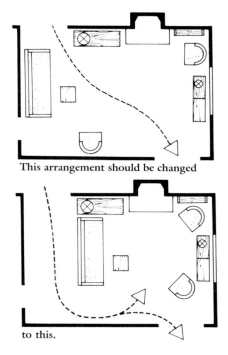

This arrangement should be changed

to this.

conversation pit has had some popularity, particularly with young people, but it is restrictive. It may serve as a supplementary area where space will allow, but it is usually not preferred for the principal conversation area of a living room.

A room in which all furniture is placed along the walls is not conducive to intimate conversation. An angled or slightly curved sofa lends itself to easy conversation more than a long, straight one does, and a comfortable corner is satisfying. The curve of a sectional sofa is invariably occupied first, just as the corner table in a restaurant is the most popular. A comfortable corner in a room is an invitation to quiet repose for all who enter. Whether an actual corner invitingly arranged, a pillowed window seat, or cornered sectional seating placed free of the walls, a comfortable corner is a wise addition to any living room.

Figure 10.3. This inviting corner conversation arrangement is out of the line of traffic, and occupants face away from the light of the large windows. Conveniently placed tables and indirect artificial lighting contribute to the comfort and attractiveness. (Courtesy of Drexel Heritage Furnishings.)

A corner arrangement need not be placed against the wall.

A current solution to having a flexible seating arrangement is movable modular furniture. Two or three separate pieces that fit together may be purchased at once; others can be added later. Modular furniture can be arranged into six basic conversation groupings, depending on space and number of pieces: (1) The *straight-line* grouping is ideal for public places, but is not conducive to intimate conversation. (2) The *L-shaped* grouping is good for conversation and lends itself to both large and small areas. (3) The *U-shaped* grouping is comfortable and attractive, but requires considerable space. (4) The *box-shaped* grouping is popular where space is ample. Allowance should be made for a sufficient opening to present an inviting aspect. (5) The *parallel* grouping emphasizes an existing focal point such as a fireplace or a special wall feature. (6) The *circular* grouping may encompass an entire room or an area of a large room (see drawings).

Soft lighting gives a feeling of intimacy to a conversation area, but this does not mean the area should be in semidarkness. People need to see the features of those with whom they are talking. A low-hanging light can pull a grouping together and may serve for reading when turned to its maximum power. Hanging mirrors where people talking can look up and see themselves is inadvisable, as this is distracting and can be annoying. To

A

B

C

Figure 10.4 (*facing page*). An intimate corner arrangement enhances the room's focal point and avoids direct traffic, yet is inviting. (Courtesy of Founders Furniture.)

Figure 10.5. Sectional love seats, chairs, and ottomans may be arranged in innumerable ways for comfortable seating and conversation. The plastic laminated shelf on top of the back and arms of *A* and *B* add another dimension and serve a practical use. (Courtesy of Thayer Coggin.)

SIX BASIC CONVERSATION GROUPINGS

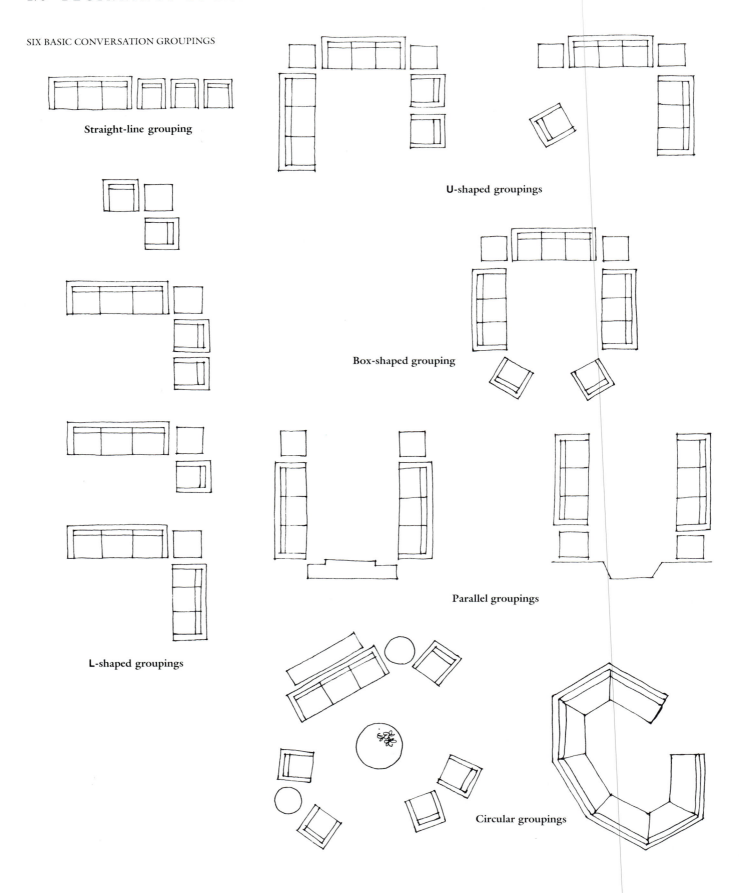

Straight-line grouping

U-shaped groupings

Box-shaped grouping

L-shaped groupings

Parallel groupings

Circular groupings

assure that household members and guests enjoy good conversation, the best possible environment should be provided.

Living room chairs should be comfortable and not of all the same type or size. Since people are built differently, what is comfortable for one person may be uncomfortable for another. Chairs should not be rigidly placed, or the guest may believe that altering the placement would be a major calamity. Near each lounge chair and sofa the right table should conveniently be placed to hold a lamp and small items such as books, magazines, and light refreshments.

With the traditional influence in today's furnishings, the use of *pairs* has returned. Identical items can be a unifying factor and hence an asset to a room. They can give balance and can pull together unrelated furniture. A pair of chairs can create a conversation grouping in a number of ways: angled about a table to give an intimate corner feeling, placed on either side of a fireplace, or placed side by side, balancing a sofa on the opposite side. Where space is adequate, a pair of love seats or sofas may be used in place of single chairs. Identical tables placed at each end of a sofa has always been a popular arrangement in American homes. Placing them in front of a sofa is a more flexible substitute for a standard coffee table. Two similar chests placed on either side of a doorway or a fireplace will enhance almost any room. Pairs of lamps, candelabra, or wall accessories can have a pleasing effect. The use of pairs, however, when carried to the extreme, can be detrimental to an interior design.

Finding the right wall space for a piano is often a problem, but an upright piano need not stand against a wall. The piano can be placed at right angles to a wall with a low screen behind it. The screen will serve as a background for a small chair and table. If the piano is low, it can be backed up to a sofa, thus providing a convenient surface for a lamp. The pianist can then face the room. A vertical piano may also serve as a room divider. The back can be covered with a piece of fabric that blends with the room.

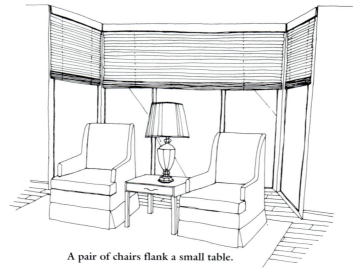

A pair of chairs flank a small table.

A grand piano may be more difficult to place in the average room, because of its size and because the straight side should in most cases be parallel to the wall. A bay window furnishes a beautiful setting for a grand piano, but the changes of temperature are hard on the instrument. In a large room, a grand piano may be placed to form a room divider. Whatever the location, the pianist should face the room.

In the living room, most tables should be used only where a functional need exists. The scale, shape, and height of each table should be right for the purpose and size of the chair or sofa it accompanies. *Console tables* can be decorative as well as functional, and when combined with a mirror or picture are an asset to almost any room. The game table is usually folding, but where a permanent one is used, it may serve other purposes,

Chairs in a corner for privacy

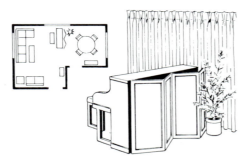

An upright piano may serve as a partial room divider.

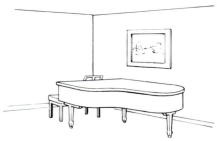

The straight side of a grand piano should be parallel to the wall.

such as for study or for guest snacks. The writing table or desk gives a room a lived-in appearance and may also serve a dual purpose. Placed with its short side to the wall near a window or as part of a wall of books, it is convenient and usually contributes more to the general attractiveness of the room than when pushed flat against a wall. When the desk is placed in front of a window, the chair should be placed behind it, facing away from the light.

Large case or wall pieces should be located to give the room a feeling of balance. Where the area is small, these pieces are usually better if centered. Where wall space is ample, a large piece can be balanced by an architectural element or by other furniture.

DINING ROOM

Dining room furniture should be suitably scaled to the room. Furniture arrangement seldom presents much choice in this room. The table is usually placed in the center of the room, with a chest or buffet for storage against the longest wall and a small serving piece near the kitchen door. If the room is large enough, a high piece such as breakfront or china cabinet can provide space for display and add dignity as well. Corner cupboards are often the answer for storage and display in smaller rooms. Chairs should not be too wide across the front. The unnecessary width takes up too much room around the table. Where space is limited, a round or oval table will allow more room for passage and will seat people more easily than a rectangular table of the same width and length. If the dining area is small, one option is to use a drop-leaf table that, when not in use, may be closed and placed against the wall along with a wall-hung shelf for serving.

Important to remember in planning the dining room is that people need space. Getting into a chair at the table requires about 2 ft. Assisting someone in seating requires about 4½ ft. The dining room often serves a number of functions, and placement of furniture should be flexible.

FAMILY AND RECREATION ROOMS

In most homes the family room and the recreation room are combined. Space does not usually permit two separate areas for activities. More than any other area of the house, the arrangement of furniture here should be flexible to permit easy adjustment for various activities. Use, convenience, and practicability should be the guiding principles in arranging furniture in these rooms.

BEDROOMS

Since furniture arrangement in a bedroom is usually more limited than in other rooms, carefully planned space is especially important. Before furniture arrangement begins, a decision should be made on the purposes the room will serve in addition to sleeping.

Because of its size, the bed will occupy the dominant place in the room, and seldom is there more than one wall large enough to accommodate it. Once the bed is established, traffic lanes should be planned, with careful attention given to nighttime walking. The foot of the bed is often a good place for a storage chest or a narrow bench. Built-in under-bed drawers will convert unused space into storage. In children's rooms, bunk beds or trundle beds are often the answer when a room must serve two or more occupants.

In arranging furniture throughout the home, the guidelines should be applied with a good measure of common sense. (See Chapter 11 for furnishing all areas of the house.)

MAKING THE MOST OF SPACE

MAKING A SMALL ROOM APPEAR LARGER

Through the adroit use of the principles and elements of design, a small room may be transformed and made to appear much larger than it is. The room should first be examined carefully and traffic lanes defined. Then, beginning with the backgrounds, space-making principles should be applied to expand the room. The results of studied efforts in creating the feeling of space may be amazing.

Walls and ceilings The most important and least costly decorating tool—color—should be taken advantage of. To camouflage unwanted architectural features and maximize the feeling of spaciousness, the same light-receding color should be applied on all backgrounds, that is, floors, walls, woodwork, ceilings, and windows. To appear the same, the walls should be lighter than the floor, and the ceiling lighter than the walls (see Chapter 5.) Wallpaper with a three-dimensional pattern used on one wall can add depth. A mirrored wall will double the space, or a corner can be opened up by the use of a mirrored panel. Pictures should be used sparingly and should have frames that blend into the background. Ample areas of plain wall should be left open.

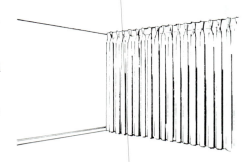

Plain, light walls and blended wall-to-wall and floor-to-ceiling drapery expand space.

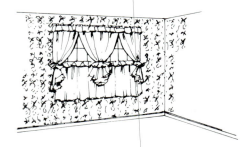

Patterned walls and ruffled curtains seem to fill up a room.

Figure 10.6. A glamorous setting for four, designed for elegance and arranged for intimacy. (Courtesy of Thayer Coggin.)

Floors   If carpeting is used, it should be laid wall to wall and should be a plain weave in a color that blends into the walls. If a hard-surface flooring is required, an unobtrusive pattern that incorporates the wall tone is a good selection.

Windows   Plain, wall-colored sheers or casements should be hung from floor to ceiling. Another approach is to hang blinds of the same color. Where feasible, windows can be left bare, using outdoor space. Hanging plants can soften the hard edges of windows and can add a feeling of warmth.

Furniture   Small-scaled furniture should be selected, but a dollhouse effect should be avoided. Case pieces that are supported on legs rather than those that are flush to the floor; high, shallow pieces for storage and display; tables with rounded corners or with clear glass or plastic tops; chairs with see-through backs; chairs of clear plastic; and those with no arms will all help to preserve space. Upholstered pieces should be covered in plain fabric or in small allover

Scale is Important When Choosing Furniture for a Small Room

Desirable

Less desirable

Desirable

Less desirable

Desirable

Less desirable

patterned fabric blended to the room's background. Using the same material on all upholstered pieces will unify the furniture and will have a space-making effect. Upholstery should be neatly tailored and without skirts. Most furniture should be aligned against the walls, leaving the center of the room free. If extended to the ceiling, shelves and high storage units attached to the wall, will visually add height, and if terminated approximately 1 ft from the floor, will allow the perimeter of the room to be seen, which also adds to the visual space. Smaller units such as serving tables, consoles, *buffets,* and desks can also be wall hung, thus eliminating the need for space-using legs.

Although the previous guidelines are safe to follow, the experienced interior designer can always do the unusual when furnishing a small room. For example, if the remainder of the room's elements are carefully chosen, a few pieces of large-scaled furniture, instead of a greater number of small ones, can be effective and will not diminish the room's apparent size.

Lighting   Lighting can do wonders in expanding space. Light cast on the ceiling or on the upper part of the wall or drapery will direct the eye upward. Lamps with inconspicuous shades that provide indirect lighting should be used.

Accessories   Clutter should be avoided. Rather than scattered about the room, items should be used sparingly and in a well-organized way. Small mirrors strategically placed can reflect a wall, the outdoors, or a particular area, thus multiplying space. A few small-leaved plants can give an airy feeling with a bonus of friendliness.

MAKING A LARGE ROOM APPEAR SMALLER
The challenge of a big room is not a common one, but when it does occur, the most important consideration is scale. Massive furniture, overscaled patterns, and large pictures should be chosen. Everything, however, should not be massive. After the large pieces have established the broad outlines of the room, lighter pieces should be used to

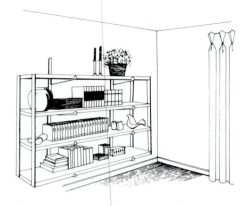

Shelves hung short of the floor will appear to use no room.

A wall-hung shelf with rounded corners takes little space.

complete the groupings. Too little furniture in a big room can result in a cold uninviting interior, and too much furniture may give a feeling of clutter. More important than the quantity, however, is the arrangement. The best technique is to plan separate areas of different sizes. Some should be small and intimate; others should be more open. *Occasional chairs* may be moved from one group to another, thus forming a link between groupings. All furniture used in the middle of a room should look attractive from all angles. A sofa-back table is a versatile and attractive piece to serve two areas. A few empty spaces in a room should not be of concern. A room that looks as though it could use one more item has a certain appeal. Someone once referred to this as "the charm of the incomplete."

Wall composition

A floor is on a horizontal plane, and its composition is primarily one of arrangement of furniture. A wall is on a vertical plane and is limited by floor, ceiling, corners, and other permanent architectural features such as doors, windows, mantels, and paneling. Because the wall is observed from a different angle, movable items such as hanging and portable lamps and pieces of furniture seen in relationship to the wall are part of the complete composition. If architectural features are not well planned, the interior designer should devise ways to disguise or emphasize wherever possible. If ceilings are below standard height (8 ft), any horizontal division of the wall should be avoided, since this will tend to make the ceiling seem even lower. Instead, vertical lines should be emphasized to add height. If ceilings are too high, they may be made to appear lower by emphasizing the horizontal line. Each wall elevation in a room should be considered individually, and each composition should present a pleasing effect suitable to the style and mood of the room.

When selecting and arranging items for a wall composition, the principles of design should be considered. Scale, proportion, and balance are of special importance. The scale relationship among the individual items, and between the overall composition and the room, should seem right. The placement of items against the wall and the proportion of wall to be covered should be carefully planned. A pleasant feeling of balance should be present. If the overall composition is one of asymmetry, it will remain interesting under constant viewing longer than if it is bisymmetrical, but some formal balance may be necessary to bring unity into the arrangement. Straight lines need to be relieved by curved lines. Since rectangles and ovals are more pleasing than squares and circles, they can successfully be used in

Figure 10.7. This eye-appealing wall composition is conveniently and artistically arranged. The wall hangings contrast with the background while echoing the wall color. The graduated heights of the small accessories, the placement of the small figure, and the overlapping greenery direct the eye into the pictures. (Courtesy of Henredon Furniture Industries.)

Bisymmmetrical balance may become monotonous.

Asymmetrical balance will remain interesting longer.

greater numbers. Also, uneven numbers are more desirable than even numbers and will be less tiring. No specific rules of measurement are available by which to produce a perfect composition. That intangible quality of taste or judgment must therefore be employed if the result is to be a comfortable one.

PICTURES

Almost everyone feels the need to add some form of decoration to the walls of his or her dwelling. From prehistoric animal paintings on the walls of caves to the supergraphics on the walls of twentieth-century homes, art has been some measure of human nature. The pictures one chooses to display reveal much of the owner's personality and individual taste. A picture worth displaying is worthy of being framed and hung with great care.

A picture can be enhanced or de-

stroyed by the way it is framed. To achieve the most pleasing result possible is more complex than one might suspect, but with a little study and observation, it can be accomplished. Some pictures do not call for a frame and are complete without one. Where a frame is used, it should never dominate the picture but should carefully be chosen to be appropriate for the subject and the style of rendering. Frames can repeat wood tones of furniture or can be painted or gilded. A traditional oil demands a rich, heavy frame, and all oils should be framed without mats. A modern painting may have a narrow wooden or metal frame, or no frame at all. Pencil sketches, *etchings,* and watercolors are more delicate and should be simply framed and usually matted. A mat will make a picture look larger, will unify pictures of various sizes, and may be a transition between picture and wall. White mats are usually preferred because they emphasize the picture, but mats may be chosen to pick up colors in the picture or in the room. When matting a picture, the size of the picture and the wall space where it is to be hung should be considered. When matting a square picture, the same space should be left at the top and the sides, with a wider margin at the bottom. For an upright rectangle, a medium margin should be left at the top, the narrowest margin at the sides, and the widest at the bottom. A rectangular frame, hung horizontally, should have a narrow margin at the top, a medium margin at the sides, and a wide margin at the bottom. Once the picture is correctly framed, it should carefully be hung flat against the wall with the wire or cord concealed.

Pictures of different sizes can be unified by the use of mats and similar frames.

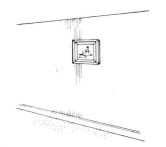

The picture seems to float when not anchored.

Picture is too small for the chest.

Picture is a pleasing proportion for the chest.

Picture is too large for the chest.

The golden mean should be considered in picture hanging. Having the center of the picture or a group of pictures midway between floor and ceiling should be avoided. A single picture should not seem to float by itself, but should be part of a grouping and should be well related in scale and proportion to the piece of furniture forming the anchor. Not all wall compositions, however, depend on furniture. In some cases, particularly in rooms with modern decor, picture groupings may reach the baseboard, with the floor becoming the anchor.

A picture hung above a chair or sofa should be placed high enough so that the head of a seated person does not touch the frame; approximately 6 in to 8 in. will provide sufficient clearance. If a

Baseboard

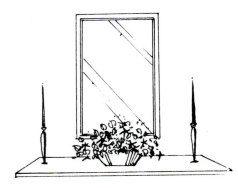

Bouquet obstructs the mirror.

Bouquet forms a link with mirror and container.

picture is important enough to be hung, it should not be obscured by an accessory, such as a lamp or a bouquet of flowers. When a plant or a bouquet is used as part of the composition, some foliage should overlap the frame, thereby forming a link between the picture and the container.

A favorite practice is to group art and other small accessories on the largest unoccupied wall space above a large piece of furniture. In the living room, the sofa is the most logical place. The hanging of a picture grouping should be approached as only part of the complete wall arrangement. The sofa, end tables, lamps, or whatever items are seen together will be part of the composition. To assemble the wall-hung components, a large sheet of brown wrapping paper the size of the area to be covered should be used. The paper is laid on the floor and pictures and other objects are arranged on it until a pleasing composition is created. Each object should then be drawn around and the point marked where it is to be hung. Next, the paper is carefully attached to the wall, and the pictures are hung. When all are in place, the paper is removed, and the composition is complete.

STORAGE UNITS

A storage unit that partially or completely covers a wall, extending from floor to ceiling, containing both open shelves and closed units, will occupy little space, provide abundant storage, and be an important architectural feature in the room. The unit can incorporate books, pictures, mirrors, and other diversified objects, as well as the television. When artfully planned and arranged into a harmonious composition, the storage wall can be a masterpiece of design and

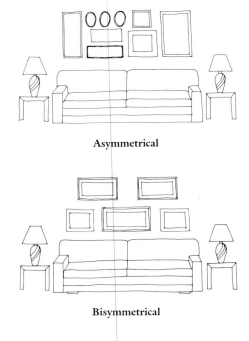

Asymmetrical

Bisymmetrical

color, and can form the room's focal point.

Since the walls of a room form the background not only for furniture but also for people, the final effect should not be an obtrusive one. With this in mind, and with an acute awareness of the importance of the relationship of form, texture, and color, a successful wall arrangement can be achieved.

Figure 10.8. Storage wall planning and organization are combined in creating a center for storage display and versatile use. The drop-down table folds up when not in use to provide extra floor space and to mask unsightly storage. (Courtesy of Interliebke.)

ASSIGNMENT 1

Carefully observe and analyze wall arrangements in magazines, studio setups, and homes. On graph paper, do some experimenting with various wall compositions until you believe that you have developed some skill. Then put your skill to a test by arranging the walls in a room of your choosing. The challenge may have rewarding results.

The specific class assignment is left to the discretion of the instructor.

ASSIGNMENT 2

In the following assignment, you are given an opportunity to apply the principles and guidelines of floor composition discussed in the chapter. Study the four living room arrangements in the Student Work Packet.

This assignment includes plans for five rooms, templates, and graph paper. Examine each of the empty rooms to determine its assets and defects. Rooms 1 and 2 present particular problems that need to be resolved. Decide on the functions of each and the areas of activity. Experiment on the graph paper until you have found a satisfactory arrangement for each room. Then arrange the templates to take the best advantage of space in creating pleasant, functional rooms. Follow the procedures as outlined in the chapter.

The following is a list of the *minimum clearances* for placement of furniture:

LIVING ROOM

Traffic path—major	4 ft to 6 ft
Traffic path—minor	1 ft, 4 in. to 4 ft
Foot room between sofa or chair and edge of coffee table top	1 ft to 15 in.
Floor space in front of chair for feet and legs	1 ft, 6 in. to 2 ft, 6 in.
Chair or bench space in front of desk or piano	3 ft

DINING ROOM

Space for occupied chairs	1 ft, 6 in. to 1 ft, 10 in.
Space to get into chairs	1 ft, 10 in. to 3 ft
Space for person to assist in seating	4 ft, 6 in.
Traffic path around table and occupied chairs	1 ft, 6 in. to 2 ft

KITCHEN

Working space in front of cabinets	2 ft to 6 ft
Counter space between equipment	3 ft to 5 ft
Ventilation for attachments in back of some appliances	3 in. to 5 in.

BEDROOM

Space for making bed	1 ft, 6 in. to 2 ft
Space between twin beds	1 ft, 6 in. to 2 ft, 4 in.
Space in front of chest of drawers	3 ft
Space in front of dresser	3 ft to 4 ft (both directions)

BATHROOM

Space between front of tub and opposite wall	2 ft, 6 in. to 3 ft, 6 in.
Space in front of toilet	1 ft, 6 in. to 2 ft
Space at sides of toilet	1 ft to 1 ft, 6 in.
Space between fronts of fixtures	2 ft to 3 ft

The completed rooms should be checked with the 12 items following. Room arrangements will be evaluated according to this list.

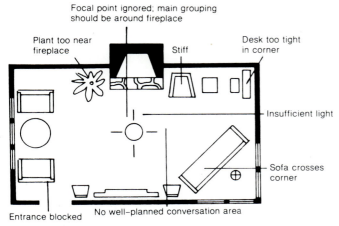

Focal point ignored; main grouping
should be around fireplace

Plant too near
fireplace

Stiff

Desk too tight
in corner

Insufficient light

Sofa crosses
corner

Entrance blocked   No well-planned conversation area

(1) Poorly arranged room

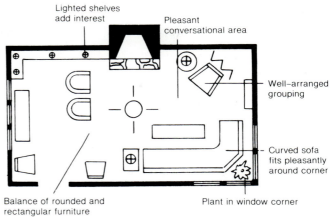

Lighted shelves
add interest

Pleasant
conversational area

Well-arranged
grouping

Curved sofa
fits pleasantly
around corner

Balance of rounded and
rectangular furniture

Plant in window corner

(2) Well-arranged room

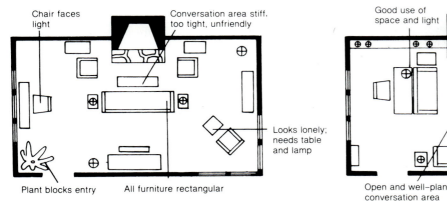

Chair faces
light

Conversation area stiff,
too tight, unfriendly

Looks lonely;
needs table
and lamp

Plant blocks entry   All furniture rectangular

(3) Poorly arranged room

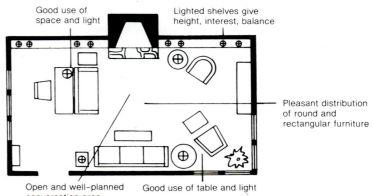

Good use of
space and light

Lighted shelves give
height, interest, balance

Pleasant distribution
of round and
rectangular furniture

Open and well-planned
conversation area

Good use of table and light

(4) Well-arranged room

CHECKLIST FOR ARRANGING FURNITURE

1 Are traffic lanes neatly marked and left free? Mark the major traffic lanes in red. (These are the lanes leading from one door to another.)

2 Where the outside door opens directly into the living room, has an entrance way been created that provides some privacy, particularly for the main conversation area?

3 Has one well-chosen center of interest been made the important, yet not completely dominating, focal point in the room? Is this grouping comfortably and conveniently arranged, out of the line of traffic, yet open enough to be inviting?

4 Are other areas of activity clearly defined, conveniently located, and artistically arranged with all necessary items?

5 In dual-purpose living-dining rooms, has a screen, a divider, or an effetive furniture arrangement been employed to provide some privacy or adequate division of space?

6 Large pieces of furniture:

□ Is each piece placed to take the best advantage of space and not pushed tightly into a corner?

□ Is each piece placed parallel to the wall (with the possible exception of a lounge chair), unless the major seating arrangement is based on a diagonal plan?

□ Does a large piece block a window?

□ Where windows go near to the floor, are large pieces placed out far enough to allow passage behind?

□ Where a grand piano is used, is the straight side parallel to and nearest the wall?

7 Does the room have a sense of balance?

□ Do opposite walls seem the same?

□ Are high and low pieces pleasingly distributed?

□ Are round and rectangular pieces pleasingly distributed?

8 Are occasional chairs placed at convenient points to be moved easily into various groupings?

9 Is lighting adequate and conveniently located? Are all electrical outlets indicated?

10 Does each living room have a feeling of comfort and interest, with a variety of activity areas for music, reading, writing, and conversation, without being crowded or cluttered? Are dining areas arranged for convenience? Are bedrooms furnished to make the best use of space, with room for nighttime walking?

11 Is there a feeling of unity?

12 Is each room's composition done with professional neatness?

CHAPTER ELEVEN

Unifying the Interior Environment

*A*nyone who has ever gone house hunting need not be reminded of the feeling of depression he or she may have experienced while traveling from one unfurnished apartment or house to another. Too often the places that are desired are beyond one's financial means, and the affordable places are badly planned or so run-down that one is hard pressed to visualize the empty spaces as comfortably designed rooms. Because most people have trouble visualizing the completed product when they look at empty rooms, real estate people invariably urge home owners to continue to live in their homes while they are selling them. In areas of tract houses, where identical homes are for sale, the more attractively designed homes consistently bring a higher price than those that are not as appealing, even though the buyer knows that the furnishings will not remain in the house.

Figure 11.1. Glowing light on a rich wall covering, floor-to-ceiling books, and oriental rugs create a friendly and fitting entrance for a traditional house. (Photograph by Mark K. Allen.)

Thinking through an interior design project

How does one go about thinking through the numerous problems involved in making a home out of empty, walled-in spaces? Of primary importance is intelligent study and insight and an accumulation of a lot of information about design principles, floor plans, colors, fabrics, materials for floors and walls, furniture selection and arrangement, and intelligent shopping. Also important is courage—courage to heed personal convictions regardless of outside pressures to follow current fads. Creative ideas that have been accumulated over a period of time and from innumerable sources are necessary as well. Thomas Carlyle once said, "He is most creative who adapts from the greatest number of sources." Carlyle's statement is particularly true when applied to interior design. Interior design is usually most successful when it proceeds slowly according to a well-organized plan—not when it is done all at once. Designing an interior is ongoing and should be based on individual or household needs and kept within a given budget.

Specific areas

A specific mood generally seems to be appropriate for each area of the house, but this necessarily varies with individual households. Also, as space becomes tighter, daily functions will increasingly be combined in multipurpose rooms. The following suggestions may be helpful in establishing the mood of specific areas of the house.

THE FRONT DOOR

More than any other architectural feature, the front door is what gives the exterior of the house individuality. Here should be created the image that the owner wishes to convey. Whether the doorway is to be a vivid focal point or blended into the facade of the house, knowledge of color and design can achieve the objective. Standard doors of every period and style are available today. If the present door is a good style but dull, it can be remodeled with molding strips, pilasters, a cornice, or a pediment. Old hardware can be replaced (the market abounds in all types), ornamental ironwork can be refinished, and shutters, side lanterns, or overhead lighting can be added. Whether the scheme is quiet or daring, paint alone can work magic and is inexpensive. When the door itself is completed, a final touch can be added with a group of potted plants, a pair of urns, or a decorative bench.

THE ENTRANCE HALL

Homes of the past almost always had an entrance hall (see Figure 11.1). The earliest seventeenth-century houses in New England had a tiny entrance from which the narrow stairway ascended to the attic. Later the entrance and stairway became the focal point of the house. With the advent of open planning, this room was abandoned, and the front door opened directly into the living room. Anyone who has lived with children knows that an entrance hall—no matter how small—that directs traffic throughout the house is an excellent use of space. The entrance hall not only can establish the character and mood of the home but also can leave a lasting impression on all who enter. With the new materials available today, a room can be formal, even luxurious in feeling, yet can also take the wear and tear of daily living. Since people do not linger in this area, the use of color and pattern can be more bold and daring than in other areas.

Whatever the general style or theme of the house, the entrance hall is a good

Figure 11.2 (*top*). An entrance way is always enhanced by a well-designed stairway. Here a telephone desk and chair add a welcoming touch. (Courtesy of Drexel Heritage Furnishings.)

Figure 11.3 (*bottom*). This spacious, uncluttered entrance is composed of beautiful flush doors, shuttered sidelights, a Berber rug, an inviting caned chair, and a Persian violet on a simply turned stand. (Photograph by Mark K. Allen, residence of Mrs. J. Hamilton Calder.)

place to enhance it. A stairway can provide a good beginning.

An entrance with a shoe-box look can benefit from some architectural interest. Lumber companies have a wealth of stock moldings and paneling from which to choose. The entrance is also an excellent place to use an attractive wall covering. If the entrance is narrow, the walls can be pushed out by the use of a mural with a three-dimensional effect that leads the eye into a distant scene. When decorative paper is used, using a dado to take the wear off the lower part of the wall is advisable.

Important to remember when selecting the floor covering is that the entrance is a passageway and must take traffic. One of the hard-surface materials such as brick, stone, terrazzo, travertine, or *quartzite* will provide a lifetime floor and will be easy to maintain. A vinyl can simulate any of these materials (see Chapter 7). A well-anchored area or throw rug can add warmth and can serve as a color transition into adjoining rooms.

The scale and the amount of furniture used in the entrance hall will be determined by the size of the room and the available wall space. Wall space is usually large enough only for the necessities: a chair to sit on while waiting or putting on boots, and a small table on which to lay such things as purses and gloves. A bench may substitute for both the chair and the table. Where space is limited, a wall-supported console that is shallow and rounded is an excellent choice, and will seem to take up no space. A mirror is important in this area. In addition to providing its functional purpose, it will expand space. Bookshelves that take little room can serve a dual purpose in an entrance. They not only will house books where they can be reached from any area of the house but also will add a warm, humanizing touch.

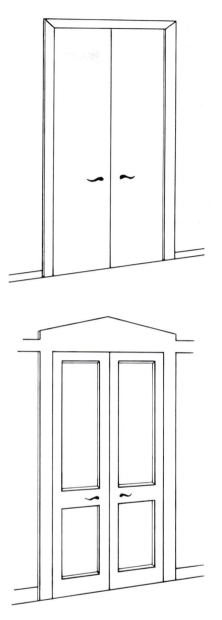

Stock moldings can change the aspect of a door either inside or out

THE LIVING ROOM

If the living room lives up to its name, it will provide for all household members and guests as well. A trend that began in the fifties, however, relegates most of the family activities to a family room and reinstates the more formal parlor—but without using the name. With today's dwindling space, however, this arrangement is not always possible, and activities are often combined. Where two living areas are permitted the living room usually takes on a more formal appearance. In planning the living room, one should keep in mind that more people share this area than any other area in the house. The general feeling of the entrance way should flow easily into the living room with a pleasant transition of color. If the walls of the entrance are papered, keeping the living room walls plain, either painted or paneled, is usually advisable. Use and personal choice will determine the type of floor covering. Since the more formal living area should be one of relaxation, neutralized backgrounds are a wise choice. Then, according to personal preference, backgrounds can be enlivened by colorful fabrics or kept in a more restrained atmosphere by the use of soft neutral tones. Since the success of the room largely depends on the windows, they should be given particular attention.

The interior of the living room should be designed gradually, beginning with the backgrounds. Decisions should be made about the floor, walls, ceiling, and the type of window treatment. Fabrics should then be selected—first the principal one, then the secondary ones, and finally the accents. The mood of the room will to a large extent be established by the fabrics that are chosen and the way they are used. To assure satisfaction, no decisions should be made until these fabrics have been observed in the room in the daytime and in artificial light.

Rarely is a home furnished by purchasing everything new. Working with exist-

Figure 11.4 (*facing page*). In this attractive living room, elegance and formality have been achieved through the use of exquisite, smooth-textured fabrics, fine woods, expertly crafted metals and glass, and accessories of exceptional beauty. (Courtesy of Drexel Heritage Furnishings.)

Figure 11.5 (*above*). Furniture covered in warm tweeds, nubby textures, and corduroy, and set against a dhurrie rug and vertical pine paneling, create a living room of informal hospitality. (Courtesy of Pennsylvania House.)

ing pieces is the usual procedure. If new furniture is needed, one piece should be purchased at a time and then lived with awhile before purchasing another piece. In this way, the owner will find pleasure with each new addition, and the final result will likely be more gratifying (see Chapter 9).

In many living rooms, the main center of interest is the fireplace, which is the most comforting feature in a house and one that deserves special consideration. The ancient Romans considered the hearth as the heart of the home. Not

until the fourteenth century was the fireplace moved from the center of the room to the side wall. Since that time, the fireplace has been a symbol of home and has provided for multiple functions.

As the center of interest, the fireplace can set the interior design theme of the room. Today, fireplaces take many shapes, from the freestanding stove to an open recess in a wall, framed with a variety of facings. Old brick or rough stone is appropriate for rooms with a country or rustic look. Wood for facing is the most versatile material and can be made to fit the decor and harmonize with other woodwork in the room. Reproductions of all the traditional styles are available, as well as a great variety of styles for the contemporary setting. Marble facing is

FIREPLACES

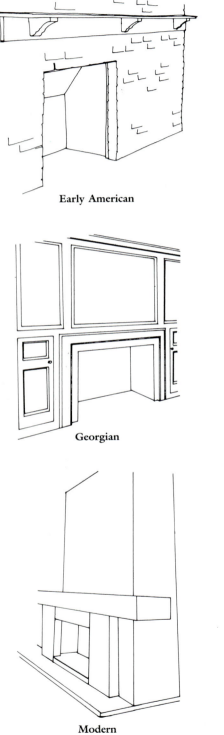

Early American

Georgian

Modern

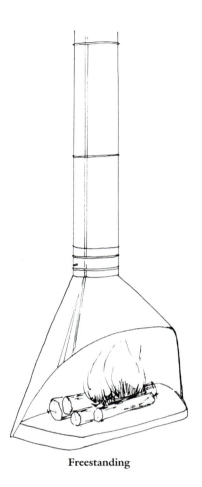

Freestanding

French provincial

appropriate for a formal room, and a wide variety of fireproof plastics are available for the less formal setting. Many of the hard-surface materials used for floors can successfully be used for fireplace facings. Fireplace tools and fittings are important accessories and should be chosen with care so that they will be in keeping with the fireplace.

With the high cost of heating, the wood-burning stove has become popular across the country. Tile stoves, descended from the beautiful alpine Kachelofen heaters of Europe, which can be traced back almost six centuries, are being manufactured today. They come in a variety of styles and provide economical ceramic radiant heat.

Figure 11.6. This handsome, hand-glazed tile stove combines advanced technology with unique design and provides efficient, economical, radiant heat. (Courtesy of Ceramic Radiant Heat, Lockmere, New Hampshire.)

THE DINING ROOM

At the turn of the century, the dining room, a big and somber room with a massive table and sideboard, a Tiffany glass chandelier, and heavily shrouded windows was the most important room of the house, where all family members gathered three times a day and in a congenial atmosphere learned manners, discipline, and the art of conversation.

After World War I, the message was that dining rooms were no longer necessary. Open planning blended kitchen, dining, and living areas into one, and as a result, family dining around a table went out of fashion. In the 1960s, however, a return of the dining room occurred. People discovered that without this greatly needed area, much that is important to family life was missing. "As you eat, so will your guests love and remember you" goes an old Roman saying. To this may well be added, "So also will your children remember you."

Friendly gatherings inevitably involve eating. Whether the food consists of hors d'oeuvres around a coffee table, a buffet supper, or a sit-down meal, space should be planned for it. The dining room, which can serve many functions, need not be formal, but privacy from the front door and distance from the clutter of the kitchen are highly desirable. In the dining room plan, colors should not be obtrusive, since they may restrict the use of a variety of table settings. The dining room is an ideal place for an attractive mural wallpaper. A dado will protect the wall from chair bumps and finger marks.

The floor covering should be practical enough for household use. Many carpets for this purpose shed dirt and clean well. A patterned carpet is a particularly good choice, since it will conceal spots. A hard-surface material might be considered; one is available for any decor, and maintenance is minimal.

Keeping the dining room in the same basic theme as the living room is wise.

Furniture should be suitably scaled to the room. The popular pedestal-base table gives maximum knee room, and round and oval tables take up less room and make it easier to squeeze in an extra guest. Two-arm chairs, or host chairs, will add dignity and can serve as occasional chairs in the living room. If the dining room is large, a breakfront with shelves for china and glass and drawers for linens and silver is a handsome addition. If space is limited, a shallow chest or a wall-hung shelf for serving can suffice.

If the dining room is one arm of an L-shaped living room, an alcove, a part-time study, a television room, or a part-time guest room, it can be just as graceful

Figure 11.7. An eating area need not be large to be inviting. This tiny space has all the attributes necessary for pleasant and intimate dining. (Courtesy of Pier 1 Imports.)

as a full-time dining room. If the table can be seen from the living room, a screen can shut off the view of the table before dinner is served. Between meals, a practical floor-length tablecloth of felt or ticking will convert the table into a place for games or study.

When the dining area is part of the living room, a number of ways are available to set it apart. The walls may be papered or painted a different but coordinated color; an area rug can define the space; pull-back curtains, paneled screens, or folding doors can shut off the view of the table when desired; and a low-hung lighting fixture can pull the group together. Tables that convert to different sizes and heights and thus do double duty are useful here. These and many other devices may give the open dining room a feeling of importance and privacy.

Because the main function of the dining room is that of serving meals, familiarity with the basic facts about table settings—silver, china, and glassware—is important for the interior designer, whether professional or nonprofessional.

Silver, china, and glassware are sure to be among the most-used items of all home furnishings. Tableware and accessories are available in any color, design, or quality. Tableware can be mixed or matched, complemented or contrasted.

The following is a list of significant terms that pertain to table settings. Familiarity with these terms will help determine appropriate usage.

Bisque   Fired, unglazed clayware.

Bone china   A fine-quality porcelain made only in England, where the bone-ash clay is preferred.

Chased   Hand decorated with cutting tools.

China or **porcelain**   Two interchangeable terms, applying only to fine, non-porous, translucent wares that have been fired at extremely high heat. They are hard and sturdy, despite their delicate appearance. Originally made only in

Figure 11.8 (*facing page*). The appeal of the country look is evident in this inviting dining room, where seventeenth-century English furniture is combined with a twentieth-century rug. Fabric-paneled shutters, greenery, and pewter complete the setting. (Courtesy of Henredon Furniture Industries.)

Figure 11.9 (*above*). A feeling of spaciousness and uncluttered dignity pervades this contemporary dining room. (Courtesy of Colwell General.)

Figure 11.10. Informality pervades this alluring dining room. The oversized plaid rug on a wide plank floor, rough plaster walls, tile fireplace, and bright plaid cushions and drapery combine to create a nostalgic look. (Courtesy of Ethan Allen.)

China, fine porcelains are now manufactured in the United States and Europe.

Crackle   A purposeful and controlled crazing that is protected by an overglaze; a decorative effect.

Crazing   A cracking in the glaze—a sign of poor quality.

Crystal   Refers to the colorless, sparkling quality of good glass.

Dirilyte   Gold plated.

Earthenware   Made of whiter, more refined clay than pottery and fired at a higher heat. It is less porous and therefore sturdier than pottery. Earthenware has many grades and qualities. Some of it is fine in texture, weight, and glaze; some of it is ovenproof.

Embossed   Decorated by die impressions.

Engraved   Hand decorated with cutting tools.

Etched   Decorated by chemical applications.

Faience   An ornamented French pottery.

Flat silver   Eating utensils: spoons, knives, forks, and servers. Flat silver may be sterling or plate.

Gadroon edge   The word *gadroon* means "half an almond" and refers to a decoration of Arabic origin. It is the oldest and most frequently used border motif for silver.

Glass   A hard substance, usually brittle and transparent, composed chiefly of silicates and an alkali fused at a high temperature.

Glaze   A thick, glasslike coating, baked into the clay body to give a smooth, highly polished finish.

Hammered silver   A procedure for hand decorating sterling hollowware.

Hand-blown glass   Air blown into a bubble of molten glass, which is then shaped by hand as it cools. Used in making fine stemware.

Hand-pressed glass   Molten glass pressed into a mold, where it is shaped and patterned at the same time. Used for intricate shapes and decorations in glass.

Handwrought silver   Completely hand shaped and decorated. The term is often incorrectly applied today, since some of the steps are usually done by machine.

Hollowware   Dishes and decorative items: bowls, pitchers, trays, coffeepots and teapots, candelabra, and so on. Hollowware may be sterling or plate.

Lead or **flint glass**   Clear and sparkling glass, with a brilliant resonance or ring when struck.

Majolica   A tin-glazed pottery made in Italy.

Opaque   Nontranslucent, as earthenware or pottery.

Open stock   Refers to patterns or styles that may be purchased by the piece rather than by the complete set. Open stock does not mean that the pattern will always be available for replacement or additions.

Oxidized   Chemically darkened to highlight the beauty and detail of ornamentation.

Patina   The soft, lustrous finish that comes with usage.

Place setting   Refers to the assorted items in one pattern that may be desired or needed for each person at the table.

Pottery   Porous and the least sturdy of baked clay products. Because it is fired (baked) at such low heat and is often unglazed or unevenly glazed, it chips and breaks easily.

Pure (fine) silver   What the name implies. In its pure form, silver is too soft and pliable for practical use.

Rock crystal   A semiprecious stone. A misleading term, for it is commonly used

by today's manufacturers to denote a polished cutting on high-quality glass.

Sheffield plate   The first substitute for sterling. The Sheffield method of fusing silver over copper went out of use in about 1840 when the silver-plating process was discovered. True Sheffield is rarely found today except in museums.

Silver plate   Pure silver coating on a base-metal shape (nickel silver for flatware, nickel silver or copper for hollowware). The cost and quality of silver plate vary with the thickness of the silver coating and the degree of finish given the base-metal form before coating.

Sterling (solid) silver   A combination of 92.5 parts pure silver with 7.5 parts alloy, usually copper. These proportions are fixed by law and are true of any silver that is stamped "sterling." The cost and quality of sterling vary with the weight or amount of silver used and the intricacy of design.

Stoneware   A hard and heavy ware made of unrefined, heat-resistant clays.

Terra-cotta   Unglazed pottery made of red or yellow clays.

Translucent   Allowing light to pass through, though not transparent. Another identifying quality of true china.

THE FAMILY ROOM

The family room came into being in the fifties. A family room should take into account the tastes, interests, and activities of all household members. This room may take many forms, depending on the individual household, but the main ob-

Figure 11.11. The mood of this contemporary kitchen and family room is one that is easy to live in. The quarry-tile-look vinyl floor and the same ivory color throughout unite the two rooms and contribute to the feeling of spaciousness. The family room can be separated by sliding wicker doors. (Courtesy of Armstrong World Industries.)

jective should be to provide a flexible room to serve many purposes. The atmosphere of the family room should be one of comfortable intimacy, planned for easy upkeep. Activities vary according to the household, but most rooms should have a place to snack, talk, nap, watch television, and listen to music. The room might also have a fireplace around which to gather with family and friends.

For ceilings in rooms of this kind, acoustical tile is usually preferred, which comes in a variety of designs and muffles noise.

For walls, wood, woodlike vinyl paneling, or scrubbable vinyl-coated wall covering will provide a sturdy background for any decor and requires little upkeep.

A hard-surface flooring is practical in this area and is easy to maintain (see Chapter 7). Vinyls simulating any of the hard-surface coverings are durable and have a resilience that may be desirable. Hardwood always makes an excellent

flooring and has a timeless warmth and beauty. Area or room-sized rugs are preferred by most households, especially where the room also serves as a recreation area, in which case special planning may be necessary to provide for a variety of activities.

Fabrics should be durable and stain resistant. Vinyl upholstering is excellent and comes in a wide range of colors, patterns, and textures.

Furniture should be sturdy but easily movable for rearranging on a moment's notice. Pieces of furniture that can serve a dual role are particularly serviceable. A sofa can serve as a bed for an overnight guest or for a member of the household who gives up his or her room. Low tables can double as stools when covered with bright cushions. Tables that can be raised and lowered may serve for coffee tables, games, and eating. A sofa-back table can become a buffet, and small stacking tables and stools can serve a number of uses. A great variety of dual-purpose furniture is available today to fill individual needs.

Of all the rooms in the house, the family room probably needs the most well-planned storage to take care of all the items that will be used in this area, such as card tables, folding chairs, games, records, books, a movie screen, and a projector. With the advent of numerous new and flexible storage units, otherwise dull rooms can be given new interest. Shelves can be added almost anywhere: between, over, and around windows, under a stairway, around and behind a

Figure 11.12. A room for family activities and television watching. The bricklike floor and painted walls for hard use and easy upkeep, the comfortable, large-scaled furniture covered in a lively print, and plenty of natural light diffused by greenery add up to a room for all seasons. (Courtesy of Armstrong World Industries.)

doorway, and flanking a fireplace. Free-standing walls or built-ins may be set up to provide floor-to-ceiling banks of drawers, cabinets, and shelves. If a smooth facade is desired, storage may be concealed behind plain or louvered doors in keeping with the other woodwork in the room. Open shelves hung from wall strips of metal or wood are probably the most flexible storage, since they can be adjusted and readjusted for height and length to accommodate a variety of items. These may be freestanding and placed against the wall, or may serve as a room divider.

In today's family room, the television is generally standard equipment. Many of the new television designs provide a wide screen and minimal cabinetry, resulting in greater flexibility than ever before in combining the television with other furniture in the home environment. The television may be housed in many ways, the most common of which is placing it in a horizontal chest, which may also hold a stereo and records, with ample, multipurpose counter space above. Locating the television in a central section of a wall of built-ins, where it may be covered by folding doors, is an excellent way to house it. It may be placed in the fireplace wall to take advantage of the furniture arrangement for convenient viewing. Whichever method is chosen, the television should be placed so that a number of people may comfortably view it at the same time.

General lighting is usually desirable in the family room, as well as area lighting for specific activities. Lighting should carefully be planned according to individual needs.

The present trend is to merge the family room and the kitchen into one big room for cooking, informal dining, and many household activities. If possible, the family room should be located where it has easy access to the outside and the kitchen, and away from the bedroom wing. Ideally, the room should be one that fills present needs and can easily be changed as household needs change.

THE ENTERTAINMENT AND RECREATION CENTER

The current "video revolution" is having a major impact on the lives and living environments of people of all ages. In the fifties, the television was in a small, comfortable room called a den. In the sixties, the color television with its hi-fi components made its appearance in the family room. In the seventies, the television with its expanded equipment was housed in the media room. Now in the eighties, as people are increasingly turning to the home for entertainment, burgeoning electronic products for the home are presenting new space problems. These products include the home computer with its many hardware and software components, video cassette recorders, videodiscs, cable and portable cameras, video game consoles, and in the near future, satellite receivers. Integrating these products into the home so that they will best serve the household and still preserve the domestic environment presents a challenge to the interior designer—both professional and nonprofessional. To meet this challenge, entertainment and educational centers are being designed to fit the vast array of electronic equipment into the home and to enhance the quality of living.

The area in which the entertainment center is located should be planned with practicality in mind, since it will most likely have continual use. Combining it with space for other recreational activities is logical.

The question is, however, where can this space be found?

A close examination may reveal underused space. The attic may have wasted space that can be put to good use. The basement may have possibilities, and noise is muffled in a downstairs location. The garage may be converted into a recreation center and the roof extended for a carport. A room already finished may be available, which can be taken over after some minor shifting. Adding a new room is another, but more costly, possibility.

Once the space is decided on, planning should start from the floor upward. Since traffic and wear will be heavy, a good-quality vinyl flooring or a heavy-duty nylon carpet should be selected. A carpet that can be rolled up for dancing and other activities will be practical. Vinyl laminated paneling is a good choice for walls. It comes in a variety of wood grains and takes hard knocks.

The first priority should be to decide where to place the entertainment center. Then, other furniture can be considered. Easily movable pieces are a good choice. To promote social interaction, lounge chairs and sofas should be comfortable. Covering them with carpet for long wear is one consideration. For some furniture, vinyl should be used. It is soft, wears well, and comes in a wide range of colors and textures.

Tables are necessary. To avoid breakage and scratches, sturdy vinyl-topped tables should be used for games such as chess, checkers, gin rummy, backgammon, and bridge. A billiard table will encourage competitive activity and develop skill. An upright piano, or an old player piano at a reasonable price, can give hours of pleasure. A fireplace with a wide hearth for

Figure 11.13. An entertainment center can comprise an entire wall, or be housed in a single piece of furniture designed to contain all the desired components. This wall unit adapts for use as an entertainment center to house television and sound systems. (Courtesy of Schweiger Industries, Inc.)

Figure 11.14. The kitchen and family room are combined in one large L-shaped room, connected by a warm brick wall. Areas of activity are defined, yet the open plan gives a feeling of spaciousness and is conducive to group interaction. (Courtesy of Armstrong World Industries.)

roasting wieners and marshmallows will add a warm, friendly atmosphere.

A pull-down screen to show home movies and slides can permanently be installed at little cost. Extra folding chairs will be needed. Canvas *director's chairs* are inexpensive, can be colorful, and are easily brought out of storage to handle a crowd. Bean bag chairs and large floor cushions will invite informality and relaxation.

A soda bar can be a popular spot. One approach is to create an old-fashioned ice cream parlor theme.

Recreation centers can be planned not only to encourage activities with household members alone but also to broaden involvement with school, church or synagogue, and community affairs. A room that is always open and ready for a committee meeting, a video game, or a rehearsal will surely become a focal point for gatherings of all ages. What better use could be made of space?

THE KITCHEN

Today's kitchens are no longer the antiseptic centers for preparing meals they once were. Many of the features requested by homemakers in a 1964 national survey, conducted by *House and Garden* magazine and the National Association of Home Builders, are still being incorporated in today's kitchens.

Homemakers requested a kitchen large enough to incorporate family dining, informal entertaining, and all the everyday household activities that are carried out spontaneously. Specifically, they wanted an informal, combination family room, living room, and kitchen, with an old-fashioned pantry, well-planned and engineered storage, built-in receptacles for trash, big broom closets, and built-in chopping blocks—all separated from the noise of the washer and dryer. The response by builders and architects to these requests is evident in the space planning that has been done during the past decade for kitchens in all types of dwellings.

Ready-made cabinets are at the disposal of those who prefer a kitchen with a sleek, modern look. For those who prefer a warm country look, finely crafted wood cabinets are available with new sealers and finishes that protect the wood. Whatever style of kitchen is chosen, durability and cleanability of all materials should be considered. Today's market abounds with new plastic materials for floors, walls, counter tops, and furniture coverings, as well as handsome molded plastic furniture that is easy to clean and maintain and resists wear and abuse. From the vast array of available products, one can select those that best serve one's individual needs. (For materials for walls and floors, along with their characteristics, uses, treatment, and care, see Chapter 7.)

Having an efficient kitchen involves keeping up-to-date on new materials. Almost every month finds new materials reaching the retail market. Before making an investment, however, one should make sure all new items have been tried, tested, and found to live up to the claims made for them. Whatever the basic style of a kitchen—traditional or modern, formal or country—it should provide personal enjoyment.

Figure 11.15 (*above*). A dream kitchen that combines the functions of food preparation, dining, and living, but with a well-defined area for each. The contemporary cabinets set the tone for the decor. The tile floor is the principal unifying element. The island work center with cooktop range and ventilating hood dominates the whole. (Courtesy of Armstrong World Industries.)

Figure 11.16 (*left*). This country kitchen, with its warmth of natural wood, quarry tiles, drying herbs, and the aroma of freshly baked bread, provides a pleasant retreat from the twentieth century. (Courtesy of Allmilmo Corporation.)

Figure 11.17. Contemporary sophistication is fundamental in this master bedroom. The sleek island bed, storage headboard, and accompanying armoires are enhanced by the mirror and lighted canopy. Colors are warm neutrals with dark accents. (Courtesy of Henredon Furniture Industries.)

THE MASTER BEDROOM

Interior design for the master bedroom is different from that of any other room in the house. This bedroom is private and personal, and one room in which the door may be closed without apology. Traffic and wear and tear need not be of concern here. The main consideration should be 24-hr comfort. Comfort does not require a large room, but does require organization of space and imagination in interior design. Important to keep in mind is that the master bedroom is a room usually shared by a couple. Each person should have input as to personal preferences for furniture style, colors, fabrics, and the general mood of the room.

The popular king- or queen-sized bed is no innovation of the twentieth century. The oversized bed was well known in Tudor England. The famous Bed of Ware measured 12 ft square and could—and often did—accommodate four couples at the same time. It is now in the Victoria and Albert Museum in London. The canopied bed is also no newcomer to this century. The Crusaders returning from the East introduced it into England and France, and its popularity has never ceased.

Sleeping grandly has been the custom of kings and queens throughout history. Tutankhamen, the Pharoah of Egypt during the fourteenth century B.C., slept on a bed of gold. The bed, however, reached its heyday in the seventeenth century, which was called "the century of magnificent beds." Louis XIV is reputed to have had over 400 beds, all lavishly draped and some inlaid with precious stones. The custom of kings holding council while lying on a sumptuous bed was common practice, and women at the court of *Versailles* received their friends while elegantly ensconced in bed.

As the predominant feature of the room, the bed is the focal point and

Figure 11.18. This handsome canopy bed sets the stage for the eighteenth-century-style bedroom. Exquisite fabrics and accessories carry out the mood. (Courtesy of Henredon Furniture Industries.)

demands special attention. No definite rules govern the choosing of a bed. The choice may be a canopy, a sturdy four-poster, a sleek chrome or bamboo, a popular brass frame, or no frame at all— only a headboard. A few personal luxuries, such as a warm throw to curl up in, attractive sheets and blankets, and a comfortable backrest for reading, can add much to the feeling of personal well-being.

Before the actual interior design is begun, the purposes the room will serve, other than repose, should be decided. A bedroom and a study can be a pleasant combination, and floor-to-ceiling bookshelves will be convenient and will lend warmth. Comfortable chairs that are appropriate for the occupant or occupants will invite relaxation. If space permits, a luxurious chaise may substitute for one of the chairs. Essential items are bedside tables containing drawers or shelves, with moisture-proof surfaces that are large enough to hold a drinking glass, a lamp (unless overhead lighting for reading is provided), and a telephone. The luxurious element in the room is fabric. It can add softness and color, and can set whatever mood is desired. For

normal use, a bedspread that is too delicate should be avoided. The market offers attractive bedspreads that are durable and do not wrinkle or show soil easily. Draw draperies or window blinds will keep morning light out when necessary. Personal preferences and individual life-style can be the guides in furnishing this most personal room.

THE BATHROOM

Since the beginning of the century, the bathroom has undergone a great many changes. From being one large family institution at the end of the hall it became a personal adjunct to the bedroom and as such became smaller and took on a utilitarian look. Then, in the twenties, color became the vogue. Appearing in all the so-called decorator colors were not only wallpaper, floors, and towels but also plumbing fixtures. In the sixties, white fixtures became the fashion, but the bathroom itself took on an aura of elegance and became the glamour room of the American home.

No longer does the bathroom serve purely functional needs. Today, function and luxury are combined, and the room once hidden behind closed doors is frequently exposed to sky, garden, terrace, and in some instances, to other rooms of the house, with screens or sliding glass doors for privacy. What was once a small, sterile room has become a powder room, a dressing room, and even a sitting room with stained glass windows, easy chairs, and a couch for lounging and massage.

The fixtures for the bathroom have kept abreast of the trend. Recalling the splendor of Rome, tubs may be sunken and deep enough for standing. They may be in the center of the room, in all shapes and sizes, and with built-in seats. Beautiful new basins are made of marble, onyx, hand-carved shells, or china. The latter may have baked-in traditional or contemporary motifs to set the theme of the room, and similar motifs are used on water closet and seat cover. Manufac-

Figure 11.20. Sleek and uncluttered, this spacious tile bathroom has all the basic luxuries. Sliding glass doors open onto an enclosed garden. Ripplefold drapery provides privacy. (Courtesy of Kirsch Company.)

turers have coordinated these motifs in all-important accessories such as shower curtains, towels, wallpaper, wall and floor tile, towel bars, and soap dishes. To further add to the feeling of luxury, flocked vinyl wallpaper, lush carpets, crystal chandeliers, miniature trees, gold-plated and crystal faucets, ornate mirrors, deep-sculptured towels, and jewel-like soap dishes are available.

For the average home owner, most of these features are undoubtedly extreme, but with the wonderful new materials available, updating a bathroom to give it a feeling of glamour can be accomplished without too much expense. When building or remodeling a bathroom, one should keep in mind, as in doing any room of the house, the kind of use it will receive. The design should then be planned accordingly. For the household bathroom, easy upkeep should be of major importance. The market offers scrubbable vinyls for every purpose in all colors and patterns (see Chapter 7). If carpet is the choice, the selection should be one that resists spots and cleans easily. A bathroom should have ample storage for such items as towels, cosmetics, and soiled clothes. Good lighting is a requisite. Mirrors for makeup and grooming are essential, and the effect they can

Figure 11.19. An efficient his-and-her bathroom with two sinks, separate toilet compartments, and no-wax floor. The bathroom is all white except for the blue fixtures, rose towels, green ferns in the wicker basket, and the fig tree. The skylight in the sloping ceiling and the sliding glass doors admit ample light. Folding louvered doors provide privacy. (Courtesy of Armstrong World Industries.)

Figure 11.21. Vinyl-coated, scrubbable, wet-look wall covering sets off an earlier vintage tub that is elevated on easy-to-clean ceramic tile. A handmade table and matching brown towels and rug complete the color scheme in this personalized bathroom. (Courtesy of Collins and Aikman Corporation.)

create by doubling light and expanding space is a bonus.

In recent years, Americans have become preoccupied with bathrooms, and the number of bathrooms in a house has taken precedence over the design or arrangement of space. During the late 1970s and early 1980s, efforts by architects and planners to cut the number and simplify the design of bathrooms met with little success. Most prospective buyers set a high priority on plenty of bathrooms with all the modern amenities.

THE CHILD'S ROOM

Home is a place where a child develops personal goals and values, where he or she learns to respect the privacy of others, and where he or she develops an appreciation for good books, art, and music. We may never know how much the houses we live in contribute to the growth of children, but a well-planned physical environment can help guide their emotional development. Often the simplest things in a house make the biggest difference. If traffic lanes are thoughtfully arranged, harmful results from unnecessary nagging may be avoided. If the child is provided a private retreat, no matter how small, it will contribute to his or her feeling of self-esteem and well-being, and can be an invaluable gift. Individual members of a household have differing concepts of personal environment, however, and what fills the needs for one does not necessarily fill the needs of another.

A child's room should be his or her private world and should be respected as such by other members of the household. The room harbors pets and friends and is a place to store, display, and hide things. It is a place to read, to work at hobbies, to snack, and to dream. The room should have storage, good lighting, a desk for study, a comfortable bed, and space for

Figure 11.22. The rainbow of color that appears when the vertical shades are drawn can delight a child. (Courtesy of Louverdrape.)

Figure 11.23. This Panda bed can be an inviting sight to a child. (Courtesy of Loards.)

play. The design should be planned with the child's input so that the room will express his or her personality. The smallest space, if skillfully planned and arranged, can meet these needs. For the young child, safety with simple, sturdy, small-scaled furniture should be of paramount concern. If furniture for the nursery is wisely chosen, it can be converted to serve as the child grows. For example, the ends of a crib can be used for head- and footboards on a youth or adult bed. A low chest of drawers can serve as a changing table for an infant and can later be used for storage for a child of any age. An infant's wardrobe can become a bookcase later on.

Since the daily habits and interests of children during their developing years vary widely, their needs may be best served by creating personal environments in which they spend their private lives and which express their individuality.

With wise long-range planning and frequent modifications, a child's room can serve from toddler to teenage years. As the child grows and changes, so should his or her room. Individual needs should always determine what changes should be made and when, but the maturing child requires ongoing alteration of his or her physical environment.

Almost any informal room that serves many needs can benefit from a generous-sized bulletin board. In the child's room, the bulletin board may range from a large rectangle to one that covers the entire wall, where the child can exhibit schoolwork, photographs, and other

prized possessions. Wallpaper, fabrics, floor coverings, and furniture should be chosen with the child's individual taste in mind.

As the child grows older, his or her interests will invariably change, and awareness of current trends, as well as a knowledge of traditional and contemporary styles, will enable the child to choose what appeals to him or her. The child will undoubtedly take pride in helping to create a private environment that reflects his or her personality—an environment in which he or she can function at an optimum level.

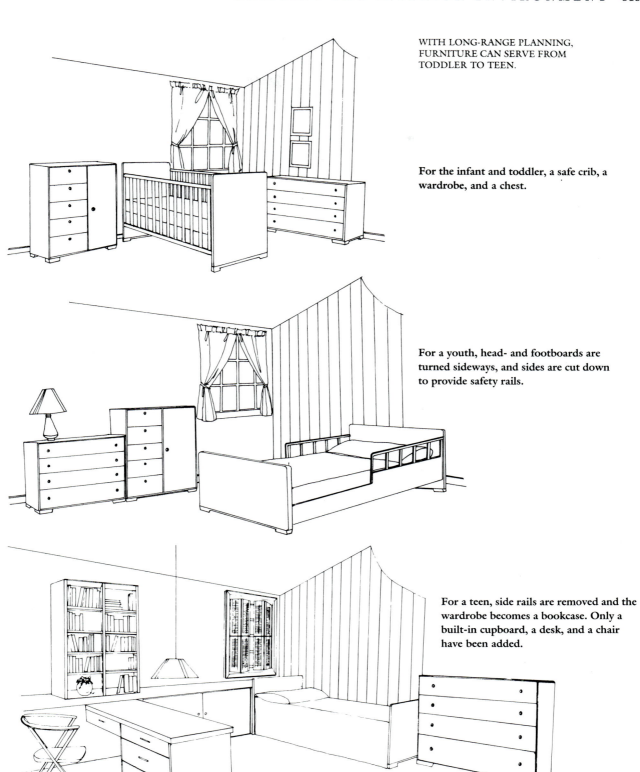

WITH LONG-RANGE PLANNING,
FURNITURE CAN SERVE FROM
TODDLER TO TEEN.

For the infant and toddler, a safe crib, a
wardrobe, and a chest.

For a youth, head- and footboards are
turned sideways, and sides are cut down
to provide safety rails.

For a teen, side rails are removed and the
wardrobe becomes a bookcase. Only a
built-in cupboard, a desk, and a chair
have been added.

Figure 11.24 (*above*). With plenty of space to display and store things, a game table, a bed for an overnight guest, and a Berber rug to take hard wear, this room should please almost any young child. (Courtesy of Drexel Heritage Furnishings.)

Figure 11.25 (*facing page*). This young girl's bedroom incorporates beauty and luxury. The bedspread and drapery fabric and the coordinated wallpaper have red tulips delicately arranged on a white ground. Bed, woodwork, and furniture are painted white. (Courtesy of Warner Company.)

Accessories

The importance of accessories should not be overlooked, for they add the finishing touches to a room and reflect personal taste and individuality. An accessory may be almost anything from a *Coromandel screen* to a door knocker, and can be a powerful tool in establishing an interior design theme. An object should never be used just to fill up space. A safe rule to follow is that if the item is neither useful, beautiful, nor meaningful to the owner, it has no place in his or her home. If an article does not meet at least one of these criteria, a prudent decision is to leave the space empty.

Among the many accessories that can complete a room and can give a desirable lived-in feeling are screens, pictures, clocks, mirrors, lamps, books, copper, brass, and fireplace tools, as well as little touches such as drapery rods, tiebacks, and hardware. Whether functional or purely decorative, each accessory can contribute to the enhancement of an interior if it is chosen with care and discrimination.

SCREENS

One graceful and economical means of individualizing an environment is through the use of a standing screen. A wide variety of screens are on the market today. The versatile shutter screen with movable louvers may be used almost anywhere. Wood frames containing light-filtering materials such as fiberglass, caning, pierced metal, or filigree, which comes in a wide assortment of designs from geometrics to exotic arabesques, are available. A decorative screen may give an architectural quality to a room, set or enhance the room's decor, provide a backdrop for a furniture grouping in a room with limited wall space, substitute for side drapery, or serve as the room's focal point.

In addition to its decorative values, a screen can serve many functional purposes. It can be the primary multipurpose item in the home, usually easily moved from one room to another. It can set off an entrance where the front door opens directly into the living room, act as a divider between a living and dining area, close off a kitchen, set off a private area by making a room within a room, redirect traffic when strategically placed, extend the apparent size of a room by replacing a door with an airy see-through effect, control the flow of air and the direction of light, camouflage an old-fashioned radiator or air-conditioning unit, and conceal storage. Whatever the theme the room, the right screen used in the right place will provide value for the money spent.

A filigreed screen can be both beautiful and functional.

PICTURES AND PAINTINGS

Displayed pictures and paintings are the most personal items in a home and can contribute much to a room's appeal and distinctiveness. In general, pictures are better when they are in keeping with the mood of the room. Sometimes, however, the opposite is true. For example, a modern painting in a traditional room can often add the variety the room needs. (For picture arranging and hanging, see "Wall Composition," Chapter 10.)

MIRRORS

Distinct in their inherent beauty, mirrors are a decorative and functional medium in today's homes, and are a helpful tool for the interior designer. They are available in almost any size and in frames to fit any decor. Through decorative know-how, mirrors can be used to add beauty, multiply space, conceal unattractive structural features, distribute and double light, brighten dark areas, and bring life into an otherwise drab room. Because of their myriad uses, mirrors have steadily increased in popularity through the years, and today they play a virtually indispensable role in all styles of interiors.

Figure 11.26. A mirror is a most helpful tool for the interior designer. Used here as a headboard, it doubles the light, adds beauty, and expands space. (Courtesy of Thayer Coggin.)

A mirror in a corner can give an illusion of space and increase the light supply.

LAMPS

The lamp is an important element of beauty and function both during the daytime and at night, and should be chosen carefully with the specific room, location, and purpose in mind (see "Artificial Lighting," Chapter 4).

BOOKS

Books can do more than anything—except people—to add friendliness to a home. Cicero said, "A room without books is a body without a soul." No room has a mood that would preclude books, and no color scheme is so complete that it cannot benefit from the warm tones and textures of books. Bookshelves can go almost anywhere. They should be planned in the initial design of the house. The entrance hall is an excellent place for bookshelves. They require little space, will create a warm, friendly atmosphere, and are accessible to all areas of the house. The living room and family room should have ample bookshelves to hold a multiplying collection of books for the entire household. Every child needs bookshelves in his or her room, at a height that can easily be reached. In any bedroom, headboards for book storage are convenient for bedtime reading,

Shelves can be built around a window to fill the entire wall. Storage is a bonus.

and kitchens need handy shelves for reference books and cookbooks. In the absence of preplanning for bookshelves, they can be fitted under stairways, into niches or odd corners, and around doors and windows to employ unused space. A room divider can hold books on one or both sides. Books, like flowers, are never out of place, and like friends, people need them always close at hand.

CLOCKS

Clocks have long been an important accessory in the home. From the handsome grandfather to the old-fashioned *wag-on-the-wall* to the contemporary sunburst, they not only serve a necessary function but also add an important

A doorway framed with books is a valuable addition to a room.

decorative touch to any room, since by their very nature they attract attention. A clock should fit appropriately into the room and should be placed where it is easily seen.

FLOWERS AND FOLIAGE

Of all the accessories that make up the final touches of a home, nothing can duplicate what a bouquet of live foliage and flowers can do for a room. The extra effort that fresh arrangements require shows that the owner loves his or her home and takes pride in its beauty.

Use wasted space under a staircase.

Create an entranceway with bookshelves.

Make a headboard or a room divider for books.

Something is always near at hand that with a little imagination can add life and beauty to the home. The sophisticated beauty of the rose, either in a full bouquet or standing alone in a graceful bud vase, is well known, but a graceful arrangement of small flowers, unknown weeds, and interesting branches can also beautify a room. Those who are serious about flower arranging may be interested in learning the principles of the three basic styles: oriental, traditional, and contemporary. If an unstudied bouquet is preferred, personal taste can be the guide.

Whatever the style of arrangement, it should be planned with a specific spot in mind. A bouquet for a coffee table should be low and attractive from any angle. On occasional tables, where space

is limited, the choice should be small containers, with blooms and foliage out of the way of lamps and other accessories. Large wall spaces and generously proportioned pieces of furniture call for larger and more impressive arrangements. Those used against the wall need to be arranged facing the room. A dull area can be brightened by a red geranium plant, a handful of daisies, or some dried yarrow. Arrangements need not always be large nor placed in key positions. Tiny bouquets in unexpected places can often do something special for a room. A small arrangement can be placed in the shelf of a nightstand or on a window ledge, ivy can be trailed from a tiny brass container over the edge of a bookshelf, or a single spray of leaves can be placed on an end table.

One of the secrets of a successful flower arrangement is the container. Selecting the right holder will help to display the flowers to better advantage. The container should be compatible with the type of flowers, the style of the arrangement, and its placement. A low, rectangular container is the most versatile and lends itself to the vertical or horizontal arrangement. The tall container calls for more formality of arranging. The

container should never detract from the flowers or foliage and should be kept simple. Many items on kitchen shelves may be appropriate. A crystal goblet will hold delicate blooms and will add a touch of refinement. For a more informal look, zinnias can be placed in an attractive baking dish or in a basket. A cup and saucer may be right for violets, a milk-glass cream pitcher for marigolds or bachelor's buttons, and a soup tureen for a mixed bouquet. A standard flowerpot and saucer can form a pyramid of fruits and flowers. A pitcher is an excellent container. The highest bloom should be placed on the handle side.

Both beginner and expert can discover continuing satisfaction in the gentle art of flower arranging. Arranging new materials and finding new ways of arranging familiar materials present an ongoing challenge. When the fresh buds of spring and the lush blooms of summer are gone, graceful berried branches, lacy weeds, and unusual dry leaves can give pleasure all winter by themselves or can be mixed with live greens, fruits, and figurines.

Queen Anne's lace is attractive in a baking dish.

Daisies look at home in a simple basket.

In this arrangement of leaves and berries, the large leaves correctly face in several directions.

A bouquet need not be large. A small one can be tucked near some books.

Figure 11.27. Plants displayed in contemporary chrome pedestals and planters. Some have built-in pots, pot-holder brackets, and places for books and favorite objects. (Courtesy of Cosco Home Products.)

Figure 11.28. Checked wallpaper in warm gold with black accents provides an appropriate background for gleaming metal and yellow chrysanthemums. From the flat, horizontal top of the television cabinet, swans in varying sizes and with graceful necks direct the eye upward to the higher bouquet, which slightly overlaps the brass tray, thus unifying the entire composition. (Photograph by Mark K. Allen, residence of Mrs. J. Hamilton Calder.)

Queen Anne's lace is a common weed, and its delicate petals and soft, slender stems make graceful and lasting arrangements. Dry flowers and leaves are natural, and their mellow, weathered look has a distinctive appeal. Twisted wood branches, after a little judicious pruning, can create interesting lines to blend with a modern room. The eye can be trained to see beauty in the commonplace things in nature.

Any house is enlivened by growing plants, but the indoor gardening fever that began sweeping the country in the late 1960s has sometimes been carried to the extreme. If used properly, however, plants can do wonders and can solve a number of interior design problems. Among their many uses, they can brighten up a somber room, serve as a room divider, substitute for curtains and drapery, and fill in where furniture is sparse.

Plants can be used in any room so long as they do not obstruct activities or traffic. Potted plants blooming on windowsills or greenery hanging in corners or trailing over shelves can bring life into a room. Corner and bay windows are excellent places to arrange a grouping. Plants can be hung at various levels, and

A window greenhouse

others can be placed on blocks of varying heights. They will make an attractive focal point, get ample light, and be out of the line of traffic. Because of the humidity in bathrooms, plants will thrive there if given artificial light.

For plant enthusiasts, a window greenhouse may be a consideration. Plants rest on metal or mesh shelving in an aluminum greenhouse window, which comes fully assembled with complete installation instructions. The feeling of perpetual springtime in a home can give year-round pleasure.

FINISHING TOUCHES

The finishing touches added to an interior design scheme can be like pieces of fine jewelry and will give a personal and final stamp of approval to a room. A contemporary room can be made strikingly modern and a traditional room can take on authenticity by the discriminating use of small details such as door knockers, doorknobs, switch plates, curtain rods, and tiebacks. Drawer pulls, escutcheons, and hinges can give a piece of furniture a definite feeling for any period. Whether the style is authentic Early American, graceful Georgian, elegant French, refined classical, romantic Spanish, exotic oriental, or sleek modern, the right hardware can convey the appropriate mood.

The desire to display one's prized possessions is universal, and the challenge is to arrange these treasured objects into a composition of uncluttered beauty. If the items collected were worth acquiring, they are worth displaying. The secret lies in training the eye to see beauty in color, form, and space relationships when grouping the items in an artistic arrangement. By themselves, small things may be insignificant, but through skillful arranging, even the simplest items can take on special meaning. When grouping small objects, one should keep in mind that they are not seen in and of themselves but against a background of walls and furniture, which should be considered

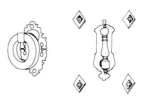

Door knockers

Doorknobs

Drawer pulls

Tiebacks

DESIRABLE   LESS DESIRABLE   DESIRABLE   LESS DESIRABLE

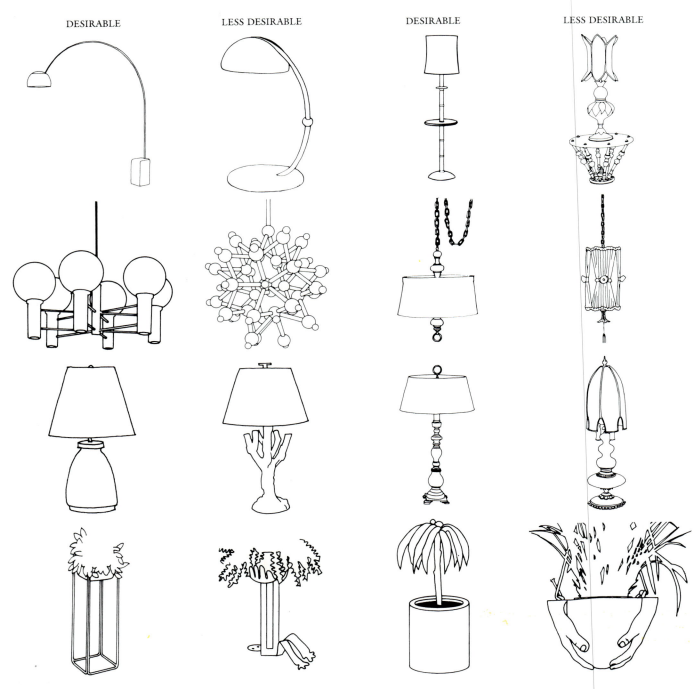

Figure 11.29. Choosing accessories.

part of the arrangement. As the interior designer brings together various items, he or she should be aware of their relationship to each other. Perhaps a grouping of round objects of varying sizes is pleasing, but adding a rectangle can provide a different perspective. In an arrangement with three elements—a horizontal piece, a higher intermediate piece, and a tall vertical piece—the eye will move from the low horizontal to the high vertical, giving a pleasant sense of transition. This transition is seen in nature when the eye observes the earth, the flowering plants, and the towering trees, which direct the sight still higher.

sprawling over the edge of a shelf to a lower level will provide an interesting effect.

If the interior designer believes that a room lacks character, he or she should search until the right elements are discovered. Whatever is used should be in keeping with the quality that has been established in the home, and should either strengthen the chosen theme or by contrast add a touch of excitement. Leaving a little empty space need not be of concern. One should remember the charm of the incomplete.

The eye is drawn from the small horizontal to the curved and upward.

A common color subtly running through each element will add unity to an arrangement.

Experimentation should be done. Even necessary articles in a kitchen, a bedroom, or a bathroom can add visual pleasure when they are grouped with an aesthetic eye. Books can be combined with an occasional figurine, a small painting, a trophy, or any small article. A plant

CHAPTER TWELVE

Interior Design as a Career

The following definition of an interior designer was formulated by the National Council for Interior Design Qualification (NCIDQ), has been endorsed by the American Society of Interior Designers (ASID), and has been approved by the Foundation for Interior Design Education Research (FIDER):

"The professional interior designer is a person qualified by education, experience and examination, who

1 identifies, researches, and creatively solves problems pertaining to the function and quality of the interior environment;

2 performs services relative to interior spaces, including programming, design analysis, space planning and aesthetics, using specialized knowledge of interior construction, building codes, equipment, materials and furnishings; and

Figure 12.1. The professional interior designer designs not only residential interiors but also commercial office space, such as this graphics studio. (Photograph courtesy of Martin Instrument Company.)

3 prepares all drawings and documents relative to the design of interior spaces in order to enhance and protect the health, safety, and welfare of the public."

The classifications of interior design

Interior design has become such a multifaceted field that many designers choose to specialize in one of the following various areas in order to develop and concentrate their expertise:

▫ Residential interior design refers to the design of an entire residence, or a part of one, in which the client is the end user or occupant.

▫ Nonresidential design, which is also referred to as "contract design," encompasses all areas of the business world, including financial, medical, and educational institutions, governmental facilities, offices, hotels, motels, retail establishments, restaurants, clubs, and so on.

▫ Additional areas of specialization in which an interior designer may choose to concentrate can include furniture, lighting, or fabric design, color consulting, interior photography, design journalism, or product representation for a manufacturer.

The responsibilities of an interior designer

The professional interior designer:

▫ Is required to be proficient in the planning, designing, and implementation of residential and nonresidential design.

▫ Must be qualified to coordinate all elements of design to create functional and aesthetically pleasing living and working environments that fulfill the total needs of the client or end user.

▫ Must be trained to make the most of space. Living and working space is diminishing in size due to increased building costs, and the designer must therefore be able to use every square foot to the best advantage.

□ Is qualified to work with an architect from the initial planning stages of an environment to completion, working from empty space until the last interior detail is in place and the client is satisfied.

□ Must be knowledgeable about and able to appropriately integrate period and contemporary styles of architecture, furniture, and decorative arts.

□ Must have knowledge of furniture materials and construction, the creative ability to custom design furnishings such as case goods, and be able to redesign or add architectural elements such as wood trim, doors, and mantels.

□ Should be concerned not only with the immediate effect but also with the construction, durability, and maintenance of fabrics and finishes. A designer should also be well qualified to select and use fabrics and textiles for the best performance and appearance as applied to all aspects of an interior, including floor, wall, window, and upholstery treatments.

□ Must be knowledgeable about lighting and its effect on interior colors, finishes, and spaces.

□ Must be familiar with a broad range of products and services, and must have a good working relationship with those people who provide the products and services, to assure that ordering, shipping, delivery, and installations go smoothly.

□ Should have, in addition to established sources, favorite cabinetmakers, artisans such as upholsterers and refinishers, workrooms, antique shops, and auction rooms from which to draw. These sources can be invaluable to the client, since access to some high-quality merchandise, labor, and services is available only through professionals.

□ Is responsible for the completed project and must see that any flaws in quality or craftsmanship are corrected.

□ Must be a good visual and oral communicator. One of the many requisites to a successful design is a sound designer-client-resource relationship.

□ Must be able to incorporate his or her artistry and expertise with the client's purposes and objectives, within the bounds of good taste.

□ Must be an effective salesperson, for without this element, the interior design profession would not exist.

Preparing for a career in interior design

For most people, deciding on a career is a searching process that requires careful examination and evaluation of one's interests and capabilities as well as one's inadequacies.

The person who is creative, sensitive to the environment, interested in America's cultural heritage and ancestral homes, as well as in today's varied architectural and contemporary design, who likes people and is concerned with improving the quality of their home, work, or recreational environments, would be wise to explore the possibility of a career in interior design.

Interior design first became a respectable profession in the early twentieth century through the efforts and achievements of Elsie de Wolfe, a remarkable woman about whom a new biography was published in 1982 (*Elsie de Wolfe: A Life in the High Style* by Jane S. Smith, published by Atheneum, New York). The accepted term for the profession for many years was *interior decoration,* and the person who provided these services was an *interior decorator.* Today these terms are seldom used, since the connotation came to derogate the profession, implying that it dealt only with the superficial embellishment of the interior.

The term *interior design,* which implies the understanding and application of highly technical and professional skills, has replaced the term *interior decoration,* and the person who performs the necessary function is an *interior designer.*

The first step toward becoming a professional interior designer is to successfully complete an interior design program at a college, university, or design school, where students are educated and trained in such areas as:

□ Visual, written, and verbal communication skills;

□ Development of knowledge of building and interior systems and codes, textiles, barrier-free design, history of art, architecture, and interiors; and

□ Interior component selection, furniture layout, space planning and estimation of floor, wall, and window coverings.

Many interior design programs require that students participate in internship or work-study courses as part of the requirements for graduation. Internship programs vary somewhat in different schools, but all have the same objective, which is to enable the student to experience firsthand the professional business world prior to graduation by combining classroom theory with practice. Students work in the interior design area of a reputable business establishment during the summer months or part-time during the school year or both. Some schools give college credits, and the monetary agreement, if any, is arranged between the student and the firm.

Internship experience is invaluable to the student. By becoming actively involved in the real world of interior design, students:

□ Experience operational procedures, policies, and various phases of design, such as client-designer relationships, interaction of designers within a firm, and observing and participating in design from concept to implementation;

□ Learn to be open to new and different attitudes and perspectives in all aspects of design;

□ Learn more about themselves in terms of potential, future desires, and goals as a professional interior designer; and

□ In general, receive valuable experience that can be entered on a job résumé for use after graduation.

Information and locations of schools offering interior design programs can be obtained from local libraries or from the Foundation for Interior Design Education Research (FIDER), Room 1501, 322-8th Avenue, New York, New York 10001.

The interior design profession offers a rewarding career for well-trained, dedicated men and women.

Opportunities for interior designers

In spite of the present economy and some apprehensions over the interior design profession, signs for cautious optimism are evident as new opportunities emerge. Today, interior design and interior designers are perceived as important by both the public and various businesses. Interior designers are being sought after by industry, which has become aware of interior designers' buying power, and manufacturers are turning to the design community for advice in product development. Major design trade centers can now be found in Texas, California, and New York. One of the most notable trade centers for residential furniture is in High Point, North Carolina, where a six-floor building is devoted entirely to the designer. Surveys have shown that interior designers' activities in both residential and contract design have increased 32 percent since 1980. An increasing source of clients is in a growing segment of the population made up of families with two wage earners who, because of limited time, are turning to professional interior designers to carry out the time-consuming project of home planning and interior design.

Some of the residential and contract career opportunities open to professional interior designers include the following:

□ An independent residential or contract interior designer may be the head or a member of a design firm or decorating studio, may own a small specialty shop, or may even work out of his or her own home and make purchases from a wide range of sources. The independent interior designer will go to a client's home or office, appraise the job, work out floor plans, assist in selecting and arranging furniture, assemble color schemes, place the orders, and supervise the job until its completion.

□ Many department and furniture stores are staffed with interior designers, drafters, buyers, and other design-related personnel. These designers follow the same procedure as the independent designer and offer a number of advantages as well: (1) a limited amount of free advice is available, (2) payment for all purchases and services can be made on the store's payment plan, and (3) store merchandise may be moderately priced due to the quantity purchases by the store.

In smaller stores, decorating and design services are usually more limited. The designer may or may not be a trained professional, he or she may not be permitted to go to the client's home, and only merchandise carried by the store may be sold. Each store establishes its own policies; therefore, services may vary.

□ A renderer, who prepares realistic, three-dimensional drawings and illustrations of a designer's concept of an interior, can work as an independent designer or for architectural and design firms.

□ A set designer works on television, theatre, and movie productions, or creates complete room displays for department stores, furniture companies, and manufacturers for advertising purposes.

□ A commercial-contract designer works for a design company, architectural firm, or corporation, and performs any of a variety of tasks such as space planning, drafting, specifying, and purchasing furnishings and materials in volume for installation in hotels, apartments, schools, health care facilities, and so on.

□ A design specialist focuses on historic preservation, solar energy, or even earth-sheltered environments.

□ A wholesale market representative sells interior-design-related merchandise in quantity to retail establishments.

□ A drafter prepares precise mechanical drawings for architects, designers, builders, and furnishing manufacturers.

□ A design journalist or photographer completes work for newspapers, magazines, or publishers on a variety of timely aspects of interior design.

□ An interior design instructor works for a school, college, or university after an advanced design degree is earned and an appropriate amount of experience is gained.

These are only some of the employment opportunities open to the trained interior designer. Other exciting opportunities are developing in government, business, and industry, where the diverse skills of design professionals are considered essential to long-range planning and product development. Experienced, professional interior designers are currently serving in key positions with large corporations in industry, manufacturing, transportation, communications, recreation, and many other areas. Designers are now members of state and federal governments. A market is rapidly evolving in some of the developing countries, such as the wealthy Gulf region of the Middle East. In 1981 Saudi Arabia held its first International Exhibition of Interior Design. This new development affords unlimited possibilities and opportunities for American interior designers.

The computer: applications for interior design

An invaluable aid now available for instruction and client presentation of space planning is the computer. Computer graphics is a science that is expanding rapidly, and provides a service whose myriad uses and benefits are only beginning to be understood. Complete packages of computerized equipment (hardware), and computer programs (software) for use with the equipment, are now available. Advanced computerized graphic design programs have been developed specifically for space planning, interior design, and facilities management, bringing a new technology to each of these disciplines. The computer design program will increase the user's capabilities in a number of ways.

The program enables the user to design workstations and floor plans right on the screen. Software includes a data base, or catalog, of furniture components. The user can also draw, describe, and specify other products to meet his or her client's needs.

Clear and concise images are displayed on the screen. Graphic display software provides representations of exteriors and interiors from any viewpoint showing shape, surface textures, light and shadow, and lighting models. With a palette of several hundred colors, the computer allows the user to see his or her design in a variety of color schemes that can instantly be changed and modified. Perspective designs in two- and three-dimensional form can be rotated on a screen and viewed from any angle. Students and clients can "walk through" a space as if it were actually there.

The program completely eliminates the need for manual drawings. Floor plans, elevations, perspectives, and full-color renderings of furniture and architecture can be produced in a fraction of the time it takes to draw them by hand. Layout drawings, required for effective space planning, are readily developed with software models.

CAD (computer-aided design) systems interfaced with high-speed drafting machines produce high-resolution working drawings, which in turn may be reproduced as traditional blueprints.

Because all the information used in the design process is filed in the computer's memory, it is retrievable. Specifications lists and facilities reports can be accessed as detailed printouts, which accurately list all the components in any design on file.

The package keeps track of all data-drawing figures and point allocations automatically so that the user does not have to keep records or items. The computer can display an area as large as the floor plan of an entire building or as minute as a single pencil on a desk top—or any area in between. Instructional packages are often available on videotape, which will aid both instructor and student. Each year, CAD systems become more "user friendly," which means less sophisticated training for those who will operate the systems. Even if the user has had no experience with computers, extensive use of tutorial menus and familiar symbols, terms, and planning concepts make the systems easy to use.

Many benefits accrue from using the computer both in classroom instruction and in client presentations. Perhaps most dramatic are speed and the ability to look quickly at a wide range of solutions to a given problem. These capabilities optimize the design and save valuable time.

A plan that formerly was possible only by making tedious hand-drawn perspectives or by building mock-ups or models can instantly be seen for student instruction or client approval. Drawings are accurate to $\frac{1}{8000}$ in., and errors are reduced. The computer can quickly help the user to respond to changing needs and project updates, and is a valuable tool for communicating ideas to students or clients.

Computer systems typically come to the user with a basic working capacity. The user may then purchase specialty packages that adapt the system to the efficient processing of a particular area, such as interior design. In time, as the user becomes more familiar with and capable of using the system, he or she can create a personalized library of components that are peculiar to his or her discipline. Standard graphic items include typical floor plan symbols such as wall types, windows, doors, cabinetry, and popular furniture types.

Architecture represents a cost-effective use of CAD, particularly because of the repeated use of standard symbols and items. A CAD system is to an interior designer what a bulldozer is to the user of a shovel. It permits each user to get the job done quicker, cheaper, and better. It strips tedium away and allows the computer and designer to work in concert with one another, each doing what it or the user does best.

Computer companies throughout the country are making every effort to make their services available to schools and industries. After the system is purchased, the company will send a member of the school or department to their one- or two-week training program to learn how to use the system. In some cities, computer companies have set up centers,

usually funded by local industries, that serve all the schools in the district.

To assist in furthering the efficient use of a given CAD system, all the users of each type of system are invited to meet at regular intervals in *user groups*. These user meetings, which typically last from three to four days, are open to users from schools throughout the country, who gather to generate a prioritized *wish list*. The group is broken down into special interest groups such as electronics, numerical control, architecture, and interior design. When priorities are established within each group, the entire body reassembles to pool their findings. As a result of these user groups, programs are generated by a vendor and are made available to all users. The interior design department that uses a computer system can have access to the programs made available through the user group, and can add them to their own programs.

A host of new computer systems are coming on the market, and both mini- and microsystems are now within the range of many universities. With costs moving downward, the computer in the near future will undoubtedly become a standard teaching tool in most schools throughout the country.

The following are some of the companies equipped to provide computer-assisted programs:

Steelcase, Inc.
Environmental Support Services
901 Forty-fourth Street SE
P.O. Box 1967
Grand Rapids, Michigan 49508

Hewlett-Packard Company
Computer Systems Division
Technical Systems Software Solutions
19447 Pruneridge Avenue
Cupertino, California 95014

Advanced Software Technology
7899 Masters Drive
Overland Park, Kansas 66204

Professional interior design societies

The American Society of Interior Designers (ASID) is a professional international organization established to enact and maintain standards of excellence to enhance the growing recognition of interior design as a profession. It was formed in 1975 through the consolidation of the American Institute of Interior Designers (AID) and the National Society of Interior Designers (NSID), but its roots date back half a century to the founding of AID in 1931. ASID is the largest organization of interior designers in the world, representing over 20,000 members in the United States as well as abroad. It represents interior design as a profession dedicated to serving people, and provides a forum for its thousands of talented members to bring their differing points of view into harmony to promote unified action. ASID fosters the development and improvement of interior design practice through a variety of activities and programs that reflect a broad spectrum of professional concerns, ranging from interior design to community service workshops.

Over 150 student chapters of ASID are in colleges across the country, and membership during the academic year 1981 to 1982 reached a record high of 7401. The society's educational program includes seminars, show-house tours, lectures, access to designers and restricted design centers, and opportunities to participate in national student competitions. Of particular importance to members is that upon graduation, they are eligible to advance automatically to associate membership in the society.

The advancement to professional membership is earned after an applicant fulfills the practical experience requirements and completes the National Council for Interior Design Qualification

(NCIDQ) exam. Professional members are distinguished by the letters *ASID* beside their names, which serve as a symbol of professional excellence. The national ASID headquarters is located at 1430 Broadway, New York, New York 10018.

The Institute of Business Designers (IBD) is an internationally established organization dedicated to the professional designer whose major field is commercial and institutional interiors and products. This includes designers responsible for offices, hotels, hospitals and health care facilities, and other institutions such as stores, schools, theaters, and banks.

The institute is dedicated to exploring new directions in design, expanding the influence of the designer, and supplementing the formal education of its members. To accomplish this, IBD is actively involved in design research, continuing education, and student design education programs. The institute also sponsors major design competitions.

As with ASID, IBD has various membership categories and requirements for membership, including education, experience, and NCIDQ examination. Information regarding this organization can be obtained by writing to the IBD national office, 1155 Merchandise Mart, Chicago, Illinois 60654.

The Interior Design Society (IDS), another national organization, is a relative newcomer to the profession. Organized in 1973, IDS is steadily growing across the country, with over 25 chapters and some 1500 members. The society, which is an arm of the National Home Furnishings Association, provides its members with a variety of sales aids and educational programs, as well as the professional recognition they deserve as retail designers. Headquarters are at 406 Merchandise Mart, Chicago, Illinois 60654.

The Interior Design Educators Council, Inc. (IDEC), incorporated in 1967, is dedicated to the development of interior design education. Its purpose is to strive to improve the teaching of interior design and, through this, the professional level of interior design practice. The IDEC program is concerned with establishing and strengthening the lines of communication among individual educators, educational institutes, and organizations concerned with interior design. It is an international organization and an associate member of the International Federation of Interior Designers (IFID). During its brief history, IDEC has been a catalyst for change and a strong contributor to most of the major accomplishments that have made the profession of interior design what it is today. Every teacher of interior design can benefit from membership in this organization. Information about IDEC can be obtained by writing IDEC, Box 8744, Richmond, Virginia 23226.

One purpose of the *National Council for Interior Design Qualification (NCIDQ)* is to establish a professional level of competence for interior designers so that they may better serve the public. Level of competence is determined through the formulation and administration of a relevant examination that qualifies the individual designer. Another purpose of NCIDQ is to investigate the advantages and disadvantages of pursuing legal registration or certification of the profession.

The incorporation charter of the council provides membership for professional design organizations only; it offers no provisions for membership to individuals. All council member organizations require the NCIDQ exam as a prerequisite for professional membership. Nonaffiliated interior designers who have the required education and experience may apply directly to NCIDQ to take the exam.

The examination, offered twice a year at various locations around the country, consists of two parts given on two consecutive days. The first part—the academic section—tests the candidate's knowledge in such areas as history, modern design, technical information, business practices, and ethics.

The second part is a 10-hr design problem testing the candidate's ability to arrive at a conceptual solution to a realistic design problem. The problem requires a design concept statement, space planning, furniture selection and arrangement, interior surfaces, interior systems, presentation skills, and project specifications. Information about the council can be obtained by writing NCIDQ, 118 East Twenty-fifth Street, New York, New York 10010.

Other professional organizations that may be of interest are the following:

Environmental Design Research
    Association, Inc.
L'Enfant Plaza Station
P.O. Box 23129
Washington, D.C. 20024

Foundation for Interior Design
    Education Research
242 West Twenty-seventh Street,
    Suite 6B
New York, New York 10001
(212) 929-8366

Interior Designers of Canada
168 Bedford Road
Toronto
Canada M5R 2K9

Getting that first job

How is that important first job obtained? First, strategies should carefully be designed and planned, and obtaining a job should be made a full-time project. Trade journals, newsletters, and periodicals dealing with the field of interior design should be read. Every available source of information, including visits to offices of agencies and professional organizations, should be explored.

Before going to the first interview, the prospective professional interior designer should

□ Examine his personal needs, assets, and weaknesses. Salary requirements and corresponding responsibilities for that salary should be determined. Does the aspiring professional know what he wants now and in the future? Is his résumé a full and honest representation? Does it say too little or too much? Is his **portfolio** a true representation of his best professional and creative work?

□ Examine carefully and objectively her personal appearance. The importance of personal appearance and presentation cannot be overemphasized. Being well groomed and appropriately dressed is important, as is standing straight and sitting properly. First impressions are lasting. The potential employer should be approached with a positive state of mind. The applicant should be articulate, straightforward, honest, and self-confident, but without arrogance. She should assume the attitude that she has something of worth to offer and should be positive in pointing out her training, skills, and desire to be of service to the company. Every opportunity for an interview should be taken, and technique should be improved each time.

Attaining visibility

A question that faces every new interior designer is, How am I going to become known? To answer this question, a few suggestions may be helpful. The new interior designer should

□ Be proud of and enthusiastic about his profession and should let people know it. He should believe in himself and in what he is doing. Before he can ask the public to believe in him, he must believe in himself.

□ Put her profession within reach of everyone in her community. She can offer to give lectures for her firm. She can contact local societies and charities which may be interested in a lecture or slide presentation. She can set up an adult education class through her local high school or college.

□ Write articles for his local newspaper. He should express a stimulating idea. A good place to start is with children's rooms, since these are quick to capture people's interest.

□ Contact people at her local radio station. They may be interested in presenting a series of daytime lectures on practical interior design problems.

□ Show courtesy and concern for every client he encounters regardless of whether they give him their job.

□ Become involved in preservation and restoration. If no preservation society exists in her community, she might organize one. Nearly every town has some building worth preserving. Getting one on the National Register of Historic Places can bring prestige and a sense of pride to her community as well as visibility and a reputation for herself.

□ Participate in national and local professional interior design or related organizations.

The interior designer's challenge for the future

In light of the impact professional design and designers have on the economic, social, cultural, and environmental life of our nation, the challenge for the interior designer as a protector of the human environment in the final decades of the twentieth century is awesome. Perhaps the first challenge and major responsibility is to design for people. Many designers are concerned primarily with the big commercial jobs that offer visible recognition. These types of jobs are most assuredly desirable and essential, but until *people* take precedence over *buildings*, the interior design profession will not have met its most important obligation: *to improve the quality of life for everyone*. To accomplish this, incumbent on the interior designer is to heighten the awareness on all levels of society of the many ways in which the interior designer can affect the living and working environment.

In today's cost-inflated world, profound social and economic changes are occurring that present new challenges requiring immediate attention. Less than twenty years ago, energy was inexpensive and abundant, and people took it for granted. Today, energy conservation must be a part of design consciousness in all aspects of both exterior and interior housing. Ever-rising costs and the change in the size and composition of families, along with their increasing mobility, present a whole new range of problems, of which one of the most crucial is *space*. The eighties have experienced a 60 percent increase in small houses for "empty nesters," childless couples, and single-parent families, with a large percentage of the population being forced to live in smaller spaces of different types. Many families are redesigning current facilities rather than building larger quarters. A shift from the group-oriented society of the sixties to a concern for personal fulfillment is seen in the enlargement of home entertainment centers such as wet bars, hot tubs, wide video screens, and health and fitness centers.

Technology is making fast inroads in residential designs. The burgeoning computer market and its corresponding technologies such as home computers, along with modified use of media equipment, specialized sound systems, and television apparatus, are making a direct impact on the interior design industry and present new problems to the interior designer, who must integrate the necessary machinery into personal living space without sacrificing the essential character of the home environment.

Another challenge to the interior designer is preservation and restoration. The awakening to the preservation of America's cultural heritage has prompted many people to buy and restore older homes. Long-standing but well-constructed buildings of all kinds are being recycled to serve a wide range of commercial and public needs.

Despite the accomplishments of the preservation movement in America in recent years, the focus has been on exterior architecture rather than on interiors, which imposes a responsibility on the interior designer to broaden his or her understanding and appreciation of the homes in which American ancestors lived out their lives. These homes provide a living record of social and cultural history, and afford a base for authentic restoration and preservation. To bring about a fuller knowledge and understanding of the living past, the Educational Foundation of ASID is undertaking a research task with a "Significant Interiors" survey, which reaches across the country.

The necessity for today's interior designer to keep up-to-date in the profession is no small order. In the rapidly changing world, some estimate that the amount of information doubles every four years, which puts excessive demands on professionals in every field of endeavor. As design has become more demanding and more technical, specialists have emerged to take over in areas where the interior designer requires particular expertise, such as in lighting and rendering.

As a practicing interior designer, one is compelled to keep abreast of the field through a continuing educational process in order to adequately serve one's clients. The interior designer must also keep in mind that each job and each client is unique. He or she must be careful with the client's money, must be truthful, and must conscientiously lead and educate—not dictate. Although the ultimate goal is to support human values, family life, and society as a whole, the designer also has a responsibility to industry.

The future will present many new conditions that will demand new design solutions. A constant recycling and renovation of the environment will be necessary to meet changing human needs. The shifting of population centers will bring about growth in some existing towns and communities, and the development of new ones, which will require new ecological designs. By the turn of the century, artificial space habitats for people may exist. The technology may already be in place to implement such dramatic changes, but will interior designers be creatively and psychologically prepared?

All of this does not mean that designers need to submit needlessly to the trends and fashions of the future. Designers must be masters of change, not blind followers. The future must be built on the appreciation of and dedication to preserving the best of the past and combining it with the best of the present. Designers should constantly and consistently reexamine old and eternal values. Environments will change, but human needs, desires, and aspirations that have endured since the beginning of time will most likely remain the same. The challenge for the designers of the future is to meet the demands of current and future technological advances while maintaining the functional and aesthetic needs of society. Interior designers are needed now and will be needed even more in the future.

Biographical notes

Aalto, Alvar (1899–1978)   A Finnish designer and Finland's greatest architect. His was the first expression of modern architecture in Scandinavia. His town hall at Saynatsalo and his tuberculosis sanatorium in Finland are two of his most famous buildings. His popular molded and bent birch plywood chair (about 1934) is a modern classic.

Alvarado, Pedro de (1485?–1541) Spanish conquistador. He was the chief lieutenant of Hernán Cortés during the conquest of Mexico and was the first to visit Taos Pueblo in New Mexico in 1540.

Belter, John Henry (1800?–1854) German born and one of the leading furniture designers in New York City during the Victorian era. In the mid-nineteenth century, his elaborately carved and laminated forms and his lacelike openwork designs were in great demand by wealthy families, whose lavish use of Belter furniture created the much-admired Belter parlor.

Breuer, Marcel Lajos (1902–1981) Hungarian-born American architect and furniture designer. During the 1920s he was both a student and a teacher at the Bauhaus. With two other architects, he designed the UNESCO headquarters in Paris and the United States embassy at The Hague. Breuer developed the tubular cantilevered steel chair, which has been the model for thousands of variations throughout the world.

Brothers Adams, the, Robert (1728–1792), **James** (1730–1794) English architects and decorative designers of Scottish parentage. They were the foremost exponents of the neoclassic style, which dominated English design about 1760 to 1790, and had a great influence on American design of the federal period.

Bulfinch, Charles (1763–1844) Possibly the first and leading professional architect of New England during the early federal period. He originally based his work on the Adam designs, but his later work became more severely classical. He designed the State House in Boston and in 1818, after Latrobe, became the architect for the national Capitol.

Chippendale, Thomas (1718–1779)   A celebrated English cabinetmaker whose book *The Gentleman and Cabinetmaker's Director,* 1754, was largely responsible for his unprecedented fame and the development of a school of eighteenth-century furniture that bore his name. During the mid-eighteenth century, the Chippendale style became popular in America, where it took on distinctive regional characteristics. The timeless designs of Chippendale furniture persist to the present time.

Downing, Andrew Jackson (1815–1852)   American horticulturist, landscape gardener, and rural architect. He is known as the father of the Gothic revival in America.

Eames, Charles (1907–1978) American-born designer. His far-reaching achievements in the field of design brought him and his wife, Ray Kaiser Eames, the most significant awards in the design field. In 1946, at the first one-man show ever given at the Museum of Modern Art, his chairs made such a sweeping impact that they are now among the biggest sellers of any furniture in the world.

Fuller, R(ichard) Buckminster (1895–1983)   American architect and engineer. He is noted for his innovative technological designs, such as his self-contained "4-D" house and designs for geodesic domes.

Gibbs, James (1682–1754)   English architect. One of his most distinguished works, St. Martin's-in-the-Fields, was the basic inspiration for many of the steepled churches of the colonial period in America. Gibbs was a proponent of the Palladian style, which flourished in America from 1750 to 1790.

Gropius, Walter (1883–1969) German architect. After World War I, he consolidated the art academy and the arts and crafts school in Weimar which he called the Bauhaus. In 1937 he came to America and became chairman of the Department of Architecture at Harvard University. Gropius was one of the most celebrated architects and teachers of the century.

Hepplewhite, George (d. 1786) English cabinetmaker whose furniture designs bridged the styles of Chippendale and Adam. In his later years he worked closely with Sheraton, and much of their furniture is indistinguishable. No authentic pieces of Hepplewhite remain, but his designs are still copied to a limited degree.

Johnson, Philip (1906–   ) A disciple of Miës van der Rohe, and one of the world's greatest living architects. Johnson's own glass and steel house in New Canaan, Connecticut, is the best residential example of Miës van der Rohe's influence. Johnson was the originator of the water garden.

Jones, Inigo (1573–1652) English architect who introduced the Renaissance style of architecture into England from Italy. He was a dominant figure in the English arts of the period. His most outstanding work was the great Banqueting House in Whitehall, London.

Latrobe, Benjamin Henry (1764–1820) English-born architect and engineer who came to America in 1796. His first Greek revival structure in America was the Bank of Pennsylvania (1799–1801). Latrobe was the architect for the new Capitol in Washington after its destruction by the British. His designs gave great impetus to the classical revival in America.

Le Corbusier (pseudonym of Charles Édouard Jeanneret) (1887–1965) French architect born in Switzerland. He based his designs on functional principles and geometric forms. Le Corbusier's hallmark is a flat-roofed floating structure on stilts with a white interior. He coined the phrase "a house is a machine for living." His Villa Savoye (1929–1931) at Poissy, France, is considered one of the four great residential buildings of the twentieth century.

McComb, John (1763–1853) American-born architect. Trained by his father, McComb's work shows the continued influence of the late colonial tradition. He is best known for his part in the architectural design of Old City Hall, New York City.

McIntire, Samuel (1757–1811) Self-taught architect and wood-carver who became the leader of his profession in Massachusetts. Through the patronage of the wealthy and powerful citizens of Salem, he turned that little shipping town into America's most beautiful federal period city.

Miës van der Rohe, Ludwig (1886–1969) German born and the last director of the Bauhaus, he became an American architect. His philosophy that "architecture is not a play with forms" but "stems from the sustaining and driving forces of civilization" is still the basis of contemporary architecture. He used steel and glass and gave the world a new concept of space. The Seagram Building in New York expresses Miës van der Rohe's famous curtain-wall design. His chairs and tables have a simple, sculptural quality, and his most famous chair is the Barcelona.

Newton, Sir Isaac (1642–1727) English physicist, natural philosopher, and mathematician. He discovered the law of universal gravitation, constructed the first reflecting telescope, and originated the emission theory of light. He is considered one of the greatest scientists, and his work profoundly influenced eighteenth-century thought.

Phyfe, Duncan (1768–1854) Born in Scotland and considered America's most renowned cabinetmaker. His furniture—particularly that produced in his early period—is famed for its excellence and artistic beauty. He is the only American cabinetmaker whose furniture is designated "period furniture."

Pirelli, Carlo A talented contemporary Italian designer who is best known for his famous Plia chair, a budget chair that folds to a thickness of 1 in. and is made of an aluminum frame with seat and back of clear or colored plastic.

Queen Anne (1665–1714) Second daughter of James II, ruled England from 1702 to 1714. The furniture style that bore her name, and for which she had no responsibility, has been referred to as the "first modern furniture period." Based on the cyma curve, Queen Anne furniture, which was further developed during the reign of George I, was a definite departure from the previous rectangular shapes. It showed a strong Chinese influence, and the use of the cabroile leg was universal. Mahogany was introduced as the furniture wood. Furniture of this style is marked by exceptional grace and beauty and timeless design.

Saarinen, Eero (1910–1961) Finnish-born architect who developed his career in America. His architectural innovations are of tremendous significance. His design for the Ingalls Hockey Rink at Yale University, Jefferson National Expansion Memorial Arch in St. Louis, Missouri, and the TWA terminal, Kennedy International Airport, New York City, are three of his most famous structures. On the furniture scene he is best known for his pedestal chair, a classic of molded plastic.

Scarpa, Tobia and Afra A prominent husband-and-wife team of Italian designers. Their Soriana chair, designed in 1970 and made of foam supported on a small wooden frame held by two steel wire clips, was a sensation in furniture design.

Sheraton, Thomas (1751–1806) English furniture designer whose style is marked by graceful delicacy and simplicity. Emphasis is on straight vertical lines, inlay decoration, reeded legs, and classical motifs. He worked closely with Hepplewhite, and their furniture designs, particularly dining room pieces, were popular during the federal period in America.

Stone, Edward Durell (1902–1978) American architect who achieved great renown for his design of the United States embassy at New Delhi (1958). He applied a lacy grillwork to his subsequent buildings, including the United States pavilions for the Brussels World Fair 1958 and Expo '67 in Montreal, Canada.

Sullivan, Louis Henry (1856–1924) American architect who studied at the Ecole des Beaux Arts and was an important figure in the evolution of modern architecture in the United States. His principle that "form should follow function" was the accepted and guiding doctrine of modern architecture throughout the world.

Thonet, Michael (1796–1871)   Of Belgian descent but born in Germany. Is best known for his development of bentwood designs, which led to the first mass production of furniture. All contemporary furniture of bentwood or plywood has been developed from Thonet's techniques.

Wegener, Hans J. (1914–   )   A Danish-born furniture designer whose chairs are characterized by refinement of shape, sculptural details, and an understanding of the inherent qualities of wood. His The Chair has probably been copied more than any other chair design.

Wren, Sir Christopher (1632–1723) English architect and foremost exponent of the Renaissance style of architecture in England, where it came to be known as "Georgian." His masterpiece was St. Paul's Cathedral in London (1675–1716), but many other important structures in the rebuilding of London after the Great Fire of 1666 were designed by him. Wren's work had a profound influence on American architecture during the eighteenth century.

Wright, Frank Lloyd (1869–1959) American architect. His philosophy of organic architecture was expressed in many of his writings. He was the first architect in America to design houses with open planning. His many radical innovations, in both structure and aesthetics, and many of his methods have become accepted internationally. Wright's best-known residence and probably the most important house of the twentieth century, Falling Water, was built during 1936 to 1937 in Bear Run, Pennsylvania, and won for him the American Institute of Architects award. He has been called the world's greatest architect.

Glossary

acoustical plaster A plaster that contains sound-absorbent ingredients.

acoustical tile A tile that is especially constructed to absorb and control the transmission of sound.

adaptation The modification of an item to make it fit more perfectly under the conditions of its environment. In furniture design, an adaptation means that only some elements of the original have been adapted to the present design.

adobe A brick of sun-dried earth and straw, or a structure made of such bricks or clay.

aesthetic Pertaining to the beautiful in art or nature.

affinity Relationship, attraction, kinship.

antebellum Existing before the Civil War.

antique A work of art, piece of furniture, or decorative object made at a much earlier period than the present, often 100 years or, according to U.S. customs laws, something made before 1830.

arabesque A leaf and scroll pattern with stems rising from a root or other motif and branching in spiral form, usually in a vertical panel.

arcade A series of adjoining arches with their supporting columns on piers.

arcaded panel A panel in whose field are two dwarf columns supporting an arch.

armoire The French term for a tall cupboard or wardrobe with doors.

artificial lighting Manufactured lighting produced in three ways: (1) combustion, (2) incandescence, and (3) fluorescence.

atrium plan A floor plan in which all major rooms open onto a central atrium or court, which may be open or enclosed in glass.

authentic Conforming to an original so as to reproduce essential features.

balcony A platform enclosed by a railing, projecting from the wall of a building or placed in the interior.

baluster An upright support of a rail, as in the railing of a staircase.

balustrade A row of balusters topped by a rail.

bas-relief A type of decoration in which the design is slightly raised from the surface or background.

batik A process of decorating fabric by wax coating the parts not to be dyed. After the fabric is dyed, the wax is removed.

Bauhaus A school of art and architecture in Weimar, Germany, organized by Walter Gropius after World War I, with the purpose of unifying art and technology. Under the Bauhaus system, artists united creative imagination with practical artisanship.

bead-and-reel A convex classical Greek molding, with disks singly or in pairs, alternating with oblong beads.

beam A horizontal timber or metal bar supported on vertical posts, used to support a roof or ceiling

bevel The edge of any flat surface that has been cut at a slant to the main surface.

blueprint   A photographic print, formerly white lines on a bright blue ground, used for copying architectural plans. The standard today is blue lines on a white ground.

boiserie   A French word, generally used to designate carved wood paneling

breakfront   A large cabinet or bookcase, the center section of which projects beyond the flanking end sections.

buffet   A cabinet for holding dining room accessories and from which food may be served.

burnish   To make brown or to make lustrous by rubbing.

Cabriole leg

cabriole leg   A furniture support designed in the form of a conventionalized animal leg, with knee, ankle, and foot.

caning   Flexible rattan or cane, woven in open mesh for chair backs, seats, and so on.

canister   A small box or case used for holding tea, coffee, flour, and sugar. Early imported canisters were prized as household items.

cantilever   A projecting beam supported at only one end.

Captain's walk

captain's walk   A balustraded observation platform built atop the roof of a coastal dwelling, providing an unobstructed view of the sea. Also called a widow's walk.

carmine   A rich crimson or scarlet; red hue in high saturation.

case furniture   A general term applied to furniture used to contain objects, such as a cabinet or bookcase.

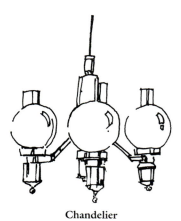

Chandelier

chandelier   A lighting fixture suspended from the ceiling, with branches to support candles or electric bulbs.

château   A castle or large country house in France.

chevron   A distinguishing mark usually consisting of two bars meeting at a point, often indicating rank or service.

chinoiserie (French)   Refers to Chinese designs or manner.

circa   Approximately.

classic   A term applied to a work of art as a recognized standard of value and excellence.

classical   A term relating to the arts of ancient Greece or Rome.

closed plan   A floor plan in which interior space is divided into separate rooms.

cluster planning   A method of arranging concentrated dwelling units, usually low-rise and either separate or attached, to take advantage of communal open spaces.

coffered   Ornamental sunken panels in a ceiling.

colonial   A term loosely used in referring to the 200-yr period that includes the settlement of the early colonies in America through the federal period (circa 1607–1825). According to some authorities, however, nothing after 1776 is rightfully colonial.

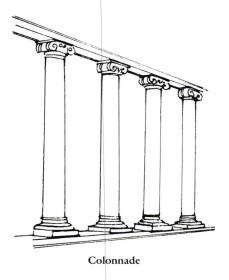

Colonnade

colonnade   Columns arranged in a straight or curved row, often supporting an entablature.

colonnette   A miniature colonnade used for decoration.

commode   A term loosely used to define a type of chest or cabinet, usually low and used against the wall.

common denominator   A common multiple or an element common to all items to which it pertains.

condominium   A multiunit structure—such as an apartment house—in which each unit is individually owned. Maintenance and services are provided, but are paid for by the residents.

console table Usually refers to a table that is designed to stand against a wall. It sometimes has only two legs or supports.

contemporary Living or occurring at the same period of time. In furniture it commonly refers to a modified type of modern design.

Corinthian The term designating the most ornate of the three Greek orders, which is characterized by its capital of small volutes (spiral, scroll-shaped ornaments) and acanthus leaves.

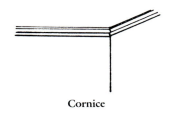

Cornice

cornice A horizontal and projecting member that crowns an architectural composition. A molding on a wall near the ceiling or under the eaves of the roof. Cornice board is a molding used with drapery instead of a valance.

Coromandel screen The name given to a screen with oriental design, originally imported from the Coromandel coast of India.

Cotswold An area of rolling green hills and limestone outcroppings, mainly in Gloucestershire, England. The region is famous for Cotswold sheep and picturesque stone houses.

counterpart An item that complements or closely resembles another.

coved ceiling A ceiling that meets the wall by means of a concave curve rather than a right angle.

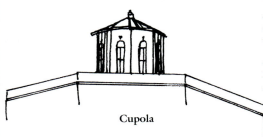

Cupola

cupola A small structure built on top of a roof for a lookout or to provide interior lighting; commonly used in Victorian structures.

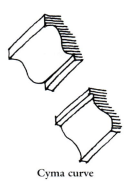

Cyma curve

cyma curve A double curve formed by the union of a concave and a convex line.

dado The lower part of an interior wall when treated in a different manner from the wall above; usually defined by a molding called a "dado cap."

decade A period of ten years.

decor Refers to the theme or style of interior design.

decoupage A process by which a picture is applied to a distressed wood backing, then alternately sanded and varnished many times to give the final appearance of great age.

dentil trim An architectural decoration composed of small, square, projecting blocks used in a cornice.

diffuse Referring to light, it means to spread throughout, usually with a softened effect.

director's chair An inexpensive folding chair, usually made with a fabric seat and backrest.

discriminate To make a distinction or separate by discerning differences.

distressed A term used to describe a wood finish that has the appearance of age.

documentary Refers to design motifs of old or ancient sources, the proof of which can be verified or documented.

doré knob A doorknob with a gilt finish; usually refers to one in a French style.

Doric Designates the simplest and oldest of the Greek orders, the principal feature of which is a large, square block at the top.

dormer A window in a small gablelike projection built out from a sloping roof.

double glazing A process of hermetically sealing two sheets of glass together with air trapped between. This type of glass provides efficient insulation against heat and cold.

double-hung window A window divided into two sections, one lowering from the top and the other rising from the bottom.

dough box A small end table with an enclosed upper section that has a surface lid. Originally used by the Pennsylvania Dutch for storing bread dough.

dovecote Originally a small, compartmented, raised house or box, used for housing domestic pigeons. Eventually became a roof type.

dower chest A chest to hold items for a prospective bride; used by most civilizations. In early Pennsylvania it was called the dower chest and took on distinctive characteristics.

Dresden Fine porcelain made in Meissen, near Dresden, Germany. Established 1710 to 1720, the factory produced some of the most famous china in Europe.

drill A twill cotton in a stout weave, often used for fabric backing for walls.

Dutch door A single-hinged door that is divided horizontally so that each section can be opened independently.

eave A protecting lower edge of a roof, which overhangs the walls of a building.

eclectic Mixing furnishings from various sources but with an eye to compatibility.

Egg-and-dart

egg-and-dart A classical Greek molding consisting of ovoid (egg-shaped) forms alternating with dartlike designs.

electromagnet A core of magnetic material surrounded by a coil of wire through which an electric current is passed to magnetize the core.

Elliptical fanlight

elliptical fanlight A fan-shaped window that topped the central doorways of federal period houses in America.

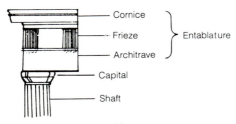

Entablature

entablature The upper part of a wall that is usually supported by columns or pilasters and that in classical orders consists of architrave, frieze, and cornice.

epergne A tiered centerpiece.

escutcheon In hardware, it refers to a shaped plate for a keyhole or a metal fitting, to which a handle or knob is attached.

étagère A series of shelves supported by columns; used chiefly for display.

etching A design produced on an etched plate or an impression taken in ink from an etched plate.

ethnic Designating races or groups of people on the basis of common traits or customs.

federal period The political and social formative era in America following the Revolution (circa 1790–1825).

felting A process of matting fibers into a fabric.

festoon A carved, molded, or painted ornament representing a decorative chain; a decorative chain or strip.

filament A threadlike conductor (as of carbon or metal) that is rendered incandescent (brilliant) by the passage of an electric current.

Finial

finial An ornament that forms the upper extremity of an architectural detail, a piece of furniture, or an accessory.

Flemish Relating to or characteristic of the low countries, now Belgium and The Netherlands.

fluorescent lighting Artificial light produced when a gaseous mixture of mercury and argon, sealed within a glass tube that is lined with a fluorescent coating, is activated by an electrical current.

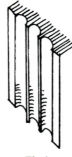

Fluting

fluting Parallel concave grooves commonly used on the shafts of classical columns.

foil Anything that serves, by contrast of color or texture, to adorn or set off another thing to advantage; also a wallpaper with the appearance of a thin sheet of metal; a background.

footcandle An international unit of light measurement. It is the illumination at a 1-ft distance from the light of one candle. The intensity of light is calculated in footcandles.

French doors Paired, single-hinged doors of paned glass—a walk-through window—which swing either inward or outward.

fresco The art of painting on moist lime plaster with water-based pigments.

Fretwork

fretwork Interlaced ornamental work either perforated or cut in low relief, usually in geometric patterns; also tracery of glazed doors and windows.

fusuma screen A freestanding, movable screen used in Japanese houses as a partition to define space.

gable The end portion of a building formed by the roof coming together at the top.

gallery A miniature railing placed along the edge of a tabletop or a shelf.

gambrel roof A roof made from two lengths of lumber, the upper one being flatter and the lower one a steeper slope.

generic The name applied to manufactured fabrics, which gives the exact fiber content.

geodesic dome A triangular patterned dome held together by a self-supporting network of rods and covered with a variety of materials. The geodesic dome was developed by R. Buckminster Fuller, an American architect and engineer.

Georgian The general name given to architecture and furniture developed in England during the eighteenth century under the reigns of George I, George II, and George III, and copied in America. Furniture included the styles of Queen Anne, Chippendale, Hepplewhite, and Sheraton.

glass blocks Hollow glass forms used in building construction to emit light.

Gothic Refers to the period from approximately 1160 to 1530, in which the ecclesiastical architecture dominated all the arts.

Greek revival The third and final phase (circa 1825–1845) of the neoclassic style in America, in which bold and monumental characteristics were related to the early forms of Greece and Rome.

half-timber Construction of timber frame, with the spaces filled with masonry or lath and plaster.

hand or **handle** The feel or drape of fabric.

hemp A tough fiber from an Asiatic herb.

henequen A sisal fiber related to maguey, found chiefly in Yucatan.

Highboy

highboy A tall chest of drawers supported on tall legs and divided horizontally into two sections.

hip roof A roof with sloping ends and sloping sides.

Hitchcock chair An American chair (1820–1850) named for Lambert Hitchcock of Connecticut. It derives from a Sheraton "fancy" chair and is often black with stenciled fruit and flower motifs.

Huguenots French Protestants.

hutch An informal chest or cabinet common to many countries, which came to America from England. The type most commonly used has bottom doors and open upper shelves for display.

incandescent lighting Light produced by heating a tungsten filament sealed in a light bulb.

indigenous Inherent; native to or living naturally in a country.

indigo A blue dye obtained from several plants but now chiefly made synthetically.

insulation The use of nonconductors to prevent the transfer of sound, heat, cold, or electricity.

international style A style of architecture based on the Bauhaus, which developed during the first two decades of the twentieth century.

Ionic The Greek order designated by the four spiral volutes of its capital.

Italianate The name given to one of the main styles of American Victorian architecture. It embodied many features of the Italian villa, which was much admired by Americans, and remained in vogue for almost 100 years (1830s–1920s).

Jacobean From the Latin *Jacobus* (James). The general term for English furniture styles from approximately 1603 to 1688. Jacobean was the prototype of most furniture made by the early colonists in New England during the seventeenth and early eighteenth centuries.

Jacquard A loom apparatus for weaving fabrics of intricate weaves and patterns; invented in France in 1801 by Charles Marie Jacquard.

jalousie window A window made of narrow, adjustable glass louvers that control ventilation.

kapok A mass of silky fibers from the ceiba tree, which are used for filling cushions.

knotty pine Pine that has a decorative distribution of knots. The knots in pine, which were originally avoided, are purposely chosen for the effect in paneling.

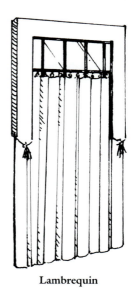

Lambrequin

lambrequin An ornamental window treatment, usually in the form of a wooden frame across the top and down the sides of the window, either painted or covered with fabric. Common in French country houses.

laminate   The binding of layers of wood together. In paneling, several layers are laid alternately across the grain for strength and durability. For decorative purposes, a thin layer of fine wood (veneer) is glued to the surface of the basic wood.

louver   A slatted panel for controlling the flow of air and the radiation of light.

lumen   A quantitative unit for measuring light output.

luminescence   Commonly referred to as fluorescence.

madder   A Eurasian herb, the root of which produces a red dye.

maguey   A fleshy-leaved Mexican agave plant that produces a liquid and a fiber, from which rope, rugs, and other items are made.

mansard roof   A roof having two slopes on all sides, the lower one being steeper than the upper one.

matte   A dull finish.

Mayan   Pertaining to an early American Indian linguistic family discovered after 1500. Their descendants live in Central America.

medieval   Pertaining to the Middle Ages, a turbulent time in history that followed the decline of the Roman Empire and extended to the Renaissance, covering roughly 1000 years, approximately A.D. 500 to 1500.

memorabilia   Things worthy of remembrance or preservation.

mode   A prevailing fashion or style.

modular   Constructed with standardized units or modules.

module   One in a series of standardized units to be integrated together, such as building construction or a set of furniture.

mordant   Any substance that serves to produce a fixed color in a textile fiber, leather, and so on.

mullion   A horizontal bar dividing the panes of a traceried window, in glazed doors of bookcases, and so on.

muntin   A vertical bar dividing the panes of a window. *Muntin* is often used interchangeably with *mullion*.

neoclassicism   Revivals simulating the ancient classical designs, such as Louis XVI, Adam, and Directoire styles.

newel post   The main post at the foot of a stairway.

occasional chair   The term applied to almost any chair that is light enough in weight to easily be moved from one location to another.

opaque   Neither reflecting nor emitting light.

open plan   A floor plan in which a minimum of fixed partitions are placed, thus allowing space to flow from one area to another.

Palladianism   Relating to a classical style in architecture based on the works of Andrea Palladio (1518–1580), the most copied of all Italian architects.

Palladian window   A window consisting of three vertical parts, with the central part higher than the flanking ones and surmounted by a fanlight. This window was a popular feature in the Palladian style of architecture in England in the seventeenth century and in America in the eighteenth century.

panetière   A decorative French bread box with open spindles.

parapet   A low wall or protective railing at the edge of a roof or platform.

parchment   Animal skin prepared for writing or a superior paper made in imitation of parchment.

parquetry   Mosaic of wood laid in geometric patterns.

patina   A mellow surface often developed with age.

patio   (Spanish)   A courtyard.

pavilion   A part of a building projecting from the main structure.

pedestal   A support at the base of a column; any base or foundation on which to display an art object.

pediment   An architectural decoration above a portico, window, or door.

pendant   An object suspended from above.

pendant chandelier   A light suspended from the ceiling, with a single fixture.

perimeter lighting   Lighting that follows the outer boundary of a room.

period style   A term used to designate a single item or a complete interior, including the architectural background, furniture, and decorative arts that were prevalent in a specific country at a particular time in history.

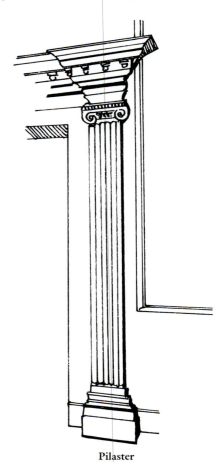

Pilaster

pilaster   An upright rectangular projection from a wall, architecturally treated as a column.

pilling Describes fiber that works out of the yarn structure and makes little balls on the surface of a carpet or fabric. In some strong, synthetic fibers, pilling creates a problem because the balls will not come off.

polyurethane A group of plastics characterized by light weight and flexibility, and varying in density, hardness, and resilience.

Pompeii A city of Italy buried A.D. 79 by the ash of Mount Vesuvius and excavated in the eighteenth century. The great interest it aroused in the classical arts inaugurated the classical revival.

Portico

portfolio A flexible case for carrying loose papers, renderings, and pictures.

portico A projection from the main structure of a building over the front entrance, supported by columns and often capped by a triangular pediment.

prefabricated (prefab) Mass produced in standardized modules or parts for later assembly at the factory or building site.

primitive painting An American primitive refers to many paintings done in the late seventeenth and early eighteenth centuries by untrained artists. The style is peculiar and unlifelike, and all primitives have a remarkable similarity that is easily distinguishable.

prototype An original from which another item is modeled.

pueblo One of the Indian tribes of New Mexico; an Indian village built in the form of commercial houses.

quartzite A hard-surface flooring derived from sandstone.

Corner quoins

quoin A solid exterior angle on a building, distinguished from the adjoining surface by material, color, size, or projection.

random plank Wood planks laid in a manner disregarding the width of individual boards.

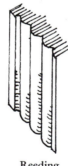

Reeding

reeding A small convex molding—the reverse of fluting. It may be used on columns and pilasters.

Renaissance The period in Europe between medieval and modern times. Beginning in Italy in the fourteenth century and lasting into the seventeenth, it was marked by a humanistic and classical revival in which an unprecedented flourishing of the arts occurred.

replica An accurate reproduction.

repoussé Relief work done on metal materials, created by hammering the material on the reverse side.

reproduction A furniture reproduction is a precise duplication of a historic style and would be a replica.

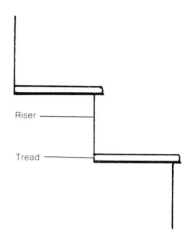

Riser

Tread

riser The upright member between two stair treads.

rococo A phase of European art that had its roots in the late Italian Renaissance, but developed in France during the reign of Louis XV in the first half of the eighteenth century. It was an extravagant style using asymmetry, shells, rocks, and all manner of elaborate decoration.

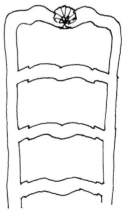

Salamander-back chair

salamander-back chair A ladder-back chair in which each crossbar resembles two salamanders. A fitting piece for country French. The salamander was the symbol of Francis I.

sash The framework (in a window or door) in which the glass is set. It may constitute a movable part.

sconce A bracket to hold a light secured to the wall.

shoji A basic element of a Japanese house, it is made of panes of rice paper and is used at the windows in place of curtains or draperies. Shoji screens are also used as panels in walls.

sisal A strong, durable, white fiber, derived from the leaves of a West Indian agave.

spectral Pertaining to or made by the spectrum.

standard milled items Items of various kinds (e.g., doors and door frames, windows and window frames, mantels) that are well designed and made in standard sizes in large quantities in the factory, thus making the cost much less than custom-made items.

Stepped gable

stepped gable A gable in which the sides ascend to the peak in steps; a style brought to America by the Dutch.

swag A festoon of flowers, fruit, or drapery.

synthetic Something artificial that simulates the genuine thing.

Taj Mahal A marble mausoleum built during 1630 to 1648 in Agra, India, by the Mogul emperor Shah Jahan in memory of his favorite wife.

tatami mat A soft straw mat, 3 ft by 6 ft by 1½ in., which is the basic element of the Japanese house and serves as a unit of measurement. It is the basis of organization and determines the size and proportion of all spaces. The black lines of its binding form an overall grid pattern, according to which rooms are sized.

templates Small patterns of furniture to be used as guides in planning rooms.

terrace Usually refers to a relatively level paved area adjoining a building.

toile de Jouy Fabric made at Jouy, France, by Oberkampf in the late eighteenth and early nineteenth centuries. Usually printed on cotton using only one color, red being an early favorite. Rural French and Chinese scenic designs are the most characteristic.

tole Painted tin used for small articles and accessories.

Tongue-and-groove joint

tongue-and-groove joint The rib on one edge of a board is made to fit into a groove in the edge of another board to make a flush joint.

Tracery

tracery Decorative openwork in the head of a Gothic window.

traditional style An inherited style of beliefs, customs, architecture, or furnishings. "Traditional" in home furnishings usually refers to styles in the English tradition.

trompe l'oeil French word meaning "to fool the eye." A term applied to wall decoration such as wallpaper showing bookshelves full of books, cupboards with dishes of fruit, and so on, in remarkably realistic renderings.

Tudor The name of the ruling house of England from 1485 to 1603.

Tudor arch

Tudor arch A low or flattened elliptical arch.

veranda An open galley or portico (usually roofed) attached to the exterior of a building.

Versailles The magnificent baroque palace built by Louis XIV in the late seventeenth century outside of Paris.

villa (Italian) A somewhat pretentious suburban residence, such as the Medici in Florence.

wag-on-the-wall One of the earliest clocks used in New England, characterized by an unenclosed, free-swinging pendulum.

wall sconce An ornamental wall bracket to hold candles or electric bulbs.

Wedgwood ware Fine English pottery, first made by Josiah Wedgwood. Forms and decoration are characteristically classical.

Yoke-back chair

yoke-back chair A typical Chippendale side chair in which the top crossbar is in the form of two S curves forming a yoke.

Bibliography

Albers, Josef. *Interaction of Color*. New Haven, Conn.: Yale Univ. Press, 1975.

Alexander, Harold. *Design: Criteria for Decisions*. New York: Macmillan, 1976.

Alexander, Patsy. *Textile Fabrics and Their Selection*. Boston: Houghton Mifflin, 1976.

Aromon, Joseph. *Encyclopedia of Furniture*. 3d ed. New York: Crown, 1965.

Barrows, Claire M. *Living Walls*. New York: Wallcoverings Council, 1968.

Better Homes and Gardens. *Creative Decorating on a Budget*. New York: Better Homes and Gardens, 1970.

———. *New Decorating Book*. New York: Better Homes and Gardens, 1982.

Bevlin, Marjorie Elliott. *Design Through Discovery*. New York: Holt, Rinehart & Winston, 1966.

Birrell, Verla. *The Textile Arts*. New York: Harper & Brothers, 1959.

Birren, Faber. *Light, Color, and Environment*. New York: Van Nostrand Reinhold, 1969.

Bradford, Barbara Taylor. *How to Solve Your Decorating Problems*. New York: Simon & Schuster, 1976.

Cobb, Hubbard H. *How to Paint Anything: The Complete Guide to Painting and Refinishing*. New York: Macmillan, 1972.

Conran, Terrence. *The House Book*. New York: Crown, 1976.

D'Arcy, Barbara. *Bloomingdales Book of Home Decorating*. New York: Harper & Row, 1973.

Debaigts, Jacques. *Interiors for Old Houses*. New York: Van Nostrand Reinhold, 1973.

Diflow, Donna. *How to Buy Furniture*. New York: Macmillan, 1972.

Downer, Marion. *Discovering Design*. New York: Lothrop, Lee & Shepard, 1963.

Draper, Dorothy. *Decorating Is Fun*. Garden City, N.Y.: Doubleday, 1962.

Fetterman, Elsie, and Charles Klamkin. *Consumer Education in Practice*. New York: Wiley, 1976.

Foley, Mary Mix. *The American House*. New York: Harper & Row, 1980.

Gains, Patricia Ellisior. *Fabric Decoration Book*. New York: Morrow, 1975.

General Electric. *The Light Book*. Cleveland, Ohio: Nela Park, 1981.

Gilliat, Mary. *Kitchen and Dining Rooms*. New York: Viking Press, 1970.

Grillo, Paul Jacques. *What Is Design?* Chicago: Paul Theobald, 1962.

Gutman, Robert, ed. *People and Buildings*. New York: Basic Books, 1972.

Helick, Martin R. *Varieties of Human Habitation*. Cambridge: MIT Press, 1970.

Hepburn, Andrew H. *Great Houses of American History*. New York: Bramhall House, 1972.

Hitchcock, Henry-Russell, and Philip Johnson. *The International Style*. 1932. Reprint. New York: Norton, 1966.

Hoffman, Hubert. *Row Houses and Chester Houses: An International Survey*. New York: Praeger, 1967.

Illuminating Engineering Society Lighting Handbook. Latest ed. New York: IES

Itten, Johannes. *The Art of Color*. New York: Van Nostrand Reinhold, 1973.

———. *Design and Form: The Basic Course at the Bauhaus*. New York: Van Nostrand Reinhold, 1964.

Jacobson, Charles W. *Check Points on How to Buy Oriental Rugs.* Rutland, Vt.: Charles E. Tuttle, 1969.

Kahlenberg, Mary Hunt, and Anthony Berlant. *Navajo Blanket.* New York: Praeger, 1972.

Kira, Alexander. *The Bathroom.* New York: Viking Press, 1976.

Kopp, Joel, and Kate Kopp. *American Hooked and Sewn Rugs.* New York: Dutton, 1975.

Kuppers, Harold. *Color: Origins, Systems, Uses.* New York: Van Nostrand Reinhold, 1973.

Larsen, Jack Lenor, and Jeanne Weeks. *Fabrics for Interiors.* New York: Van Nostrand Reinhold, 1975.

Lewis, Ethel. *Romance of Textiles.* New York: Macmillan, 1937.

Libby, William Charles. *Color and the Structural Sense.* Englewood Cliffs, N.J.: Prentice-Hall, 1974.

Lightolier. *The Light Book.* Jersey City, N.J.: Lightolier, 1981.

Liman, Ellen. *Money Saver's Guide to Decorating.* New York: Macmillan, 1972.

Maass, John. *The Victorian Home in America.* New York: Hawthorn, 1972.

Magnani, Franco, ed. *Interiors for Today.* New York: Whitney Library of Design, 1975.

Marsh, Betty. *All About Furniture.* High Point, N.C.: Southern Furniture Manufacturers, 1969.

Meadmore, Clement. *How to Make Furniture Without Tools.* New York: Pantheon Books, 1975.

Money Management Institute. *Your Home Furnishings Dollar.* Chicago: Household Finance Corp., 1973.

Munsell, Albert H. *A Color Notation.* 10th ed. Baltimore: Munsell Color Co., 1954.

Naar, Jon, and Molly Siple. *Living in One Room.* New York: Random House, 1976.

Nicholson, Arnold. *American Houses in History.* New York: Viking Press, 1965.

Phillips, Derek. *Lighting in Architectural Design.* New York: Holt, Rinehart & Winston, 1968.

Pierson, William H., Jr. *American Buildings and Their Architects: The Colonial and Neoclassical Styles.* New York: Doubleday, 1970.

Plumb, Barbara. *Young Designs in Color.* New York: Viking Press, 1972.

Pratt, Richard. *The Golden Treasury of Early American Houses.* New York: Harrison House, 1967.

Rogers, Meyric R. *American Interior Design.* New York: Bonanza Books, 1947.

Schofield, Maria, ed. *Decorative Art in Modern Interiors, 1974/75.* New York: Viking Press, 1974.

Scully, Vincent J., Jr. *Modern Architecture.* Rev. ed. New York: Braziller, 1974.

Smith, S. Jane. *Elsie de Wolfe: A Life in the High Style.* New York: Atheneum, 1982.

Sommer, Robert. *Design Awareness.* Corte Madera, California: Rinehart Press, 1972.

Sulahria, Julie, and Ruby Diamond. *Inside Design: Creating Your Environment.* San Francisco: Canfield Press, 1977.

Taylor, Lucy D. *Know Your Fabrics.* New York: Wiley, 1956.

Textile Handbook. 4th ed. Washington, D.C.: American Home Economics Assn., 1970.

Verity, Enid. *Color Observed.* New York: Van Nostrand Reinhold, 1982.

White, Wilston H. *Cluster Development.* New York: American Conservation Assn., 1964.

Wills, Royal, of Barry Associates. *More Houses for Good Living.* New York: Architectural Book Publishing, 1968.

Wilson, Jose, and Arthur Leaman. *Color in Decoration.* New York: Van Nostrand Reinhold, 1971.

Wingate, Isabel B., Karen Gillespie, and Betty Mildram. *Know Your Merchandise for Retailers and Consumers.* 4th ed. New York: McGraw-Hill, 1975.

Wright, Frank Lloyd. *The Natural House.* New York: Bramhall House, 1954.

Selected periodicals

Americana
American Heritage Publishing Co.
381 West Center Street
Marion, Ohio 43302

American Home
641 Lexington Avenue
New York, New York 10022

Antiques Magazine
551 Fifth Avenue
New York, New York 10019

Apartment Life
750 Third Avenue
New York, New York 10022

Architectural Digest
680 Fifth Avenue
New York, New York 10019

Better Homes and Gardens
750 Third Avenue
New York, New York 10017

Budget Decorating
Marco Publishing Co.
635 Madison Avenue
New York, New York 10022

Design and Environment
355 Lexington Avenue
New York, New York 10017

The Designer Magazine
1010 Third Avenue
New York, New York 10020

Home
Hudson Publishing Co.
P.O. Box 10002
Des Moines, Iowa 50340

House Beautiful Magazine
250 West 55th Street
New York, New York 10019

Interior Design
850 Third Avenue
New York, New York 10022

Interiors
1515 Broadway
New York, New York 10036

Metropolitan Home
Box AC
Des Moines, Iowa 50380

1001 Decorating Ideas Home Library
(booklets on a variety of home furnishing
subjects)
Conso Publishing Co.
635 Madison Avenue
New York, New York 10022

Waverly's Easy-to-Do Decorating
Pyramid Publications
919 Third Avenue
New York, New York 10022

Woman's Day Service Series
(a how-to series on home decorating and
repair)
Fawcett Publications
Fawcett Building
Greenwich, Connecticut 06830

Other Readings

Catalogs and brochures are published and
made available by major manufacturers of
fabrics, wallpaper, wall paneling, hard
floor coverings, carpets, and furniture.

How-to booklets on every phase of building, remodeling, and interior design are
available and advertised in current
periodicals.

Index

Student survey

Beginnings of Interior Environment, 5th edition
Phyllis Sloan Allen

Students, send us your ideas!

The author and the publisher want to know how well this book served you and what can be done to improve it for those who will use it in the future. By completing and returning this questionnaire, you can help us develop better textbooks. We value your opinion and want to hear your comments. Thank you.

YOUR NAME (OPTIONAL) _____ SCHOOL _____

YOUR MAILING ADDRESS _____ CITY _____

STATE _____ ZIP _____ INSTRUCTOR'S NAME (OPTIONAL) _____

COURSE TITLE _____ DEPARTMENT _____

1. How does this book compare with other texts you have used? (Check one)

   ☐ SUPERIOR   ☐ BETTER THAN MOST   ☐ COMPARABLE   ☐ NOT AS GOOD AS MOST

2. Circle those chapters you especially liked:

   CHAPTERS: 1   2   3   4   5   6   7   8   9   10   11   12

   COMMENTS:

3. Circle those chapters you think could be improved:

   CHAPTERS: 1   2   3   4   5   6   7   8   9   10   11   12

   COMMENTS:

4. Please rate the following. (Check one for each line)

	EXCELLENT	GOOD	AVERAGE	POOR
READABILITY OF TEXT MATERIAL	☐	☐	☐	☐
LOGICAL ORGANIZATION	☐	☐	☐	☐
GENERAL LAYOUT AND DESIGN	☐	☐	☐	☐
UP-TO-DATE TREATMENT OF SUBJECT	☐	☐	☐	☐
MATCH WITH INSTRUCTOR'S COURSE ORGANIZATION	☐	☐	☐	☐
ILLUSTRATIONS THAT CLARIFY THE TEXT	☐	☐	☐	☐
SELECTION OF TOPICS	☐	☐	☐	☐
EXPLANATION OF DIFFICULT CONCEPTS	☐	☐	☐	☐

5. List any chapters that your instructor did not assign. _____

_____

6. What additional topics did your instructor discuss that were not covered in the text? _____

_____

7. Did you buy this book new or used?   ☐ NEW   ☐ USED

   Do you plan to keep the book or sell it?   ☐ KEEP IT   ☐ SELL IT

   Do you think your instructor should continue to assign this book?   ☐ YES   ☐ NO

8. Did you purchase the Student Packet for the text?   ☐ YES ☐ NO

   How useful was the Student Packet for learning the concepts in the course? (mark the scale below)

Not useful	Adequate	Useful	Very useful

9. After taking the course, are you interested in taking more courses in this field?   ☐ YES ☐ NO

   Did you take this course to fulfill a requirement, or as an elective?   ☐ REQUIRED ☐ ELECTIVE

10. What is your major? _____

   Your class rank?   ☐ FRESHMAN   ☐ SOPHOMORE   ☐ JUNIOR   ☐ SENIOR   ☐ OTHER, SPECIFY:

   Do you hope to pursue a career as an interior designer?   ☐ YES ☐ NO ☐ UNDECIDED

11. General comments:

May we quote you in our advertising?   ☐ YES ☐ NO

Please remove this page and mail to:

L. T. OLSON
BURGESS PUBLISHING COMPANY
7108 OHMS LANE
MINNEAPOLIS, MN 55435

THANK YOU!